CONSTRUCTIBLE SETS WITH APPLICATIONS

STUDIES IN LOGIC

AND

THE FOUNDATIONS OF MATHEMATICS

NORTH-HOLLAND PUBLISHING COMPANY
AMSTERDAM

CONSTRUCTIBLE SETS WITH APPLICATIONS

A. MOSTOWSKI
University of Warsaw

1969

NORTH - HOLLAND PUBLISHING COMPANY — AMSTERDAM

PWN — POLISH SCIENTIFIC PUBLISHERS — WARSZAWA

PAŃSTWOWE WYDAWNICTWO NAUKOWE
(PWN—POLISH SCIENTIFIC PUBLISHERS)
Warszawa 1969

Library of Congress Catalog Card Number 68–54508

This book has been published by PWN jointly with
NORTH-HOLLAND PUBLISHING COMPANY
Amsterdam

PRINTED IN POLAND

PREFACE

The first (Polish) edition of a book on set theory which Professor Kuratowski and myself published in 1952 contained a chapter on selected problems concerning the independence and consistency of several set-theoretic statements. We had to omit that chapter in the second edition of our book. The English translation of our book, which appeared in 1968 in the series "Studies in Logic and the Foundations of Mathematics", does not contain any meta-mathematics of set theory, either.

The present book was originally planned as a companion volume to the above mentioned work. In the course of the writing it I realized, however, that it would not be convenient to base the exposition on the Zermelo–Fraenkel type of axioms adopted in the earlier book. It proved especially difficult to arrange the exposition of meta-mathematical results without using the notion of classes, which we had avoided in the book on the "classical" parts of set theory. I changed therefore to a stronger system, in which classes were allowed, and decided to present results concerning the Zermelo–Fraenkel set theory on the basis of Morse's theory of classes. It is debatable whether it would not have been wiser to present the meta-mathematical results concerning the Gödel–Bernays set theory on the basis of the same theory or perhaps even on the basis of a finitary meta-mathematics. I believe that there are advantages and disadvantages in each of these approaches. The advantage of basing the exposition on Morse's axioms is that the consistency of the Zermelo–Fraenkel set theory and the existence of its well-founded models are provable and need not be assumed as hypotheses.

The book contains almost nothing beyond Gödel's theory of constructible sets and Cohen's construction of models by means of generic sets. I tried to present these two theories without leaving any gaps which would have to be filled by the reader. This resulted in some places in rather lengthy calculations, which are troublesome but, I think, unavoidable unless one radically changes the whole approach. It is possible that they can be completely eliminated by using the more recent ideas of Scott and Vopěnka, who replace Cohen's forcing by the Boolean valued models, or of Sacks, who uses notions of measure theory. I did not try these approaches.

The book can roughly be divided into four parts. In Chapters I–III I define relatively constructible sets; they form a subclass of the universal class, and I prove that they form a model of the Zermelo–Fraenkel set theory. Chapters IV–VII deal with constructible sets contained in a given transitive model and obtained from an element of this model by iterating the process of construction as many times as there are ordinals in the model. Discussing these sets we arrive at Gödel's result on the consistency of the generalized continuum hypothesis. Chapters VIII–XII deal with Cohen's method of generic sets. Models which are obtained in this part of the book still consist of relatively constructible sets, and the process of construction is iterated as many times as before, but the elements one starts with are no longer elements of the given model. Cohen's theory is presented in the form which allows us to use topology; this method is due to Ryll-Nardzewski and Takeuti. Finally, Chapters XIII–XV contain applications of Cohen's method to selected proofs of independence.

ANDRZEJ MOSTOWSKI

CONTENTS

CHAPTER I

AXIOMS AND AUXILIARY NOTIONS

The present chapter contains an exposition of the Zermelo–Fraenkel axioms for set theory, describes the meta-mathematical basis on which our considerations will rest and finally gives definitions of semantical notions which are necessary for the subsequent constructions.

1. Set theory ZF of Zermelo–Fraenkel

We call ZF (set theory of Zermelo–Fraenkel) a first order theory with identity whose alphabet, formulae and axioms are defined as follows:

The *alphabet* consists of an infinite sequence $x_0, x_1, \ldots$ of variables, the binary predicates $\in$ and $=$ and the usual symbols for logical connectives and quantifiers.

Formulae are defined by induction: $x_i \in x_j$ and $x_i = x_j$ are formulae ($i, j = 0, 1, \ldots$); if H, H' are formulae, then so are $\neg H$, $H \wedge H'$ and $(x_j)H$ for $j = 0, 1, 2, \ldots$

We distinguish in the usual way the free and bound occurrences of a variable in a formula. If H is a formula, then we denote by $\mathrm{Fr}(H)$ the set of integers i such that x_i occurs freely in H.

We shall sometimes replace the letters $x_0, x_1, \ldots$ by other symbols. The connectives $\vee$, $\rightarrow$, $\equiv$ and the existential quantifier (Ex_i) are introduced in the usual way. An expression like $H(x_j, \ldots, x_k)$ will denote a formula which has free occurrences of the variables $x_j, \ldots, x_k$.

The following formulae are the *axioms of* ZF:

(I) $(z)[(z \in x) \equiv (z \in y)] \rightarrow (x = y)$ (*axiom of extensionality*),

(II) $(Ez)\,(t)\{(t \in z) \equiv [(t = x) \vee (t = y)]\}$ (*axiom of pairs*),

(III) $(Ey)(z)\{(z \in y) \equiv (Et)[(z \in t) \wedge (t \in x)]\}$ (*axiom of unions*),

(IV) $(Ex)(Ey)\Big((y \in x) \wedge (z)\big((z \in x) \rightarrow (Et)\{(t \in x) \wedge (t \neq z) \wedge \wedge (s)[(s \in z) \rightarrow (s \in t)]\}\big)\Big)$ (*axiom of infinity*),

(V) $(Ey)(z)\{(z \in y) \equiv (t)[(t \in z) \rightarrow (t \in x)]\}$ (*axiom of power sets*),

(VI_H) $(x)(E!y)H \rightarrow (a)(Eb)(y)[(y \in b) \equiv (Ex)((x \in a) \wedge H)]$ (*axiom of substitution*)[1].

In (VI_H) the formula H is supposed not to contain any free occurrence of the variable b.

Axiom (IV) states that there is a non-void set x each element of which is a proper subset of another element of x. Axiom (VI_H) says that if H defines a function (i.e., if for every x there is exactly one y such that H), then for every set a the image of a under that function is a set.

We shall assume that the reader is familiar with the derivation of the basic set-theoretic theorems in ZF to the extent in which those theorems are presented in [17][2].

2. The meta-theory of classes

The discussion of the axiom system ZF will be carried out in the theory of classes due in principle to Morse [24]. For short we call this *theory* M. In this section we describe this theory, formulate its axioms and give several definitions which we shall need later. Our presentation is based on [16], pp. 250–281, and the reader is referred to that book for further details on the subject.

From the point of view of the method it should be noted that while ZF is the object theory and M the meta-theory, the description of M is done in the meta-meta-theory.

Like ZF the theory M is a first order theory with identity. Its alphabet and its formulae are as follows:

The *alphabet* contains an infinite number of variables x_0, x_1, ..., x_j, ..., the symbols $=$ and $\in$ and the symbol $\{...: ...\}$. The last symbol

[1]) The expression $(E!y)H$ means "there is exactly one y such that H". We can define it formally as $(Ew)(y)[H \equiv (y = w)]$ where w is any variable which does not occur in H.

[2]) The system of set theory presented in [17] is slightly different from the system ZF outlined above but easy modifications of the proofs presented in [17] allow us to deduce all the theorems from axioms (I)–(VI).

is read as: the class of ... such that ... The usual logical connectives $\neg$ and $\wedge$ and the general quantifier also belong to the alphabet of M.

We define by induction the terms and formulae of M. Each variable is a *term*; if t and s are terms, then the expressions $t = s$ and $t \in s$ are *formulae*; if F and G are formulae, then so are $\neg F$, $F \wedge G$ and $(x_i)F$ for $i = 0, 1, \ldots$; if F is a formula, then $\{x_i\colon F\}$ is a term for $i = 0, 1, \ldots$

Each occurrence of a variable in a term or in a formula is either free or bound. We assume these notions as known. The operator $\{x_i\colon \ldots\}$ behaves in this respect like the quantifiers, i.e., each occurrence of the variable x_i in the term $\{x_i\colon F\}$ is a bound occurrence.

Logical connectives other than $\neg$ and $\wedge$ are introduced in the usual way as abbreviations. Also the existential quantifier is defined by means of the general quantifier and the negation symbol.

Before formulating the axioms of M we shall introduce a number of definitions. Properly speaking they will not be definitions but schemes of definitions. From each scheme we obtain an unlimited number of definitions by replacing the accented and unaccented letters $x, y, \ldots, x', y', \ldots$ occurring in the schemes by variables subject to the following rules: Letters without accents can be replaced by arbitrary variables; the kth accented letter counting from the left in the order in which the letters appear in the scheme must be replaced by the first variable x_i whose index is greater than the indices of the variables used to replace the unaccented letters and the preceding $k-1$ accented letters. Thus, for instance, in the definition scheme

$$\bigcup x =_{\mathrm{Df}} \{z'\colon (Ey')[(y' \in x) \wedge (z' \in y')]\}$$

we can replace the letter x by any variable x_j but once this is done we must replace z' and y' by x_{j+1} and x_{j+2}.

If there are no unaccented letters in the scheme, then the accented ones are to be replaced consecutively by $x_0, x_1, \ldots$ Thus the scheme $V =_{\mathrm{Df}} \{x'\colon x' = x'\}$ really means $V = \{x_0\colon x_0 = x_0\}$.

We now list our definition schemes:

x *is a set* $=_{\mathrm{Df}} (Ey')(x \in y')$,

$x \cup y =_{\mathrm{Df}} \{z'\colon (z' \in x) \vee (z' \in y)\}$ (*union of* x *and* y),

$x \cap y =_{\mathrm{Df}} \{z'\colon (z' \in x) \wedge (z' \in y)\}$ (*intersection of* x *and* y),

$-x =_{\mathrm{Df}} \{z'\colon \neg(z' \in x)\}$ (*complement of* x),

$$x - y =_{\mathrm{Df}} x \cap -y$$ (*difference of x and y*),

$$0 =_{\mathrm{Df}} \{x' \colon x' \neq x'\}$$ (*the void class*),

$$V =_{\mathrm{Df}} \{x' \colon x' = x'\}$$ (*the universal class*),

$$\bigcap x =_{\mathrm{Df}} \{z' \colon (y')[(y' \in x) \to (z' \in y')]\}$$

(*intersection of sets which belong to x*),

$$\bigcup x =_{\mathrm{Df}} \{z' \colon (Ey')[(y' \in x) \wedge (z' \in y')]\}$$

(*union of sets which belong to x*),

$$x \subseteq y =_{\mathrm{Df}} (z')[(z' \in x) \to (z' \in y)]$$ (*inclusion*),

$$P(x) =_{\mathrm{Df}} \{z' \colon z' \subseteq x\}$$ (*class of all subsets of x*),

$$\{x\} =_{\mathrm{Df}} \{z' \colon (x \in V) \wedge (z' = x)\}$$ (*the singleton of x*),

$$\{x, y\} =_{\mathrm{Df}} \{x\} \cup \{y\}$$ (*the pair of x and y*),

$$\langle x, y\rangle =_{\mathrm{Df}} \big\{\{x\}, \{x, y\}\big\}$$ (*the ordered pair of x and y*),

$$\langle x_1, \ldots, x_n\rangle =_{\mathrm{Df}} \langle x_1, \langle x_2, \ldots, x_n\rangle\rangle$$ (*the ordered n-tuple*),

$$x^n =_{\mathrm{Df}} \{z' \colon (Ey'_1) \ldots (Ey'_n)[(y'_1 \in x) \wedge \ldots \wedge (y'_n \in x) \wedge \wedge (z' = \langle y'_1, \ldots, y'_n\rangle)]\}$$ (*the n-th power of x*),

$$x \times y =_{\mathrm{Df}} \{x' \colon (Eu')(Ev')[(x' = \langle u', v'\rangle) \wedge (u' \in x) \wedge (v' \in y)]\}$$

(*the Cartesian product of x and y*),

$$\mathrm{Rel}(x) =_{\mathrm{Df}} (z')[(z' \in x) \to (Eu')(Ev')\,(z' = \langle u', v'\rangle)]$$

(*x is a relation*),

$$x \circ y =_{\mathrm{Df}} \{x' \colon (Ey')(Ez')(Et')[(x' = \langle y', z'\rangle) \wedge (\langle y', t'\rangle \in x) \wedge \wedge (\langle t', z'\rangle \in y)]\}$$ (*composition of x and y*),

$$\mathrm{Fnc}(f) =_{\mathrm{Df}} \mathrm{Rel}(f) \wedge (x')(y')(z')\{[(\langle x', y'\rangle \in f) \wedge (\langle x', z'\rangle \in f)] \to \to (y' = z')\}$$ (*f is a function*),

$$\mathrm{Dom}(f) =_{\mathrm{Df}} \{x' \colon (Ey')(\langle x', y'\rangle \in f)\}$$ (*domain of f*),

$$\mathrm{Rg}(f) =_{\mathrm{Df}} \{y' \colon (Ex')(\langle x', y'\rangle \in f)\}$$ (*range of f*),

$$\mathrm{Im}(f, x) =_{\mathrm{Df}} \{y' \colon (Et')[(t' \in x) \wedge (\langle t', y'\rangle \in f)]\}$$ (*image of x under f*),

$$x^y =_{\mathrm{Df}} \big\{f' \colon \mathrm{Fnc}(f') \wedge (\mathrm{Dom}(f') = y) \wedge (\mathrm{Rg}(f') \subseteq x)\big\}$$

(*the class of mappings of y into x*),

$$f|x =_{\text{Df}} f \cap (x \times V) \qquad \textit{(the restriction of } f \textit{ to } x\textit{)},$$

$$E =_{\text{Df}} \{x' \colon (Eu')(Ev')[(x' = \langle u', v' \rangle) \wedge (u' \in v')]\} \qquad \textit{(the membership relation)},$$

$$r \operatorname{Conn} x =_{\text{Df}} (s')(t')\{[(s' \in x) \wedge (t' \in x)] \to [(\langle s', t' \rangle \in r) \vee \vee (s' = t') \vee (\langle t', s' \rangle \in r)]\} \qquad \textit{(r is connected in x)},$$

$$\operatorname{ord}(x) =_{\text{Df}} (E \operatorname{Conn} x) \wedge (z')[(z' \in x) \to (z' \subseteq x)] \qquad \textit{(x is an ordinal)},$$

$$On =_{\text{Df}} \{x' \colon \operatorname{ord}(x')\} \qquad \textit{(the class of all ordinals)}.$$

We shall also write "x is an ordinal" instead of $x \in On$. For x, y in On we often write $x < y$ instead of $x \in y$.

$$\min x =_{\text{Df}} [\bigcap (On \cap x)] \cap [\bigcup (On \cap x)]$$

(the least ordinal in x or 0 if there is no such ordinal).

Notice that if the class $On \cap x$ is non-void, then $\bigcap (On \cap x)$ is the least element of this class; the second term $\bigcup (On \cap x)$ has been added in order to make the right-hand side void in case where $On \cap x = 0$ [1]).

$$\sup x =_{\text{Df}} \min\{t' \colon On \cap x \subseteq t'\}$$

(the least ordinal which is larger than every ordinal in x or 0 if there is no such ordinal).

Notice that if $On \cap x$ has a largest element u, then $\sup x = u+1$; if $On \cap x$ has no largest element, then $\sup x = \bigcup (On \cap x)$ [1]).

$$r^{-1} =_{\text{Df}} \{x' \colon (Eu')(Ev')[(x' = \langle u', v' \rangle) \wedge (\langle v', u' \rangle \in r)]\} \qquad \textit{(the converse of a relation)},$$

$$x \sim y =_{\text{Df}} (Ef')[\operatorname{Fnc}(f') \wedge \operatorname{Fnc}(f'^{-1}) \wedge (\operatorname{Dom}(f') = x) \wedge \wedge (\operatorname{Rg}(f') = y)] \qquad \textit{(x and y have the same power)},$$

$$x \textit{ is a cardinal number} =_{\text{Df}} (x \in On) \wedge \neg (Ey')[(y' < x) \wedge (x \sim y')],$$

$$|x| =_{\text{Df}} \operatorname{card}(x) =_{\text{Df}} \bigcap \{y' \colon (y' \textit{ is a cardinal number}) \wedge (y' \sim x)\} \qquad \textit{(the cardinal number of } x\textit{)},$$

$$r \operatorname{WO} x =_{\text{Df}} (r \operatorname{Conn} x) \wedge (y')([(y' \subseteq x) \wedge (y' \neq 0)] \to (Ez')\{(z' \in y') \wedge \wedge \neg (Es')[(s' \in y') \wedge (s' \neq z') \wedge (\langle s', z' \rangle \in r)]\}) \wedge \wedge (u')[(u' \in x) \to (\langle u', u' \rangle \in r)] \qquad \textit{(r well orders x)},$$

[1]) This remark can be established on the basis of the axioms I′–VIII′ to be given below.

x *is an integer* $=_{\mathrm{Df}} \operatorname{ord}(x) \wedge (E^{-1} \mathrm{WO}\, x)$,

$\aleph_0 =_{\mathrm{Df}} \omega =_{\mathrm{Df}} \{x'\colon x' \text{ is an integer}\}$.

Not all of these definitions are needed to express the axioms of M but we shall constantly use them in all the proofs and further definitions. We shall also introduce several new notions as our theory progresses. In these definitions we shall slightly relax our rules: We shall omit the symbol "Df" (meaning "is an abbreviation of"). We shall also state not the definition schemes, as we did above, but simply definitions in which variables and not auxiliary letters are used. Instead of the often inconvenient symbols "x_i" we shall use various other letters, usually (but not always) a capital letter for a class and a lower case letter for a set. We shall also abbreviate $\{x\colon (x \in A) \wedge \ldots\}$ as $\{x \in A\colon \ldots\}$.

In practice it is customary to use not only terms $\{x_i\colon F\}$ but more complicated terms $\{t\colon F\}$ where t is a term. We can introduce these expressions in our system in the following way:

Let t be a term and F a formula. Replace some or all free variables which occur in t or in F (or both) by accented letters $z_1', \ldots, z_k'$ in such a way that a variable which occurs simultaneously in t and in F is always replaced by the same letter in t and in F. Replace the remaining free variables by unaccented letters observing the same rule as above. Let the resulting expressions be t' and F'. We then define

$$\{t'\colon F'\} =_{\mathrm{Df}} \{x'\colon (Ez_1', \ldots, z_k')[(x' = t') \wedge F']\},$$

where x' is a new accented letter.

Thus, for instance, we can admit the definition

$$\{\langle u', v'\rangle\colon (u' \in a) \wedge (v' \in b)\}$$
$$=_{\mathrm{Df}} \{x'\colon (Eu')(Ev')[(x' = \langle u', v'\rangle) \wedge (u' \in a) \wedge (v' \in b)]\},$$

which allows us to represent the definition of the Cartesian product in the form

$$a \times b =_{\mathrm{Df}} \{\langle u', v'\rangle\colon (u' \in a) \wedge (v' \in b)\}.$$

In a similar way we can simplify the definitions of r^{-1} and of E which we gave above.

We shall now list the *axioms of* M.

I′. $(x_0)(x_1)\{(x_0 = x_1) \equiv (x_2)[(x_2 \in x_0) \equiv (x_2 \in x_1)]\}$ (*axiom of extensionality*),

II'_F. $(x_i)\{x_i \in \{x_j: F\} \equiv [(x_i \text{ is a set}) \wedge F(x_i)]\}$

(axiom scheme of class existence).

In II'_F F is a formula which does not contain the variable x_i and $F(x_i)$ is a formula obtained from F by a substitution of the variable x_i for all free occurrences of the variable x_j. No restriction is imposed on the variables which occur in F; they may, in particular, have proper classes as values.

III′. $(x_0)((x_0 \text{ is a set}) \to (Ex_1)\{(x_1 \text{ is a set}) \wedge (x_2)[(x_2 \subseteq x_0) \equiv (x_2 \in x_1)]\})$ *(axiom of power sets),*

IV′. $(x_0)(x_1)\{[(x_0 \text{ is a set}) \wedge (x_1 \text{ is a set})] \to (x_0 \cup x_1 \text{ is a set})\}$

(axiom of unions),

V′. $(x_0)\{\mathrm{Fnc}(x_0) \to (x_1)[(x_1 \text{ is a set}) \to (\mathrm{Im}(x_0, x_1) \text{ is a set})]\}$

(axiom of substitution),

VI′. $(x_0)[(x_0 \text{ is a set}) \to (\bigcup x_0 \text{ is a set})]$ *(axiom of generalized unions),*

VII′. $(x_0)\{(x_0 \neq 0) \to (Ex_1)[(x_1 \in x_0) \wedge (x_1 \cap x_0 = 0)]\}$

(axiom of regularity),

VIII′. $(Ex_0)\{[(x_0 \text{ is a set}) \wedge (0 \in x_0)] \wedge (x_1)[(x_1 \in x_0) \to (x_1 \cup \{x_1\} \in x_0)]\}$

(axiom of infinity).

This concludes the list of axioms of M. Note that their number is infinite; it seems certain that they cannot be replaced by any finite number of axioms. Note also that from II′ it follows that $(x \text{ is a set}) \equiv (x \in V)$.

We stress that we do not include the axiom of choice in the system M. Because of this we will have to be careful when dealing with topics whose usual presentation makes use of the axiom of choice. We cannot claim for instance that every set has a cardinal number as we defined it. Also later, when we use certain notions of general topology, we shall have to arrange various proofs so as to avoid the axiom of choice.

From now on all our proofs will be based exclusively on the axioms of M. In a few places we shall need the provability of certain formulae in ZF; we shall then state explicitly that we carry out the proof in the system ZF.

The axiomatic system M which we described in this section is essentially stronger than ZF. We shall see in section III.3.6 that the consistency of ZF is provable in M. According to the second undecidability theorem of Gödel the consistency of ZF cannot be proved in ZF unless ZF is inconsistent. Hence assuming the consistency of ZF we see that there are theorems provable in M but not in ZF.

On the other hand M is not much stronger than ZF. It can be shown that M is interpretable in the system ZF′ obtained from ZF by adjoining to it one additional axiom:

there is at least one strongly inaccessible cardinal.

An interpretation of M in ZF′ can be obtained as follows. Let α be a strongly inaccessible cardinal and let R_α be the family of all sets whose ranks are less than α (cf. p. 10 or [17], p. 297). We interpret classes as subsets of R_α and the symbol $\in$ as the usual membership relation. The symbol $\{x\colon F\}$ is interpreted as a set consisting of all elements of R_α which satisfy in R_α the formula F. Under this interpretation all axioms of M become theorems of ZF′.

3. Definitions by transfinite induction. Ranks

The inductive definitions will recur constantly throughout our constructions. We shall ask various questions connected with them: in the present chapter we discuss the simple problem of existence of functions satisfying given "inductive" equations. In subsequent chapters we shall deal with the problem of the definability of such functions.

Let A be a class and R a relation of partial order with domain A. Thus R is contained in $A \times A$ and, moreover, satisfies the conditions of reflexivity, antisymmetry and transitivity in A.

We denote by $O(a)$, or more exactly by $O_R(a)$, the class $\{x\colon (\langle x, a\rangle \in R) \wedge (x \neq a)\}$. We shall say that R is *well-founded* if each non-void subclass X of A contains an element a for which $X \cap O(a) = 0$. We call each a of this kind a *minimal element of X*.

3.1. *If R is a well-founded partial ordering of a class A and, moreover, $O(a) \in V$ for each $a \in A$, then for every $h \in V^{V \times A}$ there exists exactly one function $f \in V^A$ which for each a in A satisfies the equation*

(1) $$f(a) = h(f|O(a), a).$$

PROOF. If f' satisfies (1) along with f and $f' \neq f$, then the class $X = \{a: (a \in A) \wedge (f(a) \neq f'(a))\}$ is non-void. Hence for a minimal element a of X we obtain $f|O(a) = f'|O(a)$, whence by (1) $f(a) = f'(a)$, which is impossible because a is an element of X.

In order to prove the existence of f we first show that for each $b \in A$ there is exactly one function f_b with the domain $O(b) \cup \{b\}$ satisfying (1) for each a in the domain of f_b.

The uniqueness of f_b is proved as before. Let X be the subclass of A consisting of every b such that there is no f_b with the properties indicated and assume that $X \neq 0$. If b_0 is a minimal element of X, then we put

$$g = \{\langle x, f_x(x)\rangle : x \in O(b_0)\}$$

and verify that $g \cup \{\langle b_0, h(g, b_0)\rangle\}$ is a function with the domain $O(b_0) \cup \cup \{b_0\}$ which satisfies (1) for all a in $O(b_0) \cup \{b_0\}$. Thus the assumption $X \neq 0$ leads to a contradiction.

It is now sufficient to take as f the class

$$\{\langle b, f_b(b)\rangle : b \in A\}.$$

Theorem 3.1 is thus proved.

The function f constructed in 3.1 is said to be *defined by transfinite induction* and formula (1) is sometimes called the *inductive definition of* f. More complicated forms of transfinite induction are usually reducible to the one discussed in 3.1. Let us consider the following example:

3.2. *Let* A, R *be as in* 3.1; *let* p *be a set and* h_1, h_2 *mappings of* $p \times V \times V \times A$ *into* V. *Then there exist unique functions* e_1, e_2 *with domains* $p \times A$ *which for each* x *in* p *and each* a *in* A *satisfy the equations* ($i = 1, 2$):

$$e_i(x, a) = h_i\big(x, e_1|(p \times O(a)), e_2|(p \times O(a)), a\big)\ ^{1)}.$$

PROOF. We put $A' = p \times A$ and define a partial ordering R' of A':

$$\langle x, a\rangle R' \langle x', a'\rangle \equiv [(x = x') \wedge (a = a')] \vee [(aRa') \wedge (a \neq a')].$$

We easily prove that R' is well founded.

[1]) Note that the restriction of an arbitrary function to a set is a set; hence the value of h_i on the right-hand side of the equation is determined.

We denote by $\varkappa_1(x)$ the first member of x and by $\varkappa_2(x)$ the second member of x if x is an ordered pair. Otherwise we put $\varkappa_1(x) = \varkappa_2(x) = 0$. Formally this can be expressed thus:

$$\varkappa_1(x) = \bigcup \{u\colon (Ev)(x = \langle u, v\rangle)\},$$

$$\varkappa_2(x) = \bigcup \{v\colon (Eu)(x = \langle u, v\rangle)\}.$$

For any function f we denote by $\varkappa_i \circ f$ the function with domain $\mathrm{Dom}(f)$ whose value for an arbitrary argument s is $\varkappa_i(f(s))$:

$$\varkappa_i \circ f = \{\langle s, \varkappa_i(u)\rangle\colon \langle s, u\rangle \in f\}.$$

Now we put for $i = 1, 2$, $t \in V$ and $w \in A'$

$$h(t, w) = \langle h_1(\varkappa_1(w), \varkappa_1 \circ t, \varkappa_2 \circ t, \varkappa_2(w)),$$
$$h_2(\varkappa_1(w), \varkappa_1 \circ t, \varkappa_2 \circ t, \varkappa_2(w))\rangle.$$

From 3.1 we obtain a unique function $f \in V^{A'}$ satisfying the equation

(2) $$f(\langle x, a\rangle) = h(f|O_{R'}(\langle x, a\rangle), \langle x, a\rangle)$$

for arbitrary $\langle x, a\rangle$ in $p \times A$. We easily show that the functions $e_i = \varkappa_i \circ f$ satisfy the required equations and, conversely, that if e_1', e_2' satisfy these equations, then the function

$$f'(\langle x, a\rangle) = \langle e_1'(\langle x, a\rangle), e_2'(\langle x, a\rangle)\rangle$$

satisfies equation (2). This shows the existence and uniqueness of functions e_i.

Let us give a simple but important example of an inductive definition. For a function x with $\mathrm{Dom}(x) = \gamma \in On$ we put $f(x) = \bigcup \mathrm{Rg}(x)$ if γ is a limit number and $f(x) = P(\bigcup \mathrm{Rg}(x))$ otherwise. If x is not a function or if $\mathrm{Dom}(x)$ is not an ordinal, we put $f(x) = 0$. Using theorem 3.1 we infer that:

3.3. *There exists a unique function R: $On \to V$ such that for each ξ in On the equation $R_\xi = f(R|\xi)$ is true.*

Writing explicitly the value of f for the cases $\xi = 0$, $\xi = \eta+1$ and $\xi =$ a limit number, we infer that R satisfies the equations

$$R_0 = 0, \quad R_{\eta+1} = P(R_\eta), \quad R_\lambda = \bigcup \{R_\xi : \xi < \lambda\};$$

in the last equation λ is a limit number.

We shall assume the properties of the sets R_ξ as known; in particular we shall need the following lemmas proved, for example, in [17], p. 298.

3.4. *For arbitrary* ξ, η *in* On *if* $\xi \leqslant \eta$, *then* $R_\xi \subseteq R_\eta$; *if* $x \in V$, *then* $x \in R_\xi \to x \subseteq R_\xi$.

It is also easy to prove that

3.5. *If* $\xi < \eta \in On$, *then* $R_\xi \in R_\eta$.

3.6. $V = \bigcup \{R_\xi \colon \xi \in On\}$.

PROOF. Assume that the difference $V - \bigcup \{R_\xi \colon \xi \in On\}$ is not void and let a be its minimal element. Hence each x which belongs to a is an element of one of the R_ξ, say $x \in R_{\xi(x)}$ where $\xi(x)$ is the least ordinal with this property. If $\lambda = \sup \{\xi(x) \colon x \in a\}$, then $\lambda \in On$ and $a \subseteq R_\lambda$, whence $a \in R_{\lambda+1}$, which contradicts our assumption.

Let $x \in V$; the least ξ such that $x \subseteq R_\xi$ is called the *rank of* x and is denoted by $\mathrm{rg}(x)$. We easily show the following formulae:

3.7. $\mathrm{rg}(x) = \sup \{\mathrm{rg}(y) \colon y \in x\}$.

3.8. *If* $\xi \in On$, *then* $\mathrm{rg}(\xi) = \xi$.

4. Models, satisfaction

We have said before that we want to study the properties of ZF and, in particular, the models of its axioms. Since we want to carry out the discussion in the system M, we shall correlate with each formula H of ZF a set $\langle H \rangle$. These sets are objects which are to be studied in M.

With each variable x_j we correlate the ordinal j; with each of the symbols $\neg$, $\wedge$, (,), $\in$, $=$, of which the formulae of ZF are built, we correlate an ordinal: ω with $\neg$, $\omega+1$ with $\wedge$, etc. We denote by $\langle H \rangle$ the sequence of ordinals correlated with signs which appear in H: the kth term of $\langle H \rangle$ is the ordinal correlated with the kth symbol of H counting from the left.

In the sequel we shall identify formulae with the sequences correlated with them [1]).

[1]) If one wants to keep formulae and the correlated sequences apart, one has to work in a theory which contains M and the syntax of ZF. Axioms of this theory have to be chosen so that the existence of a one-to-one mapping of formulae onto sequences $\langle H \rangle$ be derivable from them.

We omit an easy proof that there exists a set of all formulae (more exactly: of the sequences $\langle H \rangle$) and that it is denumerable. We also omit the purely set-theoretical definition of the function $\mathrm{Fr}(H)$, which correlates with each formula the set of integers j such that x_j is free in the formula.

We shall now define the basic notions of the semantics of ZF.

Let A be a class (or a set), H a formula of ZF, f a mapping of $\mathrm{Fr}(H)$ into A. By $\vdash_A H[f]$ we mean that the formula H is satisfied in A by the terms of f. In order to define this expression for each concrete H it is sufficient to assume the following rules:

If H is $x_i \in x_j$, then $\vdash_A H[f] \equiv f_i \in f_j$;

If H is $x_i = x_j$, then $\vdash_A H[f] \equiv f_i = f_j$;

If H is $\neg H_1$, then $\vdash_A H[f] \equiv \neg \vdash_A H_1[f]$;

If H is $H_1 \wedge H_2$, then $\vdash_A H[f] \equiv \vdash_A H_1[f|\mathrm{Fr}(H_1)] \wedge \vdash_A H_2[f|\mathrm{Fr}(H_2)]$;

If H is $(x_i)H_1$, then $\vdash_A H[f] \equiv \vdash_A H_1[f]$ if $i \notin \mathrm{Fr}(H_1)$, $\vdash_A H[f] \equiv (a)\{a \in A \to \vdash_A H_1[f \cup \{\langle i, a \rangle\}]\}$ if $i \in \mathrm{Fr}(H_1)$.

We use throughout the abbreviation $(a)_A$ for "for every a in A" and $f^\frown \langle i, a \rangle$ (or sometimes $f^\frown a$ if the value of i is obvious) for $f \cup \{\langle i, a \rangle\}$. With these abbreviations the last part of the definition becomes

$$\vdash_A H[f] \equiv (a)_A \vdash_A H_1[f^\frown \langle i, a \rangle].$$

If $\mathrm{Fr}(H) = \{i, j, ..., k\}$ and $f(i) = a$, $f(j) = b$, ..., $f(k) = c$, then we shall sometimes write $\vdash_A H[a, b, ..., c]$ instead of $\vdash_A H[f]$.

We now want to obtain a proof that for every class A there exists a relation St_A between formulae and finite sequences of elements of A such that—speaking intuitively—

$$\langle H, f \rangle \in St_A \equiv \vdash_A H[f]$$

for each formula H and each f in $A^{\mathrm{Fr}(H)}$. We say "speaking intuitively" because we have as yet no general definition of the right-hand side of this equivalence, only a scheme which allows us to define it for each H separately.

We want also to show that there is a ternary relation St, i.e., a class of triples $\langle H, A, f \rangle$ such that if A is a set, H a formula and f a sequence in $A^{\mathrm{Fr}(H)}$, then—intuitively speaking—

$$\langle H, A, f \rangle \in St \equiv \vdash_A H[f].$$

ERRATA

Page, line	For	Read
13^{16}	E_i	E_{ij}
66^{15}	completelt	completely
66^{16}	apparen-	apparent
66_{16}	metay	meta-
66_8	nterpretations	interpretations
67_2	$\neg A(z)$	$(s)_{>z}(Et)_{z\leqslant t<s}\neg A(t)$
72^{13}	O_ϱ	$O_{\varrho(p)}$
81^{17}	$\mathrm{constr}_{A,T}$	$\mathrm{constr}_{B,T}$
83^1	5.1	5.2
89_1	IV 2	IV 3
182_{10}	sqeuence	sequence
184_7	γ	ϱ
190^6	We denote,	We denote
198_1	$\vartheta[P(a)]^\alpha$	$\vartheta([P(a)]^\alpha)$
208^{12}	is a one-to-one function	is a function

A. Mostowski, *Constructible sets*

We shall obtain proofs of these theorems by transforming the inductive rules given above into an explicit definition. We carry this out as follows:

First we define the operations Neg, Con, Qu which—speaking intuitively—lead from the classes

$$\{f \in A^{\mathrm{Fr}(H)}: \vdash_A H[f]\}, \quad \{f \in A^{\mathrm{Fr}(H')}: \vdash_A H'[f]\}$$

to the classes

$$\{f \in A^{\mathrm{Fr}(\neg H)}: \vdash_A \neg H[f]\}, \quad \{f \in A^{\mathrm{Fr}(H \wedge H')}: \vdash_A H \wedge H'[f]\},$$

$$\{f \in A^{\mathrm{Fr}((x_j)H)}: \vdash_A (x_j)H[f]\}.$$

We also define explicitly the classes E_{ij} and I_{ij} of those sequences f in $A^{\{i,j\}}$ which satisfy the atomic formulae $x_i \in x_j$ and $x_i = x_j$ (both these classes depend on A).

To say that f satisfies H in A amounts to the same as to say that there exists a function s whose domain consists of all subformulae of H and which has the following properties:

(i) if P is an atomic formula $x_i \in x_j$ or $x_i = x_j$, then $s(P) = E_i$ or $s(P) = I_{ij}$,

(ii) if $P = \neg P'$, then $s(P) = \mathrm{Neg}(s(P'))$,

(iii) if $P = P' \wedge P''$, then $s(P) = \mathrm{Con}(s(P'), s(P''))$,

(iv) if $P = (x_j)P'$, then $s(P) = \mathrm{Qu}(j, P')$,

(v) $f \in s(H)$.

To see this it is sufficient to notice that the inductive clauses (i)–(iv) imply the equivalence

$$g \in s(P) \equiv \vdash_A P[g]$$

for each subformula P of H and each g in $A^{\mathrm{Fr}(P)}$.

The difficulty now is this: we have in our language no means to speak about functions whose values are classes. We overcome this difficulty by replacing s by a class K such that $\mathrm{Dom}(K)$ is the set of all subformulae of H; the class $s(P)$ is then replaced by $\{x: \langle P, x\rangle \in K\}$ [1].

[1]) The device of replacing s by K, which enables us to speak (indirectly) about finite sequences of classes without extending the language of M, is due to Robinson [28]. For the whole content of this section compare Tarski [34].

We now pass to formal proofs.

4.1. *There is a unique class* St *of triples* $\langle x, y, z\rangle$ *in which* x *has the form* $\langle H\rangle$, y *is a set*, $z \in y^{\mathrm{Fr}(H)}$, *and which satisfies the conditions*:

(1) $$\langle\langle x_i \in x_j\rangle, y, z\rangle \in St \equiv z(i) \in z(j),$$

(2) $$\langle\langle x_i = x_j\rangle, y, z\rangle \in St \equiv z(i) = z(j),$$

(3) $$\langle\langle \neg H\rangle, y, z\rangle \in St \equiv \neg(\langle\langle H\rangle, y, z\rangle \in St),$$

(4) $$\langle\langle H_1 \wedge H_2\rangle, y, z\rangle \in St \equiv (\langle\langle H_1\rangle, y, z|\mathrm{Fr}(H_1)\rangle \in St) \wedge \wedge (\langle\langle H_2\rangle, y, z|\mathrm{Fr}(H_2)\rangle \in St),$$

(5) $$\langle\langle (x_i)H\rangle, y, z\rangle \in St \equiv (a)_y \langle\langle H\rangle, y, z \cup \{\langle i, a\rangle\}\rangle \in St$$

provided that $i \in \mathrm{Fr}(H)$; *otherwise*

(6) $$\langle\langle (x_i)H\rangle, y, z\rangle \in St \equiv \langle\langle H\rangle, y, z\rangle \in St.$$

4.2. *For every class* A *there is a unique class* St_A *of pairs of the form* $\langle\langle H\rangle, z\rangle$ *where* $z \in A^{\mathrm{Fr}(H)}$ *such that*

(1′) $$\langle\langle x_i \in x_j\rangle, z\rangle \in St_A \equiv z(i) \in z(j),$$

(2′) $$\langle\langle x_i = x_j\rangle, z\rangle \in St_A \equiv z(i) = z(j),$$

(3′) $$\langle\langle \neg H\rangle, z\rangle \in St_A \equiv \neg(\langle\langle H\rangle, z\rangle \in St_A),$$

(4′) $$\langle\langle H_1 \wedge H_2\rangle, z\rangle \in St_A \equiv (\langle\langle H_1\rangle, z|\mathrm{Fr}(H_1)\rangle \in St_A) \wedge \wedge (\langle\langle H_2\rangle, z|\mathrm{Fr}(H_2)\rangle \in St_A),$$

(5′) $$\langle\langle (x_i)H\rangle, z\rangle \in St_A \equiv (x)_A(\langle\langle H\rangle, z \cup \{\langle i, x\rangle\}\rangle \in St_A)$$

provided that $i \in \mathrm{Fr}(H)$; *otherwise*

(6′) $$\langle\langle (x_i)H\rangle, z\rangle \in St_A \equiv \langle\langle H\rangle, z\rangle \in St_A.$$

If A is a class, then $\vdash_A H[f]$ means the same as $\langle\langle H\rangle, f\rangle \in St_A$.

We shall sketch a proof of 4.1; the proof of 4.2 is entirely analogous.

PROOF OF 4.1. Let $i, j \in \omega$, let X, X_1, X_2 be classes and p, p_1, p_2 sets. We introduce the following abbreviations:

$E_{ij} = \{\langle y, z\rangle\colon (y \text{ is a set}) \wedge (z \in y^{\{i,j\}}) \wedge (z(i) \in z(j))\}$;

$$I_{ij} = \{\langle y, z\rangle: (y \text{ is a set}) \wedge (z \in y^{\{i,j\}}) \wedge (z(i) = z(j))\};$$
$$\mathrm{Neg}(X, p) = \{\langle y, z\rangle: (y \text{ is a set}) \wedge (z \in y^p) \wedge (\langle y, z\rangle \notin X)\};$$
$$\mathrm{Con}(X_1, X_2, p_1, p_2) = \{\langle y, z\rangle: (y \text{ is a set}) \wedge (z \in y^{p_1 \cup p_2}) \wedge \wedge (z|p_1 \in X_1) \wedge (z|p_2 \in X_2)\};$$
$$\mathrm{Qu}(i, X, p) = \{\langle y, z\rangle: (y \text{ is a set}) \wedge (z \in y^{p-\{i\}}) \wedge \wedge (i \in p) \wedge (u)_y\, (z \cup \{\langle i, u\rangle\} \in X)\}.$$

If X is a class of ordered triples $\langle a, b, c\rangle$ whose terms a, b, c are sets, i.e., if $X \subseteq V^3$, then we denote by $X^{(a)}$ and $\mathrm{Dom}(X)$ the classes

$$X^{(a)} = \{\langle b, c\rangle: \langle a, b, c\rangle \in X\} \quad (\textit{projection of } X),$$
$$\mathrm{Dom}(X) = \{a: (Eb)(Ec)\langle a, b, c\rangle \in X\} \quad (\textit{domain of } X).$$

In the rest of this proof the letters A, B, C, D, E, F will denote formulae (i)–(vi) below, in which R, Q, S are arbitrary formulae of ZF:

(i) $(i)(j)[(\langle Q\rangle = \langle x_i \in x_j\rangle) \rightarrow (K^{(\langle Q\rangle)} = E_{ij})]$,

(ii) $(i)(j)[(\langle Q\rangle = \langle x_i = x_j\rangle) \rightarrow (K^{(\langle Q\rangle)} = I_{ij})]$,

(iii) $(\langle Q\rangle = \langle \neg R\rangle) \rightarrow \big(K^{(\langle Q\rangle)} = \mathrm{Neg}(K^{(\langle R\rangle)}, \mathrm{Fr}(R))\big)$,

(iv) $(\langle Q\rangle = \langle R \wedge S\rangle) \rightarrow \big(K^{(\langle Q\rangle)} = \mathrm{Con}(K^{(\langle R\rangle)}, K^{(\langle S\rangle)}, \mathrm{Fr}(R), \mathrm{Fr}(S))\big)$,

(v) $(i)[(\langle Q\rangle = \langle (x_i) R\rangle) \wedge (i \notin \mathrm{Fr}(R)) \rightarrow (K^{(\langle Q\rangle)} = K^{(\langle R\rangle)})]$,

(vi) $(i)\big[(\langle Q\rangle = \langle (x_i) R\rangle) \wedge (i \in \mathrm{Fr}(R)) \rightarrow \rightarrow \big(K^{(\langle Q\rangle)} = \mathrm{Qu}(i, K^{(\langle R\rangle)}, \mathrm{Fr}(Q))\big)\big]$.

With this notation and with H denoting an arbitrary formula of ZF we let $\Phi_H(K)$ be the abbreviation of

$$(K \subseteq V^3) \wedge (\mathrm{Dom}(K) = \{\langle Q\rangle: Q \text{ is a subformula of } H\}) \wedge$$
$$\wedge (Q, y, z)((\langle\langle Q\rangle, y, z\rangle \in K) \rightarrow (z \in y^{\mathrm{Fr}(Q)})) \wedge$$
$$\wedge (Q, R, S)[(\langle Q\rangle \in \mathrm{Dom}(K)) \rightarrow (A \wedge B \wedge C \wedge D \wedge E \wedge F)].$$

By induction on the number of logical symbols in H we prove that for every formula H of ZF there is a unique class K satisfying $\Phi_H(K)$. If H is the formula $x_i \in x_j$ or $x_i = x_j$, then the unique K in question is $\{H\} \times E_{ij}$ or $\{H\} \times I_{ij}$. If H has the form $\neg H_1$, then the unique K is $K_1 \cup \big(\{H\} \times \mathrm{Neg}(K_1^{(\langle H_1\rangle)}, \mathrm{Fr}(H_1))\big)$ where K_1 is the unique class such that $\Phi_{H_1}(K_1)$. If H has the form $H_1 \wedge H_2$ and K_1, K_2 are unique classes satisfying $\Phi_{H_1}(K_1)$ and $\Phi_{H_2}(K_2)$, then

$$K_1 \cup K_2 \cup \left(\{H\} \times \mathrm{Con}\left(K_1^{(\langle H_1\rangle)}, K_2^{(\langle H_2\rangle)}, \mathrm{Fr}(H_1), \mathrm{Fr}(H_2)\right)\right)$$

is the unique class satisfying $\Phi_H(K)$. If H has the form $(x_i)H_1$, then the required class is either $K_1 \cup \{H\} \times K_1^{(\langle H_1\rangle)}$ if $x_i \notin \mathrm{Fr}(H_1)$ or

$$K_1 \cup \left(\{H\} \times \mathrm{Qu}\left(i, K_1^{(\langle H_1\rangle)}, \mathrm{Fr}(H_1)\right)\right)$$

where K_1 is the unique class satisfying $\Phi_{H_1}(K_1)$.

Finally we take

$$St = \{\langle\langle H\rangle, y, z\rangle : (EK)[\Phi_H(K) \wedge (\langle\langle H\rangle, y, z\rangle \in K)]\}.$$

We shall verify that St has the required ɼroperties.

It is obvious that elements of St are triples $\langle\langle H\rangle, y, z\rangle$, where H is a formula and $z \in y^{\mathrm{Fr}(H)}$. If H is the formula $x_i \in x_j$ and $\langle\langle H\rangle, y, z\rangle \in K$, where K is a class satisfying $\Phi_H(K)$, then $z(i) \in z(j)$ according to A and the definition of E_{ij}. Conversely, if $z \in y^{\{i,j\}}$ and $z(i) \in z(j)$, then $\langle y, z\rangle \in E_{ij}$; since the class $\{\langle x_i \in x_j\rangle\} \times E_{ij}$ satisfies the condition $\Phi_H(K)$, it follows that $\langle\langle H\rangle, y, z\rangle \in St$.

If H is the formula $x_i = x_j$, the proof is analogous.

Now let H be the formula $\neg H_1$ and let K and K_1 be unique classes satisfying $\Phi_H(K)$ and $\Phi_{H_1}(K_1)$. In this case

$$K = K_1 \cup \left(\{H\} \times \mathrm{Neg}\left(K_1^{(\langle H_1\rangle)}, \mathrm{Fr}(H_1)\right)\right)$$

whence $\langle\langle H\rangle, y, z\rangle \in K$ is equivalent to $\langle y, z\rangle \in \mathrm{Neg}\left(K_1^{(\langle H_1\rangle)}, \mathrm{Fr}(H_1)\right)$, i.e. to $\langle y, z\rangle \notin K_1^{(\langle H_1\rangle)}$. Thus, if $\langle\langle H\rangle, y, z\rangle \in K$, then there is a class K_1 such that $\Phi_{H_1}(K_1)$ and $\langle\langle H_1\rangle, y, z\rangle \notin K_1$. Since K_1 is unique, we infer that St does not contain $\langle\langle H_1\rangle, y, z\rangle$ as an element. Conversely, if $\langle\langle H_1\rangle, y, z\rangle \notin St$, then $\langle\langle H_1\rangle, y, z\rangle \notin K_1$ and by the definition of Neg we obtain $\langle\langle H\rangle, y, z\rangle \in K$, whence $\langle\langle H\rangle, y, z\rangle \in St$.

The proofs in cases where H is $H_1 \wedge H_2$ or $(x_i)H_1$ are similar and can be left to the reader.

Using the class St_A, we can define the basic semantical notion of satisfaction more precisely than we did at the beginning of this section: $\vdash_A H[f] \equiv \langle\langle H\rangle, f\rangle \in St_A$. If A is a set, this is also equivalent to $\langle\langle H\rangle, A, f\rangle \in St$.

5. Derived semantical notions; the Skolem–Löwenheim theorem

Using the satisfaction relation we can define several semantical notions which will be of great importance in our proofs.

Validity. A formula of ZF, say H, is *valid* in a class (or a set) A if $\vdash_A H[f]$ for arbitrary f in $A^{\mathrm{Fr}(H)}$.

In all subsequent definitions we shall speak exclusively of formulae of ZF; thus the word "formula" means henceforth the same as "formula of ZF".

Models. A set (or a class) A is a *model* for a set of formulae if all those formulae are valid in A. In particular, A is a model for ZF if all axioms of ZF are valid in A.

Elementary equivalence. Let A, B be two classes; in particular one of them, or both, may be sets. We say that they are *elementarily equivalent* if $\vdash_A H \equiv \vdash_B H$ for each formula H without free variables. We then write $A \equiv B$.

One easily shows that two elementarily equivalent classes are models of the same sets of formulae. Thus if one of them is a model of ZF, then so is the other.

Elementary subsystems and extensions. Let A, B be two classes; as before, one of them or both may be sets. We say that A is an *elementary subclass* (or subset) *of* B and that B is an *elementary extension of* A if $A \subseteq B$ and the following condition is satisfied: for each formula H and each sequence $f \in A^{\mathrm{Fr}(H)}$ the conditions $\vdash_A H[f]$ and $\vdash_B H[f]$ are equivalent. In symbols we write $A \prec B$.

Obviously $A \prec B$ implies that $A \equiv B$; one can show on examples that the conditions $A \subseteq B$ and $A \equiv B$ do not imply that $A \prec B$.

Definability. A class R is called an *n-ary relation* if it is a subclass of V^n. We say that an n-ary relation R is *definable in a class A* if $R \subseteq A^n$ and there is a formula H with exactly n free variables $x_1, \ldots, x_n$ such that

$$\langle a_1, \ldots, a_n \rangle \in R \equiv \vdash_A H[a_1, \ldots, a_n]$$

for arbitrary $a_1, \ldots, a_n$ in A.

The formula H is said to define R in A.

For $n = 1$ we obtain the notion of definability of subsets of A; since functions are binary relations, we also obtain the notion of definability of functions.

Parametric definability. An n-ary relation $R \subseteq A^n$ is *parametrically definable in A* if there exist an integer $p \geqslant 0$, a formula H with the free variables $x_1, \ldots, x_n, x_{n+1}, \ldots, x_{n+p}$ and a sequence with p terms $f_1, \ldots, f_p$ in A such that

$$\langle a_1, \ldots, a_n \rangle \in R \equiv \vdash_A H[a_1, \ldots, a_n, f_1, \ldots, f_p]$$

for arbitrary $a_1, \ldots, a_n$ in A.

The elements $f_1, \ldots, f_p$ are called *parameters* and we express the above formula by saying that H together with the sequence of parameters define R in A. The notion of parametric definability is applicable also to subsets of A and to mappings of A into itself.

It is clear that definability entails parametric definability but not conversely.

We shall now state and prove a theorem to which we shall refer as "the Skolem–Löwenheim theorem" although it is only a special case of the so-called downward Skolem–Löwenheim theorem, known from the theory of models (see e.g. [27]).

5.1. *If A is a well-ordered class, $b \subseteq A$ and b is a set, then there is a set a such that $b \subseteq a \prec A$ and* $\operatorname{card}(a) \leqslant \max(\aleph_0, \operatorname{card}(b))$.

PROOF. Without loss of generality we assume that $b \neq 0$. We shall construct the required a by consecutive extensions of b. We therefore first define functions which will be used to extend b.

Let $H = (x_j)K$ be a formula such that $j \in \operatorname{Fr}(K)$. We denote by F_H the unique function whose domain is $A^{\operatorname{Fr}(H)}$ and which satisfies the condition that $\langle f, a \rangle \in F_H$ if a is the earliest element of A such that $\vdash_A \neg K[f \cup \{\langle j, a \rangle\}]$ provided that such elements a exist; if there are no such elements a, then $\langle f, 0 \rangle \in F_H$.

The function F_H depends obviously on A and on the well-ordering of A, which we assumed to exist. If H does not have the form $(x_j)K$, then we put $F_H(f) = 0$ for each f in $A^{\operatorname{Fr}(H)}$.

We let X be the class

$$\{\langle H, f, a \rangle : (H \text{ is a formula}) \wedge (\langle f, a \rangle \in F_H)\}.$$

Also this class depends on A and its well-ordering.

LEMMA. *Let B be a subclass of A with the property that whenever H is a formula, $f \in B^{\mathrm{Fr}(H)}$ and $\langle f, a\rangle \in F_H$, then $a \in B$. Under these assumptions $B \prec A$.*

PROOF. Let K be any formula. We have to show that for every f in $B^{\mathrm{Fr}(K)}$

$$\vdash_A K[f] \equiv \vdash_B K[f].$$

This equivalence is obvious if K is an atomic formula. From the definition of the satisfaction relation we immediately infer that if the equivalence holds for the formulae K and K', then it does so for the formulae $\neg K$, $K \wedge K'$ and $(x_j)K$ where $j \notin \mathrm{Fr}(K)$. Thus it remains to show that if H is the formula $(x_j)K, j \in \mathrm{Fr}(K)$ and $f \in B^{\mathrm{Fr}(H)}$, then

$$\vdash_A H[f] \equiv \vdash_B H[f].$$

The implication from left to right still follows solely from the definition of the satisfaction relation: for the left-hand side means that for every a in A the sequence $f \cup \{\langle j, a\rangle\}$ satisfies K in A. If $a \in B$, then we can use the inductive assumption and state that this sequence satisfies K in B, and so we obtain the right-hand side of the equivalence.

Let us now assume that the left-hand side of the equivalence is false. Since H belongs to the domain of X, we obtain $F_H(f) \in B$. Thus B contains an element $a = F_H(f)$ such that $\vdash_A \neg K[f \cup \{\langle j, a\rangle\}]$. From the inductive assumption we infer that we can replace A by B, which shows that f does not satisfy the formula H in B. The lemma is thus proved.

Now in order to prove the theorem we put

$$a = \bigcup_{n<\omega} b_n \quad \text{where} \quad b_0 = b \text{ and } b_{n+1} = b_n \cup \bigcup_H \mathrm{Im}(X^{(H)}, b_n^{\mathrm{Dom}(F_H)}) .$$

It is obvious that $b \subseteq a$ and that a satisfies the assumption of the lemma: a is closed under the operations of forming values of functions F_H for the arguments in $a^{\mathrm{Fr}(H)}$. By the lemma we thus obtain $a \prec A$.

If b is finite, then so are all b_n and a is at most denumerable. If b is infinite, then all b_n have the same power as b and hence so does their union. Notice that this evaluation of the power of a uses the denumerability of the set of all formulae but does not require the axiom of choice since all the sets considered are contained in the well-ordered class A. Theorem 5.1 is thus proved.

6. The contraction lemma

We call a set or a class *transitive* if it satisfies the condition $(x \in y \in A) \to (x \in A)$.

Two classes A and B are called *isomorphic* if there is a one-to-one function F with domain A and range B such that

$$(x \in y) \equiv [F(x) \in F(y)]$$

for arbitrary x, y in A.

6.1. CONTRACTION-LEMMA. *Every class A in which axiom* (I) *is valid is isomorphic with a transitive class.*

PROOF. By the axiom of foundation there is at least one minimal element m in A. Hence $x \in m$ for no x in A, and since we assume that (I) is valid in A, we see that there is at most one minimal element in A. We put

$$M_0 = \{m\} \quad \text{and} \quad M_\xi = \{a \in A: (x)_A(x \in a \to x \in \bigcup_{\eta<\xi} M_\eta)\}.$$

We see by induction that each M_ξ is a set and that $M_\xi \subseteq M_\eta$ for $\xi < \eta$. The union $\bigcup_{\xi \in On} M_\xi = A$. Let us assume that this is not the case and let a be a minimal element of $A - \bigcup_{\xi} M_\xi$. Hence $x \in a$ implies $x \in \bigcup_{\xi} M_\xi$ for each x in A and thus there is a $\xi(x)$ such that $x \in M_{\xi(x)}$ for each x in $A \cap a$. If $\eta = \sup\{\xi(x): x \in A \cap a\}$, then we infer from the definition of M_η that $a \in M_\eta$, which is a contradiction.

Now we define $\varphi(x)$ by transfinite induction on the least ξ such that $x \in M_\xi$. For $\xi = 0$, i.e. $x = m$, we put $\varphi(x) = 0$. If $\varphi(y)$ is defined for $y \in \bigcup_{\eta<\xi} M_\eta$ and $x \in M_\xi$, then we put

$$\varphi(x) = \{\varphi(y): y \in A \cap x\}.$$

We prove by induction that

$$(*) \qquad \varphi(x) = \varphi(y) \to x = y.$$

Let ξ, η be the minimal ordinals for which $x \in M_\xi$ and $y \in M_\eta$ and let us assume that the implication $(*)$ is true for $\max(\xi, \eta) < \zeta$. Let x, y be such that $\max(\xi, \eta) = \zeta$ and $\varphi(x) = \varphi(y)$. If $x \neq y$, e.g. $x - y \neq 0$, then there is a $z \in x - y$, and since we assume the axiom (I) to be true in A we may assume that $z \in A$. Hence there is a $\zeta' < \zeta$ such that $z \in M_{\zeta'}$. From $z \in x$ we obtain $\varphi(z) \in \varphi(x) = \varphi(y)$. But $\varphi(y)$ is the set of all $\varphi(t)$ where $t \in A$ and $t \in y$. Hence $\varphi(z) = \varphi(t)$ for some t in $A \cap y$. Since $t \in M_\tau$ for a $\tau < \zeta$, we obtain $z = t$ by inductive assumption and hence $z \in y$, which contradicts the assumption that $z \notin y$.

The class $B = \{\varphi(x): x \in A\}$ is transitive; for, if $u \in v \in \varphi(x)$, then v has the form $v = \varphi(y)$ where $y \in x \cap A$, and hence u has the form $\varphi(z)$ where $z \in y \cap A$. Hence $u \in B$.

Finally $x \in y \equiv \varphi(x) \in \varphi(y)$ for arbitrary x, y in A. If $x \in y$, then $\varphi(x) \in \varphi(y)$ by definition. If $\varphi(x) \in \varphi(y)$, then $\varphi(x) = \varphi(z)$ for a z in y, whence $x = z \in y$. Theorem 6.1 is thus proved.

We note two simple additional facts:

6.2. *Under the assumption of* 6.1 *there is exactly one function* φ *which maps* A *isomorphically onto a transitive class.*

PROOF. φ must map m onto 0 since 0 is the unique minimal element of each transitive class. By induction on ξ we show that if $x \in M_\xi$, then $\varphi(x)$ must be equal to $\{\varphi(y): y \in x \cap A\}$.

The unique φ is called a *contracting function* of A [1]).

6.3. *Under the assumptions of* 6.1 *if* $a \in A$ *and* a *is transitive, then the contracting function of* A *satisfies the equation* $\varphi(x) = x$ *for all* $x \in a \cup \cup (P(a) \cap A)$.

PROOF. If $\varphi(x) = x$ for all $x \in a \cap \bigcup_{\eta<\xi} M_\eta$ and $x \in a \cap M_\xi$, then $\varphi(y) = y$ for all y in x and hence $\varphi(x) = x$. If $x \subseteq a$ and $x \in A$, then $\varphi(y) = y$ for all y in x and hence $\varphi(x) = x$.

[1]) The term "collapsing function" is also in use.

CHAPTER II

GENERAL PRINCIPLES OF CONSTRUCTION

1. Sufficient conditions for a class to be a model

We state several simple lemmas which express sufficient conditions for a class to be a model of ZF. Throughout this section A is a transitive class.

1.1. *Axiom* (I) *is always valid in* A.

1.2. *Axiom* (II) *is valid in* A *if and only if* A *is closed under the operation of forming pairs.*

1.3. *Axiom* (III) *is valid in* A *if and only if* A *is closed under the operation of forming unions, i.e.,* $a \in A \rightarrow \bigcup a \in A$.

1.4. *Axiom* (IV) *is valid in* A *if and only if* A *contains a non-void set* a *such that whenever* b *is in* a, *there is a set* c *which properly contains* b *and is an element of* a.

All these lemmas are proved in a straightforward way. E.g., to prove 1.2 we notice that axiom (II) is valid in A if and only if for arbitrary x, y in A there is a z in A which together with x and y satisfies in A the formula

$$(t)\{(t \in z) \equiv [(t = x) \vee (t = y)]\}.$$

From this we infer that $z = \{x, y\}$, which proves the theorem.

1.5. *Axiom* (V) *is valid in* A *if and only if* $a \in A \rightarrow P(a) \cap A \in A$.

This theorem is proved by showing that $P(a) \cap A$ is the unique element which together with a satisfies the formula

$$(z)[z \in y \equiv (t)(t \in z \rightarrow t \in x)].$$

1.6. *In order that axioms* (VI_H) *be valid in* A *it is necessary and sufficient that for all parametrically definable mappings* φ

$$(a \in A) \rightarrow (\mathrm{Im}(\varphi, a) \in A).$$

PROOF. If φ is defined by H and f, then the antecedent of (VI_H) is satisfied by f. Hence if (VI_H) is valid in A, then the consequent of (VI_H) is satisfied by f and we infer that for every a in A there is a b in A such that for every y in A

$$(1) \qquad (y \in b) \equiv (Ex)_a \vdash_A H[x, y, f_i, \ldots, f_k].$$

Thus $b = \mathrm{Im}(\varphi, a)$ and $\mathrm{Im}(\varphi, a) \in A$. Conversely, if $\mathrm{Im}(\varphi, a) \in A$, then denoting $\mathrm{Im}(\varphi, a)$ by b we have formula (1) and so the consequent of (VI_H) is satisfied.

In view of 1.1–1.6 it would seem that the simplest way to obtain a model would be to start with an arbitrary set and to close it with respect to the operations enumerated in 1.2–1.6. We must remember, however, that operations defined in 1.5 and 1.6 depend on the set A which we want to construct, and thus this simple method is not practicable: operations 1.5 and 1.6 are really not defined until we have defined an A. In order to overcome this difficulty we shall start with an arbitrary A_0 and gradually extend it, using a suitable transfinite process, to a class which has all the required properties. In order to see how to define the extensions we first prove some theorems on models represented as transfinite unions.

2. The reflection theorem

Let $A = \bigcup_{\xi \in On} A_\xi$ where the A_ξ are sets and $A_\xi \subseteq A_\eta$ for $\xi < \eta$ and $A_\lambda = \bigcup_{\xi < \lambda} A_\xi$ if λ is a limit ordinal. Then the following theorem holds.

2.1. THE REFLECTION THEOREM[1]). *For every formula H there is a strictly increasing continuous mapping $F = F_H$: $On \to On$ such that if $\varkappa$ is a critical number of F (i.e. if $F(\varkappa) = \varkappa > 0$) and $f \in A_\varkappa^{\mathrm{Fr}(H)}$, then*

$$(1) \qquad \vdash_A H[f] \equiv \vdash_{A_\varkappa} H[f].$$

PROOF. If H has no quantifiers it is clearly sufficient to take the identity mapping as F. If H is $\neg H'$ or $H' \wedge H''$, then we take $F_H = F_{H'}$ or $F_H = F_{H'} \circ F_{H''}$. We easily check that (1) is then true for H provided

[1]) This theorem is sometimes called the Scott–Scarpellini lemma. Cf. Scarpellini [29]; Scott first used this result in his lectures of 1963.

it was true for H' and for H''. In the case of the formula $\neg H'$ there is nothing to prove and in the case of the formula $H' \wedge H''$ all that we have to notice is that if $\varkappa$ is a critical number of F_H, then it is a critical number of $F_{H'}$ and of $F_{H''}$.

Now let H be the formula $(x_i)H'$. If $i \notin \mathrm{Fr}(H')$, then we take $F_H = F_{H'}$; since the quantifier is a dummy, H can be replaced everywhere by H'. Now let $i \in \mathrm{Fr}(H')$. For arbitrary f in $A^{\mathrm{Fr}(H)}$ we denote by $\varrho(f)$ the smallest ordinal η such that there is an element a in A_η satisfying $\vdash_A \neg H'[\{\langle i, a\rangle\} \cup f]$; if no such η exists, we put $\varrho(f) = 0$. Further, we put

(2) $$\sigma(\xi) = \sup\{\varrho(f)\colon f \in A_\xi^{\mathrm{Fr}(H)}\}.$$

It is obvious that the function σ is non-decreasing:

(3) $$\sigma(\xi) \leqslant \sigma(\eta) \quad \text{for} \quad \xi \leqslant \eta.$$

If λ is a limit number > 0, then

(4) $$\sigma(\lambda) \leqslant \sup\{\sigma(\xi)\colon\ \xi < \lambda\}.$$

To see this, let $f \in A_\lambda^{\mathrm{Fr}(H')}$; then there is a $\xi < \lambda$ such that $f \in A_\xi^{\mathrm{Fr}(H)}$ and hence

$$\varrho(f) < \sigma(\xi) < \sup\{\sigma(\xi)\colon\ \xi < \lambda\}.$$

Taking sup with respect to f ranging over $A_\lambda^{\mathrm{Fr}(H)}$, we obtain (4).

Since σ is not necessarily strictly increasing, we replace it by another function defined by induction:

$$G(0) = \sigma(0), \qquad G(\xi+1) = \max\big(G(\xi), \sigma(\xi+1)\big)+1,$$
$$G(\lambda) = \sup\{G(\xi)\colon\ \xi < \lambda\}.$$

G is strictly increasing and continuous and satisfies the inequality

(5) $$G(\xi) \geqslant \sigma(\xi),$$

as we immediately see from (4) using induction.

Let $F_H = F_{H'} \circ G$. This function is again strictly increasing and continuous; its critical numbers are critical for $F_{H'}$ and for G. Let $F_H(\varkappa) = \varkappa > 0$ and $f \in A_\varkappa^{\mathrm{Fr}(H)}$. If $\vdash_A H[f]$, then for every a in A we have

$$\vdash_A H'[\{\langle i, a\rangle\} \cup f],$$

and hence by the inductive assumption we obtain

$$\vdash_{A_\varkappa} H'[\{\langle i, a\rangle\} \cup f]$$

for every a in $A_\varkappa$, which proves that $\vdash_{A_\varkappa} H[f]$. If non $\vdash_A H[f]$, then there is an element a in A such that non $\vdash_A H'[\{\langle i, a\rangle\} \cup f]$. Hence we can find an a of this kind already in $A_{\varrho(f)}$. Since $f \in A_\varkappa^{\mathrm{Fr}(H)}$, there is a $\xi < \varkappa$ such that $f \in A_\xi^{\mathrm{Fr}(H)}$ and hence

$$\varrho(f) < \sigma(\xi) \leqslant G(\xi) \leqslant F_H(\xi) < F_H(\varkappa) = \varkappa .$$

Thus there is an a in $A_\varkappa$ such that

$$\text{non } \vdash_A H'[\{\langle i, a\rangle\} \cup f],$$

whence by the inductive assumption we obtain

$$\text{non } \vdash_{A_\varkappa} H'[\{\langle i, a\rangle\} \cup f] \quad \text{and} \quad \text{non } \vdash_{A_\varkappa} H[f].$$

Our theorem is thus proved.

The reflection theorem can be strengthened to the following theorem.

2.2. *Let A be a function with domain On such that $A_\xi \subseteq A_\eta$, whenever $\xi < \eta$ and $A_\lambda = \bigcup \{A_\xi \colon \xi < \lambda\}$ whenever λ is a limit number. There is an increasing continuous function ϕ which maps On into On and is such that if $\phi(\xi) = \xi > 0$, then $A_\xi \prec \bigcup \mathrm{Rg}(A)$.*

In order to obtain this result we must first prove a strengthened version of the reflection theorem: *There is a function G with the following properties*:

(i) *the domain of G consists of all pairs $\langle H, \xi\rangle$ where H is a formula and ξ an ordinal*;

(ii) *the values of G are ordinals*;

(iii) *if H is a formula, then the function $F_H(\xi) = G(H, \xi)$ is an increasing and continuous mapping of On into On*;

(iv) *if H is a formula and $F_H(\xi) = \xi > 0$, then for every a in $A_\xi^{\mathrm{Fr}(H)}$*

$$(*) \qquad \vdash_{A_\xi} H[a] \equiv \vdash_{\bigcup \mathrm{Rg}(A)} H[a].$$

In the proof of the reflection theorem we indicated how to obtain functions $F_{\neg H'}$, $F_{H' \wedge H''}$, $F_{(x_i) H'}$ from functions $F_{H'}$ and $F_{H''}$. The operation O which yields F_H when applied to $F_{H'}$ and $F_{H''}$, can be described as follows: $O(F_{H'}, F_{H''})$ is $F_{H'}$ if H is $\neg H'$; it is $F_{H'} \circ F_{H''}$ if H is $H' \wedge H''$; finally $O(F_{H'}, F_{H''})$ is ... $F_{H'}$ ... i ... if H is $(x_i)H'$. The blanks ... are to be filled here by the description of $F_{(x_i)H'}$ given on p. 24.

We now define G. If H is a formula, then we include a pair $\langle H, \langle \xi, \eta \rangle \rangle$ into G if and only if there is a class K consisting of pairs $\langle H', \langle \alpha, \beta \rangle \rangle$ where H' is a subformula of H and α, β are ordinals and which has the following properties: for each subformula H' of H the class $K^{(H')}$ is a function; if H' is an atomic formula, then

$$K^{(H')} = \mathrm{Id} = \{\langle \gamma, \gamma \rangle : \gamma \in On\};$$

if H' is either $\neg H^*$ or $H^* \wedge H^{**}$ or $(x_i)H^*$, then $K^{(H')}$ is equal to $O(K^{(H^*)}, K^{(H^{**})})$; $\langle \xi, \eta \rangle \in K^{(H)}$.

In this definition $K^{(H)}$ has the same meaning as in Section I.4, i.e., $K^{(H)}$ is the set of those $\langle \alpha, \beta \rangle$ for which $\langle H, \langle \alpha, \beta \rangle \rangle \in K$.

We can easily show that the function G defined above satisfies the conditions (i)–(iv).

In order to finish the proof of theorem 2.2 we construct a continuous and increasing mapping of On into On such that each critical number of this mapping is at the same time a critical number of each of the functions F_H.

We define the required mapping by induction:

$$\phi(0) = 0; \quad \phi(\lambda) = \sup\{\phi(\xi) : \xi < \lambda\} \text{ if } \lambda \text{ is a limit number;}$$

$$\phi(\xi+1) = \sup\{F_H(\xi+1) : H \text{ is a formula}\} + 1.$$

It is obvious that ϕ is an increasing and continuous mapping and that $\phi(\xi) \geqslant F_H(\xi)$ for each ξ and each formula H. Hence if $\phi(\xi) = \xi > 0$, then $F_H(\xi) = \xi$ and thus (*) holds for arbitrary a in $A^{\mathrm{Fr}(H)}$. It follows that $A_\xi \prec \bigcup \mathrm{Rg}(A)$ and theorem 2.2 is proved.

Take in particular $A_\xi = R_\xi$ where R_ξ are sets defined in I.3.3; obviously $\bigcup \mathrm{Rg}(A) = V$ (the universal class).

The assumptions of the reflexion theorem are satisfied and we infer that:

2.3. *There is an increasing continuous mapping* $\phi: On \to On$ *such that* $R_\varkappa \prec V$ *for each of its critical numbers* $\varkappa$.

All axioms of ZF are obviously valid in V. Hence

2.4. *There are arbitrarily high ordinals* $\varkappa$ *such that* $R_\varkappa$ *is a model for* ZF.

Sets $R_\varkappa$ with these properties are called *natural models* for ZF.

Note that there always exist critical numbers of a continuous increasing function ϕ which are cofinal with ω. E.g. we obtain such a number putting $\varkappa = \sup_n \varkappa_n$, where $\varkappa_0$ is arbitrary and $\varkappa_{n+1} = \phi(\varkappa_n)$. Thus we have (Montague–Vaught [23])

2.5. *There are natural models* $R_\varkappa$ *for* ZF *for which* $\varkappa$ *is cofinal with* ω.

3. Predicatively closed classes

We put for a set a and a formula H

$$D_H(a) = \{f \in a^{\mathrm{Fr}(H)}\colon \vdash_a H[f]\},$$

$$S_H(a,f) = \big\{x \in a\colon \{\langle 0, x\rangle\} \cup f \in D_H(a)\big\}.$$

We call $D_H(a)$ the *diagram* of H in a. This set consists of all finite sequences with terms belonging to a which satisfy H in a. The set $S_H(a,f)$ is called a *section* of $D_H(a)$ determined by f; f is here a sequence whose domain is $\mathrm{Fr}(H)-\{0\}$. We can describe the section as follows: If $0 \notin \mathrm{Fr}(H)$, then the section $S_H(a,f)$ is void. Otherwise let us select those sequences g in $D_H(a)$ which contain f (i.e. satisfy the equations $g_j = f_j$ for $j \neq 0$). The set of all g_0's is the section $S_H(a,f)$.

We call a class A *predicatively closed* if conditions $a \in A, f \in a^{\mathrm{Fr}(H)-\{0\}}$ imply $S_H(a,f) \in A$ for all formulae H.

3.1. *Let* $A = \bigcup_{\xi \in On} A_\xi$ *and let the following assumptions be satisfied*:

$$A_\xi \subseteq A_\eta \quad \text{for} \quad \xi < \eta; \qquad A_\lambda = \bigcup_{\xi<\lambda} A_\xi \quad (\lambda \text{ is a limit number}),$$

$$A_\xi \in A, \qquad A_\xi \text{ is transitive}, \qquad (x, y \in A) \to (x \cap y \in A).$$

If A *is predicatively closed, then axioms* (V) *and* (VI$_H$), H *being arbitrary, are valid in* A.

PROOF FOR AXIOM (V). Let $a \in A$; we have to show that $P(a) \cap A \in A$. For each $x \in P(a) \cap A$ there is a smallest $\xi(x)$ such that $x \in A_{\xi(x)}$. If $\alpha = \sup\{\xi(x)\colon x \in P(a) \cap A\}$, then $P(a) \cap A \subseteq A_\alpha$ and therefore

$$x \in P(a) \cap A \equiv [(x \in A_\alpha) \wedge (x \subseteq a)].$$

If H is the formula

$$(t)[(t \in x_0) \to (t \in x_1)],$$

then obviously $\vdash_{A_\alpha} H[x, a] \equiv x \subseteq a$ for arbitrary x, a in A_α. Thus

$$x \in P(a) \cap A \equiv \vdash_{A_\alpha} H[x, a] \equiv x \in S_H(A_\alpha, \{\langle 1, a\rangle\}).$$

Since all sections belong to A we obtain $P(a) \cap A \in A$.

Proof for axioms (VI_H). Let φ be a function parametrically definable in A:

$$y = \varphi(x) \equiv \vdash_A H[x, y, f_1, \ldots, f_k]$$

and let $a \in A$. We have to show that $\mathrm{Im}(\varphi, a) \in A$.

For every x in a the element $\varphi(x)$ is in A and hence there is a smallest $\xi(x)$ such that $\varphi(x) \in A_{\xi(x)}$. Let α be an ordinal $\geqslant \sup\{\xi(x)\colon x \in a\}$ such that $a \in A_\alpha$ and $f_1, \ldots, f_k \in A_\alpha$. Thus we have

(1) $$y \in \mathrm{Im}(\varphi, a) \equiv (Ex)_a \vdash_A H[x, y, f_1, \ldots, f_k] \wedge (y \in A_\alpha).$$

Now we use the reflection theorem and obtain a $\varkappa > \alpha$ such that whenever $x, y, f_1, \ldots, f_k \in A_\varkappa$

$$\vdash_A H[x, y, f_1, \ldots, f_k] \equiv \vdash_{A_\varkappa} H[x, y, f_1, \ldots, f_k].$$

Since $a \subseteq A_\alpha \subseteq A_\varkappa$ we infer from (1) that:

(2) $$y \in \mathrm{Im}(\varphi, a) \equiv (Ex)_a \vdash_{A_\varkappa} H[x, y, f_1, \ldots, f_k] \wedge (y \in A_\alpha).$$

Now the right-hand side of (2) can be represented as

$$(y \in A_\alpha) \wedge \vdash_{A_\varkappa} H'[y, a, f_1, \ldots, f_k].$$

It is sufficient to take as H' the formula

$$(Ex_2)[(x_2 \in x_1) \wedge H(x_2, x_0, x_3, \ldots, x_{k+2})].$$

We easily verify that the sequence

$$\{\langle 0, y\rangle, \langle 1, a\rangle, \langle 3, f_1\rangle, \ldots, \langle k+2, f_k\rangle\}$$

satisfies H' in $A_\varkappa$ if and only if there is an element x in a such that $\vdash_{A_\varkappa} H[x, y, f_1, \ldots, f_k]$. Thus $\mathrm{Im}(\varphi, a)$ is equal to the intersection

$$A_\alpha \cap S_{H'}(A_\varkappa, g), \quad \text{where} \quad g = \{\langle 1, a\rangle, \langle 3, f_1\rangle, \ldots, \langle k+2, f_k\rangle\}.$$

Since this intersection is in A, our proof is complete.

4. The fundamental operations

In view of theorem 3.1 it is important to have criteria for a class to be predicatively closed. We shall show in this section that if a class, which in particular can of course be a set, is closed with respect to 7 "fundamental operations" A_1–A_7, then this class is predicatively closed [1]).

The operations are as follows:

$$A_1(a, b) = \{\{\langle 0, x\rangle, \langle 1, y\rangle\}:\ (x \in y)\wedge(x \in a)\wedge(y \in a)\},$$
$$A_2(a, b) = \{a, b\},$$
$$A_3(a, b) = \bigcup a,$$
$$A_4(a, b) = \{\{\langle x, y\rangle\}:\ (x \in a)\wedge(y \in b)\},$$
$$A_5(a, b) = \{x \cup y:\ (x \in a)\wedge(y \in b)\},$$
$$A_6(a, b) = \{x - y:\ (x \in a)\wedge(y \in b)\},$$
$$A_7(a, b) = \{x \circ y:\ (x \in a)\wedge(y \in b)\}.$$

The meaning of operations A_2, A_3 is clear. $A_1(a, b)$ really depends on a only and is the set of all sequences f with domain $\{0, 1\}$ such that $f_0 \in f_1$ and $f_0, f_1 \in a$. $A_4(a, b)$ is a kind of Cartesian product of a and b; we obtain $A_4(a, b)$ from $a \times b$ by taking the set of all singletons $\{z\}$ where z ranges over $a \times b$.

Operations A_5–A_7 are called *internal union*, *internal difference*, and *internal relative product* of a and b.

In the lemmas 4.1–4.10 below X is a set or a class closed with respect to the operations A_1–A_7 and such that $0 \in X$. Letters i, j, m, n denote elements of ω, s, s', ... finite subsets of ω.

4.1. $a, b \in X \rightarrow a \cup b,\ a - b,\ a \circ b,\ a \cap b \in X$.

PROOF. $a \cup b = \bigcup A_5(\{a\}, \{b\}) = A_3\big(A_5(A_2(a, a), A_2(b, b)), 0\big)$.

[1]) This criterion for the predicative closure of a class was first established by Bernays [2] and Gödel [13] in their proofs of the "class-theorem" and the "general existence theorem M1". The idea can be traced back to von Neumann's axiomatic system of set theory [26]. We have selected fundamental operations different from those which were used by Bernays and Gödel in order to let the proof of theorem 4.12 below run parallel to the definition of satisfaction given in I.4.

The proofs for the other operations are similar; note that $a \cap b = a - (a-b)$.

4.2. $\omega \subseteq X$.

PROOF. $0 \in X$ by our assumptions. If $n \in X$, then $\{n\} \in X$ since $\{n\} = A_2(n, n)$ and hence $n \cup \{n\} \in X$ by 4.1.

4.3. $\omega^s \subseteq X$.

Proof by induction on the number of elements of s. If $s = 0$, then $\omega^s = \{0\} \subseteq X$.

If $s = \{n\}$, then $\omega^s = \{\{\langle n, m\rangle\}: m \in \omega\}$, and since $\{\langle n, m\rangle\} = A_4(\{n\}, \{m\})$ belongs to X for each m in ω (see 4.2), we obtain $\omega^s \subseteq X$.

If $s = s' \cup s''$ where s' and s'' are disjoint and both have fewer elements that s, then each x in ω^s is a union $x' \cup x''$ where $x' \in \omega^{s'}$, $x'' \in \omega^{s''}$. Hence by 4.1 and the inductive assumption we obtain $x \in X$.

4.4. *If* $a \in X$, *then* $a^s \in X$.

If $s = 0$, the theorem is obvious. If $s = \{n\}$, then

$$a^s = \{\{\langle n, x\rangle\}: x \in a\} = A_4(\{n\}, a) = A_4(A_2(n, n), a) \in X.$$

If s has at least two elements and $s = s' \cup s''$ where $s' \neq 0 \neq s''$, then each z in a^s can be represented as $x' \cup x''$, where $x' \in a^{s'}$, $x'' \in a^{s''}$, and each such union is in a^s. Hence $a^s = A_5(a^{s'}, a^{s''})$ and the theorem follows by induction.

4.5. *If* $f \in \omega^s$, $b \in X$, *then* $\{f \circ x: x \in b\} \in X$.

PROOF. This set $= A_7(\{f\}, b)$ and $f \in X$ by 4.3.

4.6. *If* $n \in s$, a, $b \in X$, $b \subseteq a^s$, *then*

$$\{x \in a^{s-\{n\}}: (Eu)(\{\langle n, u\rangle\} \cup x \in b)\} \in X.$$

PROOF. Denote this set by Z and put $T = \{\langle n, u\rangle: u \in a\}$. Then each y in b contains exactly one pair which belongs to T, and removing this pair from y we obtain an element of Z. Conversely, each x in Z can be obtained from an element y of b by removing from y the unique pair which belongs to T. This proves that $Z = \{y-T: y \in b\} = A_6(b, \{T\})$. Since $T = \bigcup a^{\{n\}}$ the theorem is proved.

4.7. *If* $n \notin s$, a, $b \in X$, $b \subseteq a^s$, *then*

$$\{\{\langle n, x\rangle\} \cup y: (x \in a) \wedge (y \in b)\} \in X.$$

PROOF. This set is equal to $A_5(a^{\{n\}}, b)$.

4.8. *If* $n \notin s$, $a \in X$, $a \subseteq X$, $y \in a^s$, *then*

$$\{\{\langle n, x\rangle\} \cup y\colon\ x \in a\} \in X.$$

The required set is equal to $A_5(a^{\{n\}}, \{y\})$ and hence belongs to X since $y \in X$ (because it is a finite set of pairs $\langle i, t\rangle$, where $i \in s \subseteq X$ and $t \in a \subseteq X$).

4.9. *If* $n \notin s$, $a \in X$, $a \subseteq X$, $y \in a^s$, $b \subseteq a^{s \cup \{n\}}$ *and* $b \in X$, *then*

$$\{x \in a\colon\ \{\langle n, x\rangle\} \cup y \in b\} \in X.$$

PROOF. Let Z be the required set. We first construct the set T of all sequences of the form $\{\langle n, x\rangle\} \cup y$ where $x \in a$ and y is the given sequence. Then $T \in X$ by 4.8 and hence $T \cap b = T'$ is also an element of X. If we subtract y from a sequence t in T' we obtain a one-term sequence $\{\langle n, x\rangle\}$ such that $\{\langle n, x\rangle\} \cup y \in b$ and each such one-term sequence can be obtained from a sequence t in T' by subtracting y. Hence if we put

$$S = \{\{\langle n, x\rangle\}\colon\ \{\langle n, x\rangle\} \cup y \in b\},$$

then

$$S = A_6(T', \{y\}) \quad \text{and} \quad S \in X.$$

Now Z is the set of elements which are second terms of pairs whose singletons belong to S and hence

$$x \in Z \to x \in \{n, x\} \in \langle n, x\rangle \in \{\langle n, x\rangle\} \in S,$$

which proves that $Z \subseteq \bigcup\bigcup\bigcup S$. If $x \in \bigcup\bigcup\bigcup S$, then there are p, q, r such that $x \in p \in q \in r \in S$. Hence $r = \{\langle n, z\rangle\}$ where z is such that $\{\langle n, z\rangle\} \cup y \in b$ and q is $\langle n, z\rangle$; hence p is either $\{n, z\}$ or $\{n\}$; consequently x is either z or n. Thus $\bigcup\bigcup\bigcup S \subseteq Z \cup \{n\}$ and Z is either $\bigcup\bigcup\bigcup S$ or $\bigcup\bigcup\bigcup S - \{n\}$. In both cases $Z \in X$.

4.10. *If* $a \in X$, *then* $\{\{\langle 0, x\rangle, \langle 1, x\rangle\}\colon\ x \in a\} \in X$.

PROOF. The set $\{\langle 0, 1\rangle, \langle 1, 1\rangle\} \circ \{\langle 1, x\rangle\}$ is equal to $\{\langle 0, x\rangle, \langle 1, x\rangle\}$. Hence the required set is $A_7(\{f\}, a^{\{1\}})$ where $f = \{\langle 0, 1\rangle, \langle 1, 1\rangle\}$.

After these lemmata we can prove two theorems:

4.11. *If* $0 \in X$ *and* X *is closed with respect to* A_1–A_7, *then* $D_H(a) \in X$ *for every* a *in* X *and every* H.

PROOF. We use induction with respect to the length of the formula. First, let H be the formula $x_i \in x_j$. If $i = j$, then $D_H(a) = 0$ and there is nothing to prove. If $i = 0$, $j = 1$, then $D_H(a) = A_1(a, a)$, and hence $D_H(a) \in X$. If $i \neq j$, but $\langle i, j\rangle \neq \langle 0, 1\rangle$, then we put $f = \{\langle i, 0\rangle, \langle j, 1\rangle\}$ and $b = A_1(a, a)$ and verify that

$$D_H(a) = \{f \circ x \colon x \in b\}.$$

Hence $D_H(a) \in X$ by 4.3 and 4.5.

In the case of the formula $x_0 = x_1$ we obtain $D_H(a) \in X$ by 4.10. For H: $x_i = x_i$ we have

$$D_H(a) = \big\{\{\langle i, x\rangle\} \colon x \in a\big\} = A_4(\{i\}, a)\,.$$

Finally, the formula $x_i = x_j$ for $i \neq j$ is treated in the same manner as $x_i \in x_j$.

Since $D_{\neg H}(a) = a^{\mathrm{Fr}(H)} - D_H(a)$, we infer that if the theorem is true for H it is true for $\neg H$.

Now assume that the theorem is true for H' and H'' and let H be $H' \wedge H''$. If $\mathrm{Fr}(H') = \mathrm{Fr}(H'')$, then obviously $D_H(a) = D_{H'}(a) \cap D_{H''}(a)$ and hence $D_H(a) \in X$. If $\mathrm{Fr}(H') \neq \mathrm{Fr}(H'')$ we need a small adjustment at the beginning. Let $s = \mathrm{Fr}(H) = \mathrm{Fr}(H') \cup \mathrm{Fr}(H'')$ and let $n \in s - \mathrm{Fr}(H')$, $b = D_{H'}(a)$. Using 4.7 we obtain from b a set of all sequences f with domain $\mathrm{Fr}(H') \cup \{n\}$ whose restrictions to $\mathrm{Fr}(H')$ belong to b. Repeating this process for all integers $n \in s - \mathrm{Fr}(H')$ we obtain a set $b_1 \in X$ whose elements are all sequences $f \in a^{\mathrm{Fr}(H)}$ such that $f|\mathrm{Fr}(H') \in b$. We perform the same process on the set $c = D_{H''}(a)$ and obtain a set $c_1 \in X$ consisting of all sequences $f \in a^{\mathrm{Fr}(H)}$ for which $f|\mathrm{Fr}(H'') \in c$. Clearly $D_H(a) = b_1 \cap c_1$ and the theorem is proved for conjunction.

Finally, if H is $(x_n)H'$, then we consider two cases: (i) $n \notin \mathrm{Fr}(H)$, (ii) $n \in \mathrm{Fr}(H)$. In case (i) $D_H(a) = D_{H'}(a)$ and the theorem is obvious. In case (ii) we notice that $D_{\neg H'}(a) \in X$ and hence, by 4.6, there is a set c in X such that $c \subseteq a^{\mathrm{Fr}(H)-\{n\}}$ and

$$x \in c \equiv (Eu)\big\{\{\langle n, u\rangle\} \cup x \in D_{\neg H'}(a)\big\}.$$

We easily verify that $a^{\mathrm{Fr}(H)-\{n\}} - c = D_H(a)$. Thus 4.11 is proved.

4.12. *If* $0 \in X$ *and* X *is transitive and closed with respect to* A_1–A_7, *then* X *is predicatively closed.*

PROOF. Let H be a formula such that $0 \in \mathrm{Fr}(H)$ (otherwise there is nothing to prove) and let a be in X and $f \in a^{\mathrm{Fr}(H)-\{0\}}$. Since $D_H(a) \in X$ by 4.11, we infer by 4.9 that

$$\{x \in a \colon \{\langle n, x\rangle\} \cup f \in D_H(a)\} \in X,$$

i.e., that $S_H(a,f) \in X$. This proves the theorem. Note that we have used the transitivity of X since we can use 4.9 only if we know that $D_H(a) \subseteq X$.

Theorem 4.12 jointly with 3.1 allows us to formulate a sufficient condition for a class to be a model of ZF:

4.13. *If a class A is representable as a union*

$$A = \bigcup \{A_\xi \colon \xi \in On\}$$

where

(i) $$A_\xi \subseteq A_\eta \quad \textit{for} \quad \xi < \eta \in On,$$

(ii) $$A_\lambda = \bigcup \{A_\xi \colon \xi < \lambda\} \quad \textit{if } \lambda \textit{ is a limit number},$$

(iii) $$A_\xi \in A \quad \textit{for each } \xi \textit{ in } On,$$

(iv) $$A_\xi \textit{ is transitive for each } \xi \textit{ in } On,$$

(v) $$0 \in A$$

and if

(vi) $$A \textit{ is closed under the operations } A_1\text{–}A_7,$$

then A is a model of ZF.

PROOF. By 4.12 the class A is predicatively closed. All the other assumptions of theorem 3.1 have been incorporated in the present theorem with the exception of the closure of A under intersections. This condition, however, follows from the closure of A under operations A_1–A_7 (see 4.1). Hence A satisfies all the assumptions of theorem 3.1 and hence axioms (V) and (VI) are valid in A. The validity of axioms (I)–(III) follows from theorems 1.1–1.3, whose assumptions are obviously satisfied. Finally, to show that the axiom of infinity (IV) is valid in A we define by induction an increasing sequence ξ_n of ordinals such that ξ_{n+1} is the least ordinal for which A_{ξ_n} is an element of $A_{\xi_{n+1}}$. The existence of such ordinals follows from assumption (iii).

If $\lambda = \sup\{\xi_n\colon n < \omega\}$, then $A_\lambda = \bigcup\{A_{\xi_n}\colon n < \omega\}$ and A_λ is such that each of its elements is properly contained in another element. For if $b \in A_\lambda$, then b is an element of one of the sets A_{ξ_n}, and hence, by (iv), b is contained in A_{ξ_n}. The inclusion must be proper because no set is its own element. Since moreover $A_{\xi_n} \in A_\lambda$ we see that A_λ satisfies the assumption of 1.4 and the axiom of infinity is valid in A.

Theorem 4.13 may appear forbidding at first sight because of the large number of assumptions. A closer inspection reveals however, that these assumptions are easily checked in each particular case. What is more important, it is very easy to construct classes which satisfy these assumptions. Owing to this, theorem 4.13 can very well serve as a basis for the construction of various models of ZF. We shall perform one such construction in the next chapter.

CHAPTER III

CONSTRUCTIBLE SETS

In this chapter we shall define models which will be the main object of our study. The idea underlying their construction is very simple. We start with an arbitrary transfinite sequence whose terms form a transitive set and whose order type is an ordinal in *On* (a more exact formulation of the assumptions concerning the initial sequence is given at the beginning of Section 3). We shall form new sets of the terms of this sequence by performing suitable operations. The process will go on by stages: at stage ξ we shall construct a set, called $C_\xi(a)$, out of the sets constructed at the previous stages. We call $C_\xi(a)$ the *ξth set constructible in a.*

The operations used to build the ξth constructible set will be so chosen that the class of all constructible sets will satisfy the assumptions of theorem II.4.13. To each ordinal ξ there will be attached a special operation which will have to be performed at stage ξ. There will also be specified functions of ξ which will name the places from which we have to draw the arguments of the operation performed at stage ξ.

Having in view assumption (iii) of II.4.13, we shall arrange the definitions so that there will be a class, cofinal with *On*, of indices ξ such that the operation to be performed at stage ξ will consist of forming the set of all the preceding $C_\eta(a)$'s. Since we want the terms of the initially given sequence to be constructible, we shall single out a class of ordinals ξ such that the operation to be performed at stage ξ will yield the first term not yet used of the initially given sequence or 0 if all the terms have already been used.

The role of the remaining operations will be twofold. One part of them will ensure the predicative closure of constructible sets. There will even exist a sequence cofinal with *On* of ordinals ξ such that $C_\xi(a)$ will be predicatively closed. In order to achieve this alone it would be sufficient to perform in a suitable order the fundamental operations on terms $C_\xi(a)$. However, this method would not yield the desired result because we would not obtain transitive sets and so condition (iv) of II.4.13 would be jeopardized. Therefore we shall use, instead of the fundamental operations, certain ternary operations closely connected with them. They are defined as $A_i(x, y) \cap z$ where the A_i are the fundamental operations. In order to ensure that the class of constructible sets be closed under the fundamental operations we shall have to add two more operations: $(x - y) \cap z$ and $(x \circ y) \cap z$.

The other operations are to a great extent arbitrary and in many cases can be dispensed with altogether. However, they can be used to ensure that certain formulae which are not axioms of ZF be valid in the class of constructible sets. In the present book we shall avail ourselves of this freedom of choice of the additional operations only to a very limited extent: we shall consider an operation which secures the validity of the axiom of choice in the class of constructible sets. Also we shall define another operation which ensures that each ordinal α should appear in the sequence $C_\xi(a)$ at a well-determined place which can be calculated once α is known. There are other operations that could be used for various purposes but we shall not investigate them here.

The constructible model whose detailed description will be presented below was introduced by Gödel [11] in the special case where the initial sequence is void and there are no additional operations. The modifications consisting of adding the initial sequence and new operations have been proposed by various authors; see, e.g., Hajnal [14] and Cohen [4].

1. Enumeration

In this section we define four mappings I, K, L, M of On into On. The value of $I\xi$ tells us which operation we have to perform at stage ξ and $K\xi$, $L\xi$, $M\xi$ determine the places from which we take the arguments of the operation to be performed at stage ξ [1]).

Let r be an integer. We define $\delta(r, \xi)$ by induction on ξ. We suppress

[1]) The particular enumeration presented in this section is due to Cohen [4].

the variable r in the subsequent formulae to make them more readable; sometimes we shall write $\delta\xi$ or δ_ξ instead of $\delta(r, \xi)$.

$$\delta_0 = 0, \quad \delta_{\xi+1} = \delta_\xi + 1 + r \cdot \delta_\xi^3, \quad \delta_\lambda = \sup\{\delta_\xi : \xi < \lambda\}$$

(λ is a limit number). Thus $\delta_1 = 1$, $\delta_2 = r+2$, $\delta_3 = r+3+r(r+2)^3$ etc., $\delta_\omega = \omega$, $\delta_{\omega+1} = \omega^3$, $\delta_{\omega+2} = \omega^9$ etc., $\delta_{\omega\cdot 2} = \omega^\omega$.

1.1. *If $\xi \geqslant \omega$, then $\delta\xi$ is a power of ω and $\delta_{\xi+1} = \delta_\xi^3$.*

We prove this by induction using the fact that if $\alpha < \omega^\beta$, $\beta > 0$, then $\alpha + r\omega^\beta = \omega^\beta$.

1.2. *δ is an increasing and continuous function.*

It follows from the definition that the set $X_\xi = \{\sigma: \delta_\xi < \sigma < \delta_{\xi+1}\}$ has the order type $r\delta_\xi^3$. Thus there is a one-to-one mapping of the set X_ξ onto the set of quadruples $\langle i, \alpha, \beta, \gamma\rangle$ where $1 \leqslant i \leqslant r$, $\alpha, \beta, \gamma < \delta_\xi$. We denote the quadruple which corresponds to σ by $\langle I\sigma, K\sigma, L\sigma, M\sigma\rangle$. We thus have

1.3. *If $\delta_\xi < \sigma < \delta_{\xi+1}$, then $1 \leqslant I\sigma \leqslant r$ and $K\sigma, L\sigma, M\sigma < \delta_\xi$.*

It is not very important how exactly we fix the mapping of $r \cdot \delta_\xi^3$ onto X_ξ; but for the sake of definiteness we may agree to order (anti-lexicographically) the quadruples $\langle i, \mu, \nu, \varrho\rangle$ where $1 \leqslant i \leqslant r$, $\mu, \nu, \varrho < \delta_\xi$ and correlate with each quadruple the order type of the set of all quadruples which precede it.

Additionally we define $I\delta_\xi = K\delta_\xi = L\delta_\xi = M\delta_\xi = 0$.

We stress the fact that I, K, L, M are really functions of two variables and thus a more appropriate notation for them would be $I(r, \xi)$, $K(r, \xi)$, etc.

We shall make use of a function which enumerates the class of all ordinals ξ satisfying the condition $I\xi = k$ where k is an integer and $1 \leqslant k \leqslant r$. We denote this functions by $\mathrm{pl}_k(\alpha)$ or, more accurately, $\mathrm{pl}_k(r, \alpha)$:

$$\mathrm{pl}_k(0) = \min_\xi (I\xi = k),$$
$$\mathrm{pl}_k(\alpha) = \min_\xi [(\beta)_\alpha (\xi > \mathrm{pl}_k(\beta)) \wedge (I\xi = k)].$$

Since we shall really use only the functions pl_{10}, pl_{11} and pl_{12}, we introduce a simplified notation:

$$\mathrm{pl}_{10} = \mathrm{pl}', \quad \mathrm{pl}_{11} = \mathrm{pl}^*, \quad \mathrm{pl}_{12} = \mathrm{pl}.$$

We shall prove that the functions pl_k do not increase fast:

1.4. $\mathrm{pl}_k(\xi) < \delta(\xi+1)$ *for each* $\xi > 0$.

PROOF. For $\xi = 1$ the theorem is obvious. Let us assume it for all $\beta < \alpha$. Since $\delta_{\beta+1} \leqslant \delta_\alpha < \delta_{\alpha+1}$ and the interval $(\delta(\alpha), \delta(\alpha+1))$ contains at least one ordinal ξ such that $I\xi = k$ holds, we infer that $(\beta)_\alpha(\xi > \mathrm{pl}_k(\beta))$. Hence, by definition, $\mathrm{pl}_k(\alpha) \leqslant \xi$ and thus $\mathrm{pl}_k(\alpha) < \delta_{\alpha+1}$.

Besides pl_k we shall use the function $\overline{\mathrm{pl}}_k$ defined thus:

$$\overline{\mathrm{pl}}_k(\beta) = \min\{\alpha\colon \mathrm{pl}_k(\alpha) \geqslant \beta\};$$

a more correct notation for this function would obviously be $\overline{\mathrm{pl}}_k(r, \beta)$ but we shall often omit the symbol r.

If ξ_α is the increasing transfinite sequence of all ordinals ξ satisfying the equation $I\xi = k$, then $\mathrm{pl}_k(\alpha) = \xi_\alpha$ while $\overline{\mathrm{pl}}_k(\beta)$ is the first index α satisfying the inequality $\xi_\alpha \geqslant \beta$.

We obviously have

$$\overline{\mathrm{pl}}_k(\mathrm{pl}_k(\alpha)) = \alpha.$$

Since $\mathrm{pl}_k(\alpha)$ strictly increases with α, we also have

$$\overline{\mathrm{pl}}_k(\beta) \leqslant \beta.$$

For $k = 10, 11, 12$ we shall use the more convenient notation $\overline{\mathrm{pl}}'$, $\overline{\mathrm{pl}}^*$ and $\overline{\mathrm{pl}}$ instead of $\overline{\mathrm{pl}}_k$. Thus

$$\overline{\mathrm{pl}}'(\beta) = \overline{\mathrm{pl}}_{10}(\beta), \quad \overline{\mathrm{pl}}^*(\beta) = \overline{\mathrm{pl}}_{11}(\beta), \quad \overline{\mathrm{pl}}(\beta) = \overline{\mathrm{pl}}_{12}(\beta).$$

1.5. *If* $1 \leqslant k \leqslant r$, *then* $\mathrm{pl}_k(\alpha) = \mathrm{pl}_1(\alpha)+k-1$.

PROOF. It follows from the definition of the antilexicographic ordering that if $1 \leqslant i < r$, then the element $\langle i+1, \alpha, \beta, \gamma\rangle$ is an immediate successor of the element $\langle i, \alpha, \beta, \gamma\rangle$. Hence if $\xi_0, \xi_1, \ldots, \xi_\varrho, \ldots$ is the increasing transfinite sequence of all ordinals satisfying $I\xi = 1$, then $\xi_0+k-1, \xi_1+k-1, \ldots, \xi_\varrho+k-1, \ldots$ is the increasing transfinite sequence of all ordinals η satisfying $I\eta = k$. Hence

$$\mathrm{pl}_k(\alpha) = \xi_\alpha+k-1 = \mathrm{pl}_1(\alpha)+k-1.$$

2. Constructible sets

Let S be the class of all transfinite sequences. Thus $a \in S$ if and only if there is an ordinal $\xi \in On$, called the *type* or the *length* of a, such that a is a function and $\mathrm{Dom}(a) = \xi$. For a in S we shall often write $\mathrm{lh}(a)$ instead of $\mathrm{Dom}(a)$.

In order to make our subsequent notation uniform we introduce two new operations, A_8 and A_9, which complete the list of 7 operations defined in II.4:

$$A_8(x, y) = x - y, \quad A_9(x, y) = x \circ y.$$

We now consider a function B of two variables a, f ranging over S such that

(B.0) $$B(a,f) \subseteq \mathrm{Rg}(f) \cup \bigcup \mathrm{Rg}(f).$$

We assume that B satisfies the following conditions, in which r is an integer (determined by B) and σ stands for $\mathrm{lh}(f)$:

(B.1) *If* $I(r, \sigma) = 0$, *then*

$$B(a,f) = \mathrm{Rg}(f);$$

(B.2) *If* $0 < I(r, \sigma) \leqslant 9$, *then*

$$B(a,f) = A_{I(r,\sigma)}(f_{K(r,\sigma)}, f_{L(r,\sigma)}) \cap f_{M(r,\sigma)};$$

(B.3) *If* $I(r, \sigma) = 10$ *and* $\overline{\mathrm{pl}}'(r, \sigma) < \mathrm{lh}(a)$, *then*

$$B(a,f) = a_{\overline{\mathrm{pl}}'(r,\sigma)};$$

(B.4) *If* $I(r, \sigma) = 10$ *and* $\overline{\mathrm{pl}}'(r, \sigma) \geqslant \mathrm{lh}(a)$, *then*

$$B(a,f) = 0.$$

From the theorem on inductive definitions we infer that:

2.1. *There is exactly one function* C: $S \times On \to V$ *such that* $C(a, \xi) = B(a, C|\xi)$ *where* $C|\xi$ *is the function* C *restricted to ordinals* $< \xi$, *i.e.*, $C|\xi = \{\langle \eta, C(a, \eta)\rangle : \eta < \xi\}$.

A more appropriate symbol for the function C would be C^B since C is determined by the choice of B. Usually we shall omit the index B in order to simplify the notation. We shall also frequently use the symbol $C_\xi(a)$ or C_ξ for the values of C. The last symbol will be used in cases where a is fixed. We shall also omit the symbol r in the expressions $I(r, \sigma)$, $K(r, \sigma)$, etc.

The class consisting of all sets $C_\xi^B(a)$ is denoted by $K^B(a)$. Its elements are called constructible; more exactly: constructible from a by means of the function B. Our whole discussion will be concerned with these sets.

From the definition of C we immediately obtain:

2.2. $C_\sigma(a) = \{C_\xi(a)\colon \xi < \sigma\}$ *if* $I\sigma = 0$.

2.3. $C_\sigma(a) = A_{I\sigma}(C_{K\sigma}(a), C_{L\sigma}(a)) \cap C_{M\sigma}(a)$ *if* $1 \leqslant I\sigma \leqslant 9$.

2.4. $C_\sigma(a) = a_{\overline{\mathrm{pl}'(\sigma)}}$ *if* $I\sigma = 10$ *and* $\overline{\mathrm{pl}'(\sigma)} < \mathrm{lh}(a)$.

2.5. $C_\sigma(a) = 0$ *if* $I\sigma = 10$ *and* $\overline{\mathrm{pl}'(\sigma)} \geqslant \mathrm{lh}(a)$.

2.6. $C_\sigma(a) \subseteq \bigcup_{\varrho<\sigma} C_\varrho(a) \cup \{C_\varrho(a)\colon \varrho < \sigma\}$ *if* $I\sigma > 10$.

We add a few comments on these definitions. The transfinite sequence $C_\xi(a)$ of constructible sets is defined in such a way that for each of its terms $C_\xi(a)$ one of the following cases occurs: (i) $C_\xi(a)$ arises from the previous term by means of operations $A_i(x, y) \cap z$ (cases 2.3); (ii) $C_\xi(a)$ is the set X of all the terms previously constructed (case 2.2); (iii) $C_\xi(a)$ is a subset of X or of $\bigcup X$ (cases 2.5 and 2.6); (iv) $C_\xi(a)$ is one of the terms of a (case 2.4). Which of these cases occurs is determined by the value of ξ; also the values of i, x, y, z in case 2.3 are determined by ξ. Thus if B is given, then each sequence a determines uniquely a sequence of constructible sets. Terms of a are among the constructible sets and they appear there in the same order in which they appeared in a: the set a_α occupies the place $C_\xi(a)$ where ξ is the αth ordinal such that $I\xi = 10$. The whole sequence a is not necessarily a set constructible in a.

3. Properties of constructible sets

From now on we shall assume that

(1) $$a_\xi \subseteq a|\xi \quad \text{for each } \xi < \mathrm{lh}(a).$$

Thus elements of a_ξ are some a_η with $\eta < \xi$ and in particular $a_0 = 0$. Sequences a satisfying (1) will be called *transitive*.

We fix a function B satisfying (B.0)–(B.4) and a transitive sequence a. Since B, r, a will be fixed throughout this section we shall write simply

C_ξ for $C_\xi^B(a)$, and shall suppress the symbol r in writing the values of the functions δ, I, K, etc.

We want to show that if λ is a limit number, then $C_{\delta(\lambda)}$ is predicatively closed.

3.1. $0 \in C_{\delta(\lambda)}$ *for* $\lambda > 0$.

For $0 = a_0 \in \mathrm{Rg}(C|\delta(\lambda)) = C_{\delta(\lambda)}$.

3.2. $C_\xi \subseteq \mathrm{Rg}(C|\xi)$ *for each* $\xi \in On$.

PROOF. We use induction on ξ. Since $C_0 = 0$, the theorem is true for $\xi = 0$; assume that it holds for $\eta < \xi$ and consider the various cases according to the value of $I\xi$. If $I\xi = 0$, then $C_\xi = \mathrm{Rg}(C|\xi)$ by 2.2. If $1 \leqslant I\xi \leqslant 9$ and $x \in C_\xi$, then $x \in C_{M\xi}$ by 2.3 and hence $x \in \mathrm{Rg}(C|M\xi)$ by the inductive assumption. Hence $x \in \mathrm{Rg}(C|\xi)$. If $I\xi = 10$, then either $C_\xi = 0$ or $C_\xi = a_{\overline{\mathrm{pl}}'(\xi)}$; hence $C_\xi \subseteq a|\overline{\mathrm{pl}}'(\xi)$ since we have assumed that a is transitive. For each $x \in C_\xi$ there is an $\eta < \overline{\mathrm{pl}}'(\xi)$ such that $x = a_\eta$. If ζ is the ηth ordinal such that $I\zeta = 10$, then $\zeta < \xi$ since ξ was the $\overline{\mathrm{pl}}'(\xi)$th such ordinal. Hence $x = C_\zeta \in \mathrm{Rg}(C|\xi)$.

Finally if $I\xi > 10$ and $x \in C_\xi$, then by 2.6 we have either $x = C_\varrho$ for a $\varrho < \xi$ or $x \in C_\varrho$ for a $\varrho < \xi$. Thus by the inductive assumption we have in both cases $x = C_\sigma$ for a $\sigma < \xi$. Thus the proof of 3.2 is complete.

As a corollary we find that:

3.3. $C_{\delta(\xi)}$ *is transitive for each* ξ.

We shall now prove that $C_{\delta(\lambda)}$ is closed under the operations A_1–A_7. It will be convenient to state a more general lemma:

3.4. *For each* i, $1 \leqslant i \leqslant 7$, *there is an integer* $p = p_i$ *such that whenever* α *is any ordinal and* $x, y \in C_{\delta(\alpha)}$, *then* $A_i(x, y) \in C_{\delta(\alpha+p)}$.

PROOF. We start with the case $i = 2$. Here we have $A_2(a, b) = \{a, b\} = \{a, b\} \cap C_{\delta(\alpha)}$. If $a = C_\xi$, $b = C_\eta$, then we determine a ζ such that $I\zeta = 2$, $\xi = K\zeta$, $\eta = L\zeta$, $\delta(\alpha) = M\zeta$ and obtain $\{a, b\} = A_{I_\zeta}(C_{K_\zeta}, C_{L_\zeta}) \cap \cap C_{M_\zeta}$. Since a ζ with these properties can be found among numbers $< \delta(\alpha+2)$, we obtain $\{a, b\} \in C_{\delta(\alpha+2)}$.

$i = 1$. The set $A_1(a, b)$ consists of pairs $\{\langle 0, x\rangle, \langle 1, y\rangle\}$ where $x, y \in a$ and $x \in y$.

Let x, y be arbitrary elements of a and b respectively. Since we have assumed that a and b are elements of $C_{\delta(\alpha)}$, we obtain $\alpha > 0$ and $x, y \in C_{\delta(\alpha)}$. Hence $0 \in C_{\delta(\alpha)}$ and by our previous result $1 \in C_{\delta(\alpha+2)}$. Using 3.3 we infer that the four elements x, y, 0, 1 belong to $C_{\delta(\alpha+2)}$. It follows that the singletons $\{0\}$ and $\{1\}$, and also the pairs $\{0, x\}$ and $\{1, y\}$, are elements of $C_{\delta(\alpha+4)}$, and hence the ordered pairs $\langle 0, x\rangle$, $\langle 1, y\rangle$ are elements of $C_{\delta(\alpha+6)}$. Thus we have proved that each element of $A_1(a, b)$ belongs to $C_{\delta(\alpha+6)}$. If $a = C_\xi$ and $b = C_\eta$, then $A_1(a, b) = A_1(C_\xi, C_\eta) \cap \cap C_{\delta(\alpha+6)}$. We now determine a ζ such that $I\zeta = 1$, $K\zeta = \xi$, $L\zeta = \eta$, $M\zeta = \delta(\alpha+6)$ and have $A_1(a, b) = C_\zeta$. Since ζ can be found among the numbers $< \delta(\alpha+8)$, the theorem is proved.

$i = 3$. Since $a \in C_{\delta(\alpha)}$ implies $\bigcup a \subseteq C_{\delta(\alpha)}$, we can find a $\zeta < \delta(\alpha+2)$ such that $A_3(C_\xi, C_\eta) = A_3(C_{K\zeta}, C_{L\zeta}) \cap C_{M\zeta} = \bigcup C_\xi = \bigcup a$ and $\zeta < \delta(\alpha+2)$.

$i = 4$. If $a = C_\xi$, $b = C_\eta$ where $\xi, \eta < \delta(\alpha)$, then each pair $\langle x, y\rangle$ with $x \in a$ and $y \in b$ belongs to $C_{\delta(\alpha+4)}$ and hence $\{\langle x, y\rangle\} \in C_{\delta(\alpha+6)}$. It follows that $A_4(a, b) \subseteq C_{\delta(\alpha+6)}$ and we obtain $A_4(a, b) \in C_{\delta(\alpha+8)}$ by the same method as above.

$i = 5$. If $a = C_\xi$, $b = C_\xi$ where $\xi, \eta < \delta(\alpha)$, then $x \in a$ implies $x \in C_{\delta(\alpha)}$ and $y \in b$ implies $y \in C_{\delta(\alpha)}$. Hence $x \cup y = \bigcup \{x, y\}$ is an element of $C_{\delta(\alpha+4)}$ according to the cases already discussed. It follows that $A_5(a, b) \subseteq C_{\delta(\alpha+4)}$ and the theorem follows as in the previous cases.

$i = 6$. Again all we have to show is $A_6(a, b) \subseteq C_{\delta(\alpha+1)}$. Let us assume that $x \in a$, $y \in b$, whence $x, y \in C_{\delta(\alpha)}$. Let $x = C_\xi$, $y = C_\eta$. Hence $x - y = A_8(x, y) \cap x = A_8(C_\xi, C_\eta) \cap C_\xi$ and we obtain $x - y = C_\gamma$ for any γ such that $I\gamma = 8$, $K\gamma = \xi$, $L\gamma = \eta$, $M\gamma = \xi$. Hence $x - y \in C_{\delta(\alpha+1)}$ since a γ with these properties exists among the numbers $< \delta(\alpha+1)$.

$i = 7$. It will be sufficient to show that $A_7(a, b) \subseteq C_{\delta(\alpha+6)}$. An element $x \circ y$ of $A_7(a, b)$ consists of pairs $\langle p, q\rangle$ such that $\langle p, r\rangle \in x$ and $\langle r, q\rangle \in y$ for a set r. Hence if $a = C_\xi$, $b = C_\eta$ where $\xi, \eta < \delta(\alpha)$, then $p, q \in C_{\delta(\alpha)}$ and $\langle p, q\rangle \in C_{\delta(\alpha+4)}$ by the case $i = 1$ discussed above. It follows that $x \circ y = A_9(x, y) \cap C_{\delta(\alpha+4)}$ is an element of $C_{\delta(\alpha+6)}$. Thus theorem 3.4 is proved.

An immediate corollary is

3.5. *If λ is a limit number > 0, then $C_{\delta(\lambda)}$ is predicatively closed; also the class $K = K(a)$ of sets constructible in a is predicatively closed.*

The first part results from 3.4. In order to prove the second it is sufficient to note that $K = \bigcup_{\alpha \in On} C_{\delta(\alpha)}$.

Using theorem 3.4 we can now establish the main result of the present chapter:

3.6. *For each function B which satisfies the conditions* (B.0)–(B.4) *and each transitive sequence a the class $K^B(a)$ of sets constructible from a by means of B is a model of* ZF.

For the proof it is sufficient to verify the assumptions of theorem II.4.13. We let λ_ξ be the increasing sequence of all limit ordinals and put $A_\xi = C_{\delta(\lambda_\xi)}$. It is then obvious that the A_ξ form an increasing sequence and that $K^B(a)$ is their union. Assumption (ii) is satisfied because $\delta(\lambda) = \sup\{\delta(\xi) : \xi < \lambda\}$ for each limit ordinal λ. Assumption (iii) is satisfied because each constructible set, and in particular each set $C_{\delta(\lambda_\xi)}$, is an element of $K^B(a)$. Assumption (iv) was proved in 3.3, assumption (v) is obvious and assumption (vi) was proved in 3.4.

Theorem 3.6 furnishes examples of classes which are models of ZF. Since the choice of a and B is to a great extent arbitrary, we obtain an unlimited number of such models. If we want to obtain models which are sets and not classes as in 3.6, then all that we have to do is to apply theorem II.2.2 to the class $K^B(a)$. In this way we obtain

3.7. *For each function B which satisfies the conditions* (B.0)–(B.4) *and each transitive sequence a there is a continuous increasing function ϕ: $On \to On$ such that $C^B_{\delta(\lambda_\varkappa)}(a) \prec K^B(a)$ for every critical number $\varkappa$ of ϕ; thus in particular $C^B_{\delta(\lambda_\varkappa)}(a)$ is a model of* ZF.

We can also prove the existence of transitive sets which are models of ZF and have a prescribed cardinality.

3.8. *For every ordinal α there is a transitive set t which is elementarily equivalent to $K^B(a)$ and has the power $\aleph_\alpha$.*

Proof. Let b be any subset of $K^B(a) = K$ of power $\aleph_\alpha$. Since K is a well ordered class, we can use the Löwenheim–Skolem theorem I.5.1 and obtain a set d of power $\aleph_\alpha$ such that $b \subseteq d \prec K$. Now we use the contraction lemma I.6.1 and obtain a transitive set t which is isomorphic to d. Sets t and d are elementarily equivalent (because of isomorphism) and hence t is elementarily equivalent to K. Theorem 3.8 is thus proved.

Note that isomorphism destroys, in general, the relation $\prec$; thus from $d \prec K$ it does not follow that $t \prec K$.

4. Constructibility of ordinals

In this section we shall discuss the problem which ordinals are constructible and we shall show that all of them belong to $K(a)$. We shall also obtain some more precise information about the place which a given ordinal occupies in the transfinite sequence of constructible sets.

We need the following lemma on ranks:

4.1. *If a is a transitive sequence, then* $\mathrm{rg}(a_\xi) \leqslant \xi$ *for each* $\xi < \mathrm{lh}(a)$.

P r o o f b y i n d u c t i o n: if the inequality is valid for all $\xi < \eta < \mathrm{lh}(a)$, then it is valid for η because $a_\eta \subseteq \{a_\xi \colon \xi < \eta\}$ and hence $\mathrm{rg}(a_\eta) \leqslant \sup\{\mathrm{rg}(a_\xi) \colon \xi < \eta\} \leqslant \eta$.

We can now evaluate the rank of C_ϱ.

4.2. *If B satisfies conditions* (B.0)–(B.4) *and a is a transitive sequence, then* $\mathrm{rg}\big(C_\varrho^B(a)\big) \leqslant \varrho$.

Proof. We proceed by induction. Let us assume that the inequality is valid for all $\sigma < \varrho$. We distinguish several cases:

(1) $0 < I(r, \varrho) \leqslant 9$. In this case $C_\varrho^B(a) \subseteq C_{M(r,\varrho)}^B(a)$ and hence by the inductive assumption the rank of the left-hand side is $\leqslant M(r, \varrho) < \varrho$.

(2) $I(r, \varrho) = 0$. In this case $C_\varrho^B(a) = \{C_\xi^B(a) \colon \xi < \varrho\}$ and hence by I.3.7 and the inductive assumption the rank of the left-hand side is $\leqslant \sup\{\xi \colon \xi < \varrho\} = \varrho$.

(3) $I(r, \varrho) = 10$. In this case $C_\varrho^B(a) = a_{\overline{\mathrm{pl}'(r,\varrho)}}$ or $= 0$ and hence by 4.1 the rank of the left-hand side is $\leqslant \overline{\mathrm{pl}'(r, \varrho)} \leqslant \varrho$.

(4) $I(r, \varrho) > 10$. In this case $C_\varrho^B(a) \subseteq \{C_\xi^B(a) \colon \xi < \varrho\} \cup \bigcup_{\xi < \varrho} C_\xi^B(a)$ and hence the rank of each element of $C_\varrho^B(a)$ is $< \varrho$, whence the rank of $C_\varrho^B(a)$ is $\leqslant \varrho$.

4.3. *$C_\varrho^B(a)$ contains no ordinal $\geqslant \varrho$.*

This corollary shows that if $C_\varrho^B(a) = M$ is a model of ZF, then ordinals of this models are $< \varrho$. We shall now discuss the question whether all ordinals $< \varrho$ are elements of M.

4.4. *If B satisfies* (B.0)–(B.4) *and a is a transitive sequence, then $\varrho \in C^B_{\delta(r,\,\varrho+\omega)}(a)$ for every $\varrho \in On$.*

PROOF. In order to simplify the formulae we omit everywhere the symbols B, r and a. We use induction on ϱ. For $\varrho = 0$ the theorem is obvious; therefore we assume that it holds for all $\sigma < \varrho$ and distinguish two cases:

(i) $\varrho = \sigma+1 = \sigma \cup \{\sigma\}$. By the inductive assumption $\sigma \in C_{\delta(\sigma+\omega)}$, whence $\sigma = C_\alpha$ where $\alpha < \delta(\sigma+\omega) = \lim_{n<\omega} \delta(\sigma+n)$.

It follows that $\{C_\alpha\} \in C_{\delta(\sigma+\omega)}$ and $C_\alpha \cup \{C_\alpha\} = \varrho \in C_{\delta(\sigma+\omega)}$. Since $\sigma+\omega = \varrho+\omega$, this proves the theorem in case (i).

(ii) ϱ is a limit number > 0. For $\sigma < \varrho$ we obviously have $\sigma+\omega \leqslant \varrho$ and hence $\sigma \in C_{\delta(\varrho)}$, which proves that $\varrho \subseteq C_{\delta(\varrho)}$. We now consider the formulae

$$\mathbf{Trans}\,(x)\colon\ (y)(z)[(y \in z) \wedge (z \in x) \to (y \in x)],$$

$$\mathbf{Ord}\,(x)\colon\ \mathbf{Trans}\,(x) \wedge (y)(z)\{[(y \in x) \wedge (z \in x)] \to$$
$$\to [(y \in z) \vee (y = z) \vee (z \in y)]\}.$$

We easily check that if A is a transitive class, then for every a in A

$$\vdash_A \mathbf{Trans}\,[a] \equiv a \text{ is transitive},$$

$$\vdash_A \mathbf{Ord}\,[a] \equiv (a \text{ is transitive and } E \text{ is connected in } a) \equiv a \in On.$$

Since $C_{\delta(\varrho)}$ is transitive, we obtain

$$\{a \in C_{\delta(\varrho)}\colon \vdash_{C_{\delta(\varrho)}} \mathbf{Ord}\,[a]\} = On \cap C_{\delta(\varrho)}.$$

If $\gamma = \min\{\xi\colon \xi \in On - C_{\delta(\varrho)}\}$, then the right-hand side of this equation is γ. Since $C_{\delta(\varrho+\omega)}$ is predicatively closed, we obtain $\gamma \in C_{\delta(\varrho+\omega)}$. The inclusion $\varrho \subseteq C_{\delta(\varrho)}$ proves that $\gamma \geqslant \varrho$ and hence $\varrho \in C_{\delta(\varrho+\omega)}$.

4.5. *If ϱ is a critical number of δ (i.e., $\delta(r, \varrho) = \varrho$), B satisfies* (B.0)–(B.4), *and a is a transitive sequence, then $C_\varrho^B(a)$ contains all ordinals $< \varrho$ and only such ordinals.*

PROOF. This corollary follows from 4.3, 4.4 and the remark that if $\sigma < \varrho$, then $\sigma+\omega \leqslant \delta(r, \varrho) = \varrho$ and hence $\delta(\sigma+\omega) \leqslant \varrho$.

For later purposes we shall calculate the cardinal numbers $|C_\xi^B(a)|$ of $C_\xi^B(a)$ for any transitive sequence a and B satisfying (B.0)–(B.4):

4.6. *If b is a transitive sequence, then $|b_\xi| \leqslant |\xi|$ for each ξ in* $\mathrm{Dom}(b)$; *also* $\left|\bigcup \mathrm{Rg}(b)\right| \leqslant |\mathrm{Dom}(b)|^2$.

PROOF. b_ξ is a subset of $\mathrm{Rg}(b|\xi) = \{b_\eta\colon \eta < \xi\}$. Hence the power of b_ξ is at most $|\xi|$. Since the sets b_ξ are well ordered, we can use the well known laws on the summation of cardinals and obtain

$$\left|\bigcup \mathrm{Rg}(b)\right| \leqslant \sum_{\xi \in \mathrm{Dom}(b)} |b_\xi| \leqslant \sum_{\xi \in \mathrm{Dom}(b)} |\xi| \leqslant |\mathrm{Dom}(b)|^2.$$

If a is a transitive sequence, then so is the sequence whose terms are the consecutive constructible sets (cf. 3.2). Thus we can apply 4.6 to this sequence and obtain

4.7. *If B satisfies* (B.0)–(B.4) *and a is a transitive sequence, then* $|C_\xi^B(a)| \leqslant |\xi|$ *for each ordinal ξ.*

5. Models containing with each element its mappings into ordinals

We shall prove in VII.1.3 an easy theorem to the effect that the axiom of choice is valid in a model M provided that M contains with each x a one-to-one mapping of ordinals onto a set $\supseteq x$.

In the present section we shall show how to obtain models which have this property: we shall add two new conditions, (B.5) and (B.6), to the list (B.0)–(B.4) given in Section 2 and we shall prove that if B satisfies conditions (B.0)–(B.6), then each set constructible from an arbitrary transitive sequence a by means of B is an image of ordinals obtained by a function which also is constructible from a by means of B

Let $r \geqslant 11$; we consider the condition

(B.5) *If $I(r, \sigma) = 11$, then*

$$B(a, f) = \{f_\varrho\colon (\varrho < \sigma) \wedge (I(r, \sigma) = 11)\}.$$

5.1. *If B satisfies* (B.0)–(B.5) *and* $I(r, \sigma) = 11$, *then $C_\sigma^B(a)$ is an ordinal; more precisely,* $C_\sigma^B(a) = \overline{\mathrm{pl}}^*(r, \sigma)$ *for each σ in On.*

Note that $\overline{\mathrm{pl}}^*(r, \sigma)$ is the index of σ in the increasing sequences of all ordinals satisfying the equation $I(r, \xi) = 11$ (cf. p. 38).

PROOF. It follows from (B.5) that if σ satisfies the equation $I(r, \sigma) = 11$, then $C^B_\sigma(a)$ is the set of all $C^B_\varrho(a)$ where ϱ ranges over ordinals $< \sigma$ satisfying the same equation. It follows by induction that $C^B_\sigma(a) = \xi$ where ξ is the order type of the set of ordinals $\varrho < \sigma$ satisfying this equation, which is the required result.

Theorem 5.1 shows that under conditions (B.0)–(B.5) all ordinals appear in the sequence C^B_ξ at places such that $I\xi = 11$. We showed in 4.5 that if B satisfies only (B.0)–(B.4), all ordinals are constructible but we did not obtain any simple formula which would show the place at which a given ordinal appears in the sequence of constructible sets.

Now we assume that $r \geqslant 12$ and introduce the last condition:

(B.6) *If* $I(r, \sigma) = 12$, *then*

$$B(a,f) = \{\langle\varrho, f_\varrho\rangle : \mathrm{pl}(r, \varrho) < K(r, \sigma)\} \cap f_{M(r,\sigma)} .$$

5.2. *If B satisfies* (B.0)–(B.6), *then*

$$\{\langle\varrho, C^B_\varrho(a)\rangle : \varrho < \xi\} \in C^B_\tau(a) \quad \textit{where} \quad \tau = \delta(r, \xi+7) .$$

PROOF. In order to simplify the formulae we suppress everywhere the index B and the symbols a and r. Then the formula to be proved becomes $C|\xi \in C_{\delta(\xi+7)}$.

Let $\eta < \xi$. By 1.4 we have $\mathrm{pl}(\eta) < \delta(\eta+1) < \delta(\xi+1)$ and $C_\eta \in C_{\delta(\xi+1)}$. Hence both $\eta = C_{\mathrm{pl}^*(\eta)}$ and C_η are elements of $C_{\delta(\xi+1)}$, whence $\langle\eta, C_\eta\rangle \in C_{\delta(\xi+5)}$, which proves that $C|\xi \subseteq C_{\delta(\xi+5)}$. We can determine a σ such that $\delta(\xi+6) < \sigma < \delta(\xi+7)$, $I\sigma = 12$, $K\sigma = \mathrm{pl}(\xi)$, $L\sigma = 0$, $M\sigma = \delta(\xi+5)$. It follows that

$$C_\sigma = \{\langle\varrho, C_\varrho\rangle : \mathrm{pl}(\varrho) < \mathrm{pl}(\xi)\} \cap C_{\delta(\xi+5)} = C|\xi ,$$

which proves the theorem.

Theorem 5.2 shows that if B satisfies conditions (B.0)–(B.6) and λ is a limit number, then $C_{\delta(\lambda)}$ has the property referred to at the beginning of this section. More precisely:

5.3. *If B satisfies* (B.0)–(B.6) *and λ is a limit number, then for each transitive a in S and each $x \in C^B_{\delta(\lambda)}(a)$ there are an ordinal ξ in $C^B_{\delta(\lambda)}(a)$ and a function φ in $C^B_{\delta(\lambda)}(a)$ such that* $\mathrm{Dom}(\varphi) = \xi$ *and* $\mathrm{Rg}(\varphi) \supseteq x$.

PROOF. Again we suppress the symbol a. Let $x = C_\zeta$. Since $\zeta < \delta(\lambda)$ and λ is a limit number, we infer that there is an ordinal $\xi < \lambda$ such that $\zeta < \delta(\xi)$. Hence we have $\delta(\xi+7) < \delta(\lambda)$ and $C|\xi \in C_{\delta(\lambda)}$. By 3.3 $x \subseteq \mathrm{Rg}(C|\zeta) \subseteq \mathrm{Rg}(C|\xi)$. Hence the required function is $C|\xi$.

The theorem remains valid if we replace $C^B_{\delta(\lambda)}$ by the whole class K^B.

6. Examples of functions satisfying (B.0)–(B.6)

Until now we assumed that function B is given. Now we want to give examples of such functions.

(a) *Function* $B^{\min}$. For this function we have $r = 10$; we define $B^{\min}$ as the least function satisfying (B.1)–(B.4). These conditions determine uniquely the values of $B(a,f)$ for every a, f in S. We easily show that condition (B.0) is also satisfied.

Constructible sets corresponding to this choice of B will be called *minimal constructible sets*. The class of these sets is denoted by $K^{\min}(a)$. One can show that in $K^{\min}(0)$ the axiom of choice is satisfied; this is not true, in general, if $a \neq 0$.

(b) *Function* B^0. In this case $r = 11$ and B^0 is the smallest function satisfying (B.1)–(B.5). It is again easy to show that B^0 satisfies (B.0).

(c) *Function* B^Z. In this case $r = 12$ and B^Z is the smallest function satisfying (B.1)–(B.6). This function also satisfies (B.0). In the class $K^Z(a)$ of sets which are constructible from a by means of B^Z the axiom of choice is always satisfied independently of the value of a.

Our discussion in the subsequent chapters will be concerned with the above three functions and the corresponding classes of constructible sets. Some results, however, will be stated for arbitrary functions B satisfying some or all of our conditions (B.0)–(B.6).

7. Sets constructible in a class

Constructible sets as defined above depend on a parameter a ranging over S. Later on we shall use the fact that the permissible values of a are sets. At present this assumption is not essential and it requires but little change to define constructible sets depending on a class.

Thus let T be a transfinite sequence $\{\langle\xi, T_\xi\rangle : \xi \in On\}$ such that $T_\xi \subseteq T|\xi$ for each ξ. Let B be a function satisfying the conditions (where $f \in S$, $\sigma = \mathrm{lh}(f)$, and $I(r, \sigma) \neq 10$):

(B′.0) $B(f) \subseteq \mathrm{Rg}(f) \cup \bigcup \mathrm{Rg}(f)$.

(B′.1) *If* $I(r, \sigma) = 0$, *then*

$$B(f) = \mathrm{Rg}(f).$$

(B′.2) *If* $0 < I(r, \sigma) \leqslant 9$, *then*

$$B(f) = A_{I(r,\sigma)}(f_{K(r,\sigma)}, f_{L(r,\sigma)}) \cap f_{M(r,\sigma)}.$$

From theorem I.3.1 it follows that:

7.1. *There exists exactly one transfinite sequence* $C_\xi = C_\xi^B(T)$ *such that*

$$C_\xi = B(C|\xi) \quad \text{if} \quad I(r, \xi) \neq 10,$$
$$C_\xi = T_{\mathrm{pl}'(r,\xi)} \quad \text{if} \quad I(r, \xi) = 10.$$

The terms of this sequence are called *constructible from T by B.*

All the theorems established in this chapter are valid *mutatis mutandis* or this more general notion of constructibility.

CHAPTER IV

FUNCTORS AND THEIR DEFINABILITY

The general topic of this chapter is as follows. We consider functions which correlate with each set A a set $F(A)$ contained in A. More generally, we consider functions depending on more arguments, e.g., $F(A, p_1, \ldots, p_n)$ with the variables p_i ("the parameters" as we shall call them) ranging over A. We want to inquire under what conditions there is a formula H with $n+1$ free variables such that for arbitrary a in A and arbitrary values of the parameters the condition $a \in F(A, p_1, \ldots, p_n)$ is equivalent to $\models_A H[a, p_1, \ldots, p_n]$.

Questions of this type arise very often in the discussion of models. For instance it is very natural to ask whether the set of all ordinals which belong to A is definable (or parametrically definable) in A, whether the set of all constructible sets which belong to A is definable (or parametrically definable) in A, etc. We can answer these questions if we can answer for the functions $F(A) = On \cap A$ and $F(A, p) = K^B(p) \cap A$ the general question formulated above.

If, possibly under some assumptions concerning A, we succeed in finding a formula H which has the properties indicated above, then we have a stronger result than a mere parametric definability of the set $F(A, p_1, \ldots, p_n)$ in A. We can claim that the definability of $F(A, p_1, \ldots, p_n)$ in A is in a sense uniform: the defining formula is one and the same for all classes A satisfying the assumptions, if any, which ensure the existence of the formula H.

In most cases we have to make some assumptions concerning A in order that the formula in question exist: let us say a few words about those assumptions. Since we are chiefly interested in transitive models of ZF, we might be tempted to assume that all classes A for which we shall discuss our problem are simply such models of ZF. However, this assumption would be much too strong because in many special situations we shall be interested in transitive models not necessarily of the whole ZF but of its finitely axiomatisable subsystems. For this reason we shall investigate the problem of the existence of H for a given function F restricting F to arguments A which are transitive models for a suitable finitely axiomatisable subsystem of ZF. The choice of this subsystem will of course depend on the function F. As a rule we shall not be interested in an explicit enumeration of the axioms which are assumed to be valid in A but shall content ourselves with the statement that these axioms exist and their number is finite.

The above remarks are intended to justify the somewhat involved definitions to be given in Sections 1 and 2 below, in which we introduce the notion of "strongly definable functors". In later sections we establish the general properties of those functors and give several examples of them.

1. Strongly definable functors

The following abbreviated expression will prove useful in the future. We shall say that *almost every set A has a property* P if there are finitely many axioms $K_1, \ldots, K_r$ of ZF such that whenever A is a transitive set in which these axioms are valid, A has the property P.

We shall say that *F is a functor with $n+1$ arguments* if F is a function with domain V^{n+1} (i.e., F: $V^{n+1} \to V$, where V is the universal class) such that for almost all A and arbitrary $p_1, \ldots, p_n$ in A

$$F(A, p_1, \ldots, p_n) \subseteq A\,.$$

We shall say that *F is strongly definable* if there is a formula H such that $\mathrm{Fr}(H) = \{0, 1, \ldots, n\}$ and for almost every A and arbitrary $p_1, \ldots, p_n$ in A

$$x \in F(A, p_1, \ldots, p_n) \equiv \;\vdash_A H[x, p_1, \ldots, p_n]\,.$$

We shall call H a *definition of F.*

The following theorems concerning operations on strongly definable functors are easily provable:

1.1. *If F and G are strongly definable functors with $n+1$ and $m+1$ arguments, then so are the functors*

$$N(A, p_1, \ldots, p_n) = A - F(A, p_1, \ldots, p_n),$$

$$P(A, p_1, \ldots, p_n, q_1, \ldots, q_m) = F(A, p_1, \ldots, p_n) \cap G(A, q_1, \ldots, q_m),$$

$$Q(A, p_1, \ldots, p_{n-1}) = \bigcap_{q \in A} F(A, p_1, \ldots, p_{n-1}, q).$$

Also identifications of some or all arguments $p_1, \ldots, p_n$ *and permutations of these arguments yield strongly definable functors.*

For the proof we remark that if H and K are definitions of F and G, then $\neg H$ is a definition of N, $H(x_0, x_1, \ldots, x_n) \wedge K(x_0, x_{n+1}, \ldots, x_{n+m})$ is a definition of P and $(x_n)H$ is a definition of Q. Identifications and permutations of variables in H yield formulae which define functors arising from F by identifications and permutations of its variables.

In dealing with functions, whose values not only are contained in A but also belong to A it is advantageous to use another notion of a functor.

We shall call a mapping f: $V^{n+1} \to V$ a *functor of the second kind* if for almost every set A and every $p_1, \ldots, p_n \in A$

$$f(A, p_1, \ldots, p_n) \in A.$$

It follows from the definition that every functor of the second kind is a functor. Thus the notion of strong definability applies to functors of the second kind. However, it is more convenient to associate with functors of the second kind formulae which define the value of $f(A, p_1, \ldots, p_n)$ directly. Those formulae will be described in the next theorem:

1.2. *If f is a functor of the second kind and H a formula which defines it, then the formula*

$$K(x_0, x_1, \ldots, x_n) = (u)[(u \in x_0) \equiv H(u, x_1, \ldots, x_n)]$$

has the property that for almost every A and for all $t, p_1, \ldots, p_n \in A$

(1) $t = f(A, p_1, \ldots, p_n)$ *if and only if* $\vdash_A K(t, p_1, \ldots, p_n)$.

The proof of this theorem is immediate.

A formula K satisfying (1) for almost every A and arbitrary $t, p_1, \ldots, p_n \in A$ will be called a *definition of the second kind of f*. Only functors of the second kind possess definitions of the second kind. Functors which possess definitions of the second kind are strongly definable functors of the second kind.

Finally we shall introduce strongly definable relations:

An $(n+1)$-ary relation $R \subseteq V^{n+1}$ will be called *strongly definable* if the functor χ_R:

$$\chi_R(A, p_1, \ldots, p_n) = \begin{cases} 0 & \text{if } \neg R(A, p_1, \ldots, p_n), \\ A & \text{if } R(A, p_1, \ldots, p_n) \end{cases}$$

is strongly definable. We call χ_R the *characteristic functor of R*.

It can be easily proved that if H is a definition of χ_R, then the formula $(x_0)H$ which we denote by K has the following property: for almost all A and for arbitrary $p_1, \ldots, p_n$ in A

$$R(A, p_1, \ldots, p_n) \equiv \vdash_A K[p_1, \ldots, p_n].$$

Each formula K with this property will be called a *definition of R*.

2. Properties of strongly definable functors and relations

The first four theorems given below result immediately from the definitions:

2.1. *Permutations and identifications of the variables $p_1, \ldots, p_n$ in a strongly definable functor (or relation) yield a strongly definable functor (or relation).*

2.2. *If f is a strongly definable functor of the second kind with $n+1$ arguments and F is a strongly definable functor with $m+1$ arguments, then the functor*

$$G(A, p_1, \ldots, p_n, q_1, \ldots, q_{m-1}) = F(A, q_1, \ldots, q_{m-1}, f(A, p_1, \ldots, p_n))$$

is strongly definable; if F is of the second kind, then so is G.

2.3. *Boolean operations on strongly definable relations yield strongly definable relations. If $R(A, p_1, \ldots, p_n)$ is a strongly definable relation, then so is the relation $(p_n)_A^{*} R(A, p_1, \ldots, p_n)$.*

2.4. *If $R(A, p_1, \ldots, p_n)$ is a strongly definable relation and $f(A, q_1, \ldots, q_m)$ a strongly definable functor of the second kind, then the relation $R(A, f(A, q_1, \ldots, q_m), p_2, \ldots, p_n)$ is strongly definable.*

2.5. *The ternary relations expressed by the formulae*

$$(p \in A) \wedge (q \in A) \wedge (p \in q),$$
$$(p \in A) \wedge (q \in A) \wedge (p = q)$$

are strongly definable.

PROOF. The characteristic functors En and Id of these relations have as their definitions the formulae

$$(x_0 = x_0) \equiv (x_1 \in x_2), \qquad (x_0 = x_0) \equiv (x_1 = x_2).$$

2.6. *If f, g are strongly definable functors of the second kind, then the relations $f(A, p_1, \ldots, p_n) \in g(A, p_1, \ldots, p_n)$ and $f(A, p_1, \ldots, p_n) = g(A, p_1, \ldots, p_n)$ are strongly definable.*

PROOF. The characteristic functors of these relations are obtained from En and Id by substituting $f(A, p_1, \ldots, p_n)$ and $g(A, p_1, \ldots, p_n)$ for the last two arguments.

2.7. *If F is a strongly definable functor, then so is the relation $p_{n+1} \in F(A, p_1, \ldots, p_n)$.*

PROOF. The characteristic functor of this relation has as its definition the formula

$$(x_0 = x_0) \equiv \boldsymbol{F}(x_{n+1}, x_1, \ldots, x_n),$$

where $\boldsymbol{F}$ is a definition of F.

2.8. *If F is a strongly definable functor and f a strongly definable functor of the second kind, then the relation $f(A, p_1, \ldots, p_n) \in F(A, p_1, \ldots, p_n)$ is strongly definable.*

PROOF. Its characteristic functor is obtained by a substitution and a subsequent identification of variables from the characteristic functor of the relation considered in 2.7.

The previous theorems showed how to obtain strongly definable relations from functors. Now we show how to obtain functors from strongly definable relations.

2.9. *If $R(A, p_1, \ldots, p_n)$ is a strongly definable relation, then the functor*

$$F(A, p_1, \ldots, p_{n-1}) = \{p_n \colon R(A, p_1, \ldots, p_n)\}$$

is strongly definable.

PROOF. The definition of F is $(u)H(u, x_1, \ldots, x_{n-1}, x_0)$, where H is a definition of χ_R. This results from the equivalences

$$\begin{aligned} p_n \in F(A, p_1, \ldots, p_{n-1}) &\equiv R(A, p_1, \ldots, p_n) \equiv [\chi_R(A, p_1, \ldots, p_n) = A] \\ &\equiv (a)_A[a \in \chi_R(A, p_1, \ldots, p_n)] \equiv (a)_A \vdash_A H[a, p_1, \ldots, p_n] \\ &\equiv \vdash_A \big((u)H\big)[p_1, \ldots, p_n]. \end{aligned}$$

2.10. *If R is a strongly definable relation and G_1, G_2 are two strongly definable functors, then the functor F defined thus*

$$F(A, p_1, \ldots, p_n) = \begin{cases} G_1(A, p_1, \ldots, p_n) & \text{if} \quad R(A, p_1, \ldots, p_n), \\ G_2(A, p_1, \ldots, p_n) & \text{if} \quad \neg R(A, p_1, \ldots, p_n), \end{cases}$$

is strongly definable; if G_1 and G_2 are functors of the second kind, then so is F.

To prove this it is sufficient to notice that $F = (G_1 \cap \chi_R) \cup (G_2 \cap \chi_{\neg R})$.

2.11. *If f is a strongly definable functor of the second kind, then so is the functor F defined thus:*

$$F(A, a, p) = \{f(A, x, p) \colon x \in a\}.$$

PROOF. The condition $y \in F(A, a, p)$ is equivalent to

$$(Ex)_A[(x \in a) \wedge (y = f(A, x, p))].$$

Thus by the previous theorems 2.3–2.9 the functor F is strongly definable.

In order to show that the functor F is of the second kind, we denote by $\mathbf{f}$ the definition of the second kind of f. There are finitely many axioms of ZF such that if A is a transitive set in which those axioms are valid and if x, t are in A and p in A^n, then

$$f(A, x, p) \in A,$$
$$t = f(A, x, p) \equiv \vdash_A \mathbf{f}[t, x, p].$$

Let A be a set in which, in addition, axiom ($\mathrm{VI}_{\mathbf{f}}$) is valid. If $p \in A^n$ and $a \in A$, then for every x in a there is exactly one t in A such that $\vdash_A \mathbf{f}[t, x, p]$. Thus the set of all these elements t belongs to A. Since this set is equal to $\{f(A, x, p) \colon x \in a\}$, the theorem is proved.

3. Examples of strongly definable functors

Theorems of Sections 2 and 3 allow us to establish strong definability of several simple functors. Their examples will be presented below. For brevity of exposition, we shall adopt the following notational conventions:

As a rule functors will be denoted by upper case letters in roman or in italics or a combinations of such letters starting with a capital letter. A corresponding symbol printed in bold face letters is then a definition of the functor. The same notation applies to functors of the second kind, which will be denoted by a lower case letter or a combination of such letters. The symbol made out of the same bold face letters will denote the definition of the second kind of that functor.

A few functors will be denoted by special symbols.

If $\boldsymbol{f}$ and $\boldsymbol{H}$ are definitions of the functors $f(A, x_1, \ldots, x_n)$ and $H(A, x_1, \ldots, x_m)$, then we abbreviate as

$$\boldsymbol{H}\big(x_0, x_1, \ldots, x_{q-1}, \boldsymbol{f}(x_{h+1}, \ldots, x_{h+n}), x_{q+1}, \ldots, x_m\big)$$

the formula

$$(Ex_h)[\boldsymbol{f}(x_h, \ldots, x_{h+n}) \wedge \boldsymbol{H}(x_0, \ldots, x_{q-1}, x_h, x_{q+1}, \ldots, x_m)],$$

where h is the least integer such that no variable with an index $\geqslant h$ occurs either in $\boldsymbol{f}$ or in $\boldsymbol{H}$. This formula is obviously a definition of the compounded functor $H\big(A, x_1, \ldots, x_{q-1}, f(A, y_1, \ldots, y_n), x_{q+1}, \ldots, x_m\big)$.

We now give the list of the basic functors of both kinds and of the relations which are strongly definable.

1. $f(A, p, q) = \{p, q\}$.

This is a functor of the second kind because a transitive set A in which axiom (II) is valid is closed with respect to the operation of forming pairs. A definition of the second kind of f is

$$(x_3)\{(x_3 \in x_0) \equiv [(x_3 = x_1) \vee (x_3 = x_2)]\}.$$

2. $g(A, p, q) = \langle p, q \rangle$.

The strong definability of this functor follows from 1 by the application of 2.2 because g can be obtained from f by substitution.

We always use the expressions $x_0 = \{x_1, x_2\}$ and $x_0 = \langle x_1, x_2 \rangle$ for the definitions of the functors 1, 2. The use of the same symbols as in meta-theory should not lead to a misunderstanding because it will always be clear whether we are writing a formula of ZF or a formula of the meta-theory.

3. $\mathrm{Rl}(A) = \{a \in A\colon \mathrm{Rel}(a)\}$.

The relation expressed by the formula

$$(u)_a(Ev, w)_A(u = \langle v, w \rangle)$$

is strongly definable according to 2.3, 2.5. Hence by 2.9 the set of those a in A which stand in this relation to A is a strongly definable functor.

4. $\mathrm{Fn}(A) = \{a \in A\colon \mathrm{Fnc}(a)\}$.

The proof is similar to that given above.

5. $\mathrm{dl}(A, a) = \mathrm{Dom}(a)$ *if* $\mathrm{Dom}(a) \in A$ *and* 0 *otherwise.*

This is a functor of the second kind. To show its strong definability we proceed as follows: the relation

$$(Ew)_A(\langle v, w\rangle \in a)$$

is strongly definable and hence so is the functor

$$(*) \qquad \{v \in A\colon (Ew)_A\{\langle v, w\rangle \in a\}\}.$$

The value of this functor for each a in a transitive set A is $A \cap \mathrm{Dom}(a) = \mathrm{Dom}(a)$. Now we make use of the fact that the existence of the domain of a relation is provable in ZF. Thus there is a formula $H(x_0, x_1)$ which is a definition of the functor (*) and which has the property that the formula

$$(x_1)(Ex_2)(x_0)[(x_0 \in x_2) \equiv H(x_0, x_1)]$$

is provable in ZF and hence valid in almost all models of ZF. It follows that for almost all A and arbitrary a in A the set $\mathrm{Dom}(a)$ is an element of A. Thus $\mathrm{dl}(A, a)$ is a functor of the second kind and it is strongly definable because it is identical with (*).

6. $\mathrm{dp}(A, a) = \mathrm{Rg}(a)$ *if* $\mathrm{Rg}(a) \in A$ *and* 0 *otherwise.*

The proof of the strong definability of dp is similar to that given in 5.

7. $\mathrm{restr}(A, a, b) = a|b$ $(= a \cap (b \times V))$ *if this set belongs to* A *and* 0 *otherwise.*

Again the proof is similar to that given in 5 and uses the fact that a formula which states the existence of a function restricted to a set is provable in ZF.

8. $W(A) = \{\langle u, v, w\rangle \in A^3\colon \langle u, v\rangle \in w\}$.

Strong definability follows here from the remark that

$$x \in W(A) \equiv (Eu, v, w)_A[(x = \langle u, v, w\rangle) \wedge (\langle u, v\rangle \in w)]$$

and the relation defined by the right-hand side of this formula is strongly definable in view of 2.3, 2.5 and 3.2.

9. $\mathrm{val}(A, a, t) = a(t)$ *if a is a function and* $t \in \mathrm{Dom}(a)$; *otherwise* 0.

The relation $x \in \mathrm{val}(A, a, t)$ is equivalent to a strongly definable relation

$$\big(a \in \mathrm{Fn}(A)\big) \wedge \big(t \in \mathrm{dl}(A, a)\big) \wedge (Eb)_A[(\langle t, b\rangle \in a) \wedge (x \in b)].$$

The proof is accomplished as in example 5.

10. $\mathrm{un}(A, a) = \bigcup \{a(t)\colon t \in \mathrm{Dom}(a)\}$ *if a is a function and the union of its range is an element of A*; *otherwise* 0.

The proof of strong definability is similar to that given above.

11. $\pi(A) = On \cap A$.

The defining formula **Ord** for this functor was given in III.4.4. Note that if A is transitive, then $\pi(A)$ is the least ordinal not in A, i.e., $\pi(A) = \sup A$.

12. $\mathrm{Seq}(A) = \{a \in A\colon \ \mathrm{Fnc}(a) \wedge \big(\mathrm{Dom}(a) \in On\big)\}$.

This is a functor of the first kind and $a \in \mathrm{Seq}(A)$ if and only if a is a transfinite sequence, i.e. a function whose domain is an ordinal. The strong definability of this functor follows from the observation that the relation $a \in \mathrm{Seq}(A)$ is (for almost all A) equivalent to $\big(a \in \mathrm{Fn}(A)\big) \wedge \big(\mathrm{dl}(A, a) \in \pi(A)\big)$ and this relation is strongly definable.

13. $\mathrm{Str}(A) = \{a \in \mathrm{Seq}(A)\colon a$ *is a transitive sequence*$\}$.

The strong definability of this functor results from the equivalence

$$\big(a \in \mathrm{Str}(A)\big) \equiv \big(a \in \mathrm{Seq}(A)\big) \wedge (x)_{\mathrm{Dom}(a)}\big(a(x) \subseteq \mathrm{Rg}(a|x)\big).$$

We can replace here $\mathrm{Dom}(a)$ by $\mathrm{dl}(A, a)$, $a(x)$ by $\mathrm{val}(A, a, x)$ and $\mathrm{Rg}(a|x)$ by $\mathrm{dp}\big(A, \mathrm{restr}(A, a, x)\big)$. It is thus clear that the relation $a \in \mathrm{Str}(A)$ is strongly definable.

14. $\mathrm{suc}(A, a) = a \cup \{a\}$; $\mathrm{pred}(A, a) = \bigcup a$.

These functors give the values of the successor and of the predecessor of an element a of A. Their strong definability is obvious.

15. $\mathrm{Lim}(A) = \{a \in \pi(A)\colon \ a = \mathrm{pred}(A, a)\}$.

$\mathrm{Lim}(A)$ is the set of limit ordinals which belong to A.

16. $P(A, a) = A \cap P(a)$.

This is the set of those subsets of a which belong to A. If axiom (IV) (of power-set) is valid in A, then $P(A, a) \in A$ (see II.1.5), and thus $P(A, a)$ is a functor of the second kind. Its strong definability results from the equivalence

$$(x \in P(A, a)) \equiv [(x \in A) \wedge (x \subseteq a)].$$

17. $\min\{\xi \in \pi(A) \colon \xi \notin a\}$.

That this is a functor of the second kind follows from the observation that in ZF the following theorem is provable:

$$(x_1)(Ex_0)\{\mathbf{Ord}(x_0) \wedge \neg(x_0 \in x_1) \wedge (x_2)[(x_2 \in x_0) \rightarrow (x_2 \in x_1)]\}$$

(for each set there is a smallest ordinal not in the set).

The strong definability of this functor is obvious.

Example 17 allows us to establish the following result:

18. *If f is a strongly definable functor of the second kind such that its values are ordinals, then for almost all A and all $p \in A^n$, $b \in A$*

$$\sup\{f(A, x, p) \colon x \in b\} \in A;$$

moreover, the functor whose value is this supremum is strongly definable.

PROOF. From 2.11 it follows that the set $a = \bigcup\{f(A, x, p) \colon x \in b\}$ belongs to A for almost all A and arbitrary $p \in A^n$, $b \in A$. The supremum described in the theorem is either $\min\{\xi \in \pi(A) \colon \xi \notin a\}$ or its successor and the result follows from 17.

19. *If R is a strongly definable relation with $n+2$ arguments, then the functor*

$$f(A, p) = \min\{\xi < \pi(A) \colon R(A, \xi, p)\}$$

is strongly definable of the second kind.

PROOF. The minimum in question obviously belongs to A. It is therefore sufficient to represent the condition $x \in f(A, p)$ by means of logical connectives and quantifiers limited to A applied to strongly definable relations. This representation is

$$x \in f(A, p) \equiv (y)_A[(y \in \pi(A)) \wedge R(A, y, p) \rightarrow (x \in y)] \wedge$$
$$\wedge (Ey)_A[(y \in \pi(A)) \wedge R(A, y, p)].$$

4. Definitions by transfinite induction

In this section we consider the strong definability of functors satisfying certain inductive equations.

Let S, R be strongly definable functors with $n+1$ arguments and let f be a strongly definable functor of the second kind with $n+3$ arguments. We shall abbreviate the string of n parameters $(p_1, \dots, p_n)$ by p. We assume that for almost all A and arbitrary p the following conditions are satisfied:

(1) $R(A, p)$ is a partial well-ordering of $S(A, p)$,

(2) if $b \in S(A, p)$, then the set $O_{A,p}(b) = \{c \in S(A, p)\colon (\langle c, b\rangle \in R(A, p)) \wedge \wedge (c \neq b)\}$ is in A.

We call $O_{A,p}(b)$ the *segment of* $S(A, p)$ determined by b. If φ is any function with $\mathrm{Dom}(\varphi) = S(A, p)$, then $\varphi|b$ denotes its restriction to $O_{A,p}(b)$.

4.1. *For almost all A and arbitrary $p \in A^n$ there is at most one function φ with domain $S(A, p)$ which satisfies the inductive equation*

$$\varphi(a) = f(A, \varphi|a, a, p). \tag{3}$$

Proof. Let us assume that in A are valid finitely many axioms of ZF which ensure that (1) is true for arbitrary p in A^n. If φ_1 and φ_2 both satisfy (3) and $\varphi_1 \neq \varphi_2$, then the set $\{a\colon \varphi_1(a) \neq \varphi_2(a)\}$ is not void. For any minimal element a_0 of this set we have $\varphi_1|a_0 = \varphi_2|a_0$ and hence by (3) $\varphi_1(a_0) = \varphi_2(a_0)$, which is a contradiction.

For arbitrary A and $p \in A^n$ we denote by $\mathrm{In}(A, p)$ the unique function $\varphi \subseteq A$ which satisfies (3) provided that such a function exists; otherwise we take $\mathrm{In}(A, p) = 0$.

4.2. *The functor* In *is strongly definable; moreover, for almost all A and all p in A^n the value of* $\mathrm{In}(A, p)$ *is a function which satisfies* (3) *and also the condition $\varphi|a \in A$ for each a in $S(A, p)$.*

Proof. Let $\boldsymbol{S}$, $\boldsymbol{f}$ be definitions of functors S, f. Thus for almost all A and arbitrary $p \in A^n$, $a, b \in A$ we have

$$\vdash_A \boldsymbol{S}[a, p] \equiv [a \in S(A, p)], \tag{4}$$

$$\vdash_A \boldsymbol{f}[a, b, p] \equiv [a = f(A, b, p)]. \tag{5}$$

Instead of choosing for $\boldsymbol{R}$ a formula which defines R we prefer to proceed differently in order to obtain a formula expressing the fact that $\langle x, y\rangle \in R(A, p)$ and not (as would follow if we took as $\boldsymbol{R}$ simply a definition of R) that $a \in R(A, p)$. Thus we let $\boldsymbol{R}$ be the formula $\boldsymbol{R}'(\langle y_0, y_1\rangle, x_1, \ldots, x_n)$, where $\boldsymbol{R}'$ is a definition of R. For almost all A and arbitrary $p \in A^n$, $a, b \in A$ we then have

$$\vdash_A \boldsymbol{R}[a, b, p] \equiv [\langle a, b\rangle \in R(A, p)]. \tag{6}$$

Finally, let H be the conjunction of the following three formulae:

H_1: $\mathbf{Fn}(x) \wedge \boldsymbol{S}(y, p)$,

H_2: $(s)[(s \in \mathbf{dl}(x, p)) \equiv \boldsymbol{R}(s, y, p)]$,

H_3: $(q)(t)\Big(\boldsymbol{R}(t, y, p) \wedge (r)\{(r \in q) \equiv [\boldsymbol{R}(r, t, p) \wedge (r \neq t)]\} \rightarrow$

$$\rightarrow \boldsymbol{W}\big(\langle t, \boldsymbol{f}(\mathbf{restr}(x, q), t, p), x\rangle\big)\Big).$$

The free variables of H are x, y, p and the intuitive content of this formula is the following: x is a function, y is an element of $S(A, p)$, the domain of x is $O_{A,p}(y) \cup \{y\}$, and if t precedes y in $S(A, p)$ or is equal to y, then the value of x at the point t is $f(A, x|O_{A,p}(t), t, p)$.

LEMMA 1. *For almost all A, if $p \in A^n$ and $g, b \in A$ and $\vdash_A H[g, b, p]$, then*

1° *g is a function with* $\mathrm{Dom}(g) = O_{A,p}(b) \cup \{b\}$,

2° $b \in S(A, p)$,

3° *$\langle c, b\rangle \in R(A, p)$ implies that $g|c \in A$ and $g(c) = f(A, g|c, c, p)$.*

PROOF. Let so many axioms of ZF be valid in A that for arbitrary $p \in A^n$, a, b in A the equivalences (4)–(6) will be true. Moreover, let the equivalences

$$\vdash_A \mathbf{Fn}[x] \equiv (x \text{ is a function}), \tag{7}$$

$$\vdash_A [y = \mathbf{dl}(x)] \equiv (y = \mathrm{Dom}(x)), \tag{8}$$

$$\vdash_A [z = \mathbf{restr}(x, y)] \equiv (z = x|y), \tag{9}$$

$$\vdash_A \boldsymbol{W}[\langle x, y, z\rangle] \equiv (\langle x, y\rangle \in z) \tag{10}$$

be true for arbitrary x, y, z in A; since the functors $\mathrm{Fn}(A)$, $\mathrm{dl}(A, x)$, $\mathrm{restr}(A, x, y)$ and $W(A, x)$ are strongly definable, we can fix a finite number of axioms of ZF such that these equivalences will hold whenever A is transitive and the selected axioms are valid in A.

Finally, let us fix so many axioms of ZF that (2) will be true for arbitrary p in A^n and $b \in A$ whenever these axioms are valid in A.

Since by our assumption the formula H_1 is satisfied in A by g, b, p, we infer from (7) and (4) that g is a function and $b \in S(A, p)$.

Since H_2 is also satisfied in A by g, b, p, we infer by (8) and (4) that

$$(x \in \mathrm{Dom}(g)) \equiv (\langle x, b\rangle \in R(A, p)) \equiv (x \in O_{A,p}(b) \cup \{b\}).$$

Thus 1° and 2° are proved.

Finally, let c be an element such that $\langle c, b\rangle \in R(A, p)$. From (2) it follows that $O_{A,p}(c) \in A$ and from (6) that

$$(r \in O_{A,p}(c)) \equiv \vdash_A \boldsymbol{R}[r, c, p] \wedge (r \neq c).$$

Using the assumption that H_3 is satisfied in A by g, b, p we obtain

$$\vdash_A \boldsymbol{W}\Big(\langle c, \boldsymbol{f}\big(\mathbf{restr}(g, O_{A,p}(c)), c, p\big), g\rangle\Big)$$

or, which is the same,

$$\langle c, f(A, g|O_{A,p}(c), c, p)\rangle \in g,$$

i.e.

$$g(c) = f(A, g|c, c, p).$$

Thus Lemma 1 is proved.

LEMMA 2. *For almost all A, if $p \in A^n$, $b, g \in A$ and conditions* 1°–3° *of Lemma* 1 *are satisfied, then* $\vdash_A H[g, b, p]$.

The proof is obtained by deducing in the same way as in Lemma 1 the condition $\vdash_A H[g, b, p]$ from assumptions 1°–3°.

LEMMA 3. *For almost all A and for arbitrary $p \in A$, $b \in S(A, p)$ there exists in A exactly one function g satisfying* 1°–3° *of Lemma* 1.

PROOF. We assume that so many axioms of ZF are valid in A as to ensure the validity of Lemma 1 and Lemma 2 and of formulae (1)–(10). Additionally we assume that axioms of pairs, unions and the axiom of replacement for the formula H are valid in A. Let p be a fixed sequence of parameters in A^n. We use induction with respect to the partial well-ordering $R(A, p)$. We prove exactly as in 4.1 that there is at most one function g satisfying 1°–3°. Let us now assume that there are elements b in $S(A, p)$ for which the corresponding g is not in A and let b_0 be a minimal element of this kind. For $b \in O_{A,p}(b_0)$ a unique function

g satisfying 1°–3° exists in A and we denote it by g_b. From Lemmata 1 and 2 we know that the mapping

$$b \to g_b$$

is parametrically definable in A because $(x = g_b) \equiv \vdash_A H[x, b, p]$. Thus the sets

$$\{g_b\colon b \in O_{A,p}(b_0)\} \quad \text{and} \quad h = \bigcup \{g_b\colon b \in O_{A,p}(b_0)\}$$

belong to A.

We now claim that the set

$$g = h \cup \{\langle b_0, f(A, h, b_0, p)\rangle\}$$

(which obviously belongs to A) is a function and satisfies 1°–3° for $b = b_0$. Condition 2° is obvious.

From the definition of g we infer that g is a set of pairs and that the domain of g consists of b_0 and of elements in the union $\bigcup\{\mathrm{Dom}(g_b)\colon b \in O_{A,p}(b_0)\}$. Thus the domain of g is $O_{A,p}(b_0) \cup \{b_0\}$.

g is a function. To see this let us assume that $\langle b, u\rangle$ and $\langle b, v\rangle$ are elements of g. If $b = b_0$, then $u = v = f(A, h, b_0, p)$ because g contains only one pair whose first element is b_0. Now let b be different from b_0 and let $\langle b, u\rangle \in g_{b_1}$, $\langle b, v\rangle \in g_{b_2}$. The functions g_{b_i} restricted to $O_{A,p}(b)$ satisfy conditions 1°–3° and thus are equal; hence $u = v$.

Finally we check condition 3°. Let us assume that $\langle c, b_0\rangle \in R(A, p)$. If $c = b_0$, then $g|c = g|O_{A,p}(b_0) = h$, and hence $h \in A$; condition 3° is satisfied because $g(b) = f(A, h, b_0, p)$. If $c \neq b_0$, then $g|c = g_c|c$, and hence condition 3° is true by the assumption that it is true for g_c.

We now complete the proof of 4.2. For almost all A and all p in A^n the union $G = \bigcup \{g_b\colon b \in S(A, p)\}$ is a function with domain $S(A, p)$, which satisfies the conditions $G|b \in A$ and $G(b) = f(A, G|b, b, p)$. Hence $G = \mathrm{In}(A, p)$. Since

$$(\langle b, u\rangle \in G) \equiv (Eg)_A[(\vdash_A H[g, b, p]) \wedge (\langle b, u\rangle \in g)],$$

we infer that $\mathrm{In}(A, p)$ is strongly definable.

Theorem 4.2 should be compared with theorem I.3.1. We proved there the existence and uniqueness of a function which satisfies a given "inductive" equation. From 4.2 we obtain sufficient criteria for the definability of that function:

4.3. *If A is a model of* ZF, $p \in A^n$ *and* $h = f(A, x, p)$, $S = S(A, p)$, $R = R(A, p)$, *where f is a strongly definable functor of the second kind, S and R are strongly definable and R satisfies the condition that $R(A', p')$ is a partial well-ordering of $S(A', p')$ and $O_{R(A', p')}(a') \in A'$ for almost all A' and all a' in A', p' in A'^n, then there is a unique function φ which satisfies for all b in S the conditions*

$$\mathrm{Dom}(\varphi) = S, \quad \varphi|O_R(b) \in A, \quad \varphi(b) = h\big(\varphi|O_R(b), b\big).$$

This function is parametrically definable in A.

PROOF. $\varphi = \mathrm{In}(A, p)$ and since In is a strongly definable functor, its value φ for the arguments A and p is parametrically definable in A.

We also formulate a counterpart of theorem I.3.2. We make the same assumptions concerning A, R, S as in 4.3. Let $P \in A$ and let $h_i(x, u, v, w) = f_i(A, x, u, v, w, p)$, where for $i = 1, 2$ the functors f_i are strongly definable, x ranges over P, u, v, w over A and where p is a fixed sequence of parameters in A. Under these assumptions:

4.4. *There exists a unique pair of functions e_i with domain $P \times S$ such that for arbitrary x in P and a in S the equations*

$$e_i(x, a) = h_i\big(x, e_1\big|(P \times O_R(a)), e_2\big|(P \times O_R(a)), a\big)$$

are true; these functions are parametrically definable in A.

This theorem can be deduced from 4.3 in the same way as I.3.2 was deduced from I.3.1. We leave it to the reader to verify this in detail.

We also remark that we could prove theorems 4.3 and 4.4 under a weaker assumption concerning R and S. Instead of assuming that $S = S(A, p)$ and $R = R(A, p)$, where the functors R, S are strongly definable and satisfy (1) and (2) for almost all values of the argument A and for all p in A^n, we could simply assume that S and R are parametrically definable in A (where A is a given model of ZF) and satisfy assumptions (1) and (2). The proof of theorems 4.2, 4.3 thus modified can be obtained simply by repeating the proof of 4.2 and assuming forthright in this proof that A is a model of ZF. We shall need the strengthened version of theorems 4.3 and 4.4 later on. Since, however, the proofs are practically just the repetitions of the proofs given above, we content ourselves with this brief remark and leave out the full proof of the theorem in question.

5. Why is all that necessary?

The reader must have noticed the far reaching analogy between the contents of the present chapter and that of Sections 2 and 3 of Chapter I. In Chapter I we defined several properties of classes and we have repeated them here for the elements of a model of ZF or of its finitely axiomatisable subsystems. To give one example: in Chapter I, p. 4, we formulated the property of a class to be a function; in the present chapter we have essentially repeated the definition and introduced for each set A the set $\mathrm{Fn}(A)$ consisting of those elements of A which are functions.

The relation between what we did in Chapter I and what we do in the present chapter can also be described thus: In Chapter I the universe consisted of all sets and all classes; in the present chapter we have replaced this universe by a model of ZF or of its finitely axiomatisable subsystems. For both universes we define the same properties of their elements.

It is natural to inquire whether this duplication of definitions is really necessary, and the question becomes very urgent when one reflects that Gödel, who is an unquestionable master not only of the subject but also of the manner of its presentation, completely avoids this awkward situation in his classical book [13].

The original sin for which we have to suffer by this duplication of definitions was committed at the very beginning of our exposition, where we decided to work in a very strong system of set theory, serving as a meta-theory, and to keep it apart from the theory ZF which is the system under investigation. A property of sets defined in the meta-theory is not necessarily definable in the theory if the two systems are different from each other. Theorems concerning a property definable in one system need not be provable in the other. For this reason we have had to introduce in the present chapter an auxiliary machinery which allows us to establish the existence of formulae (of ZF) serving as definitions of notions previously defined in the meta-theory. Moreover, we can establish that notions defined in models of ZF (or its finitely axiomatisable subsystems) by those formulae coincide with notions defined in the meta-theory. The formulae referred to are definitions of strongly definable functors; functors in turn, are defined in the meta-theory and can be used to express in that theory several properties of models. In this way the correlation between strongly definable functors and their definitions (which are formulae of ZF) allows us to build a bridge between the properties of sets which are expressible in the meta-theory and the properties which are expressed in ZF.

There are obviously many other ways of achieving the same aim. For instance we could eliminate functors and deal exclusively with formulae which we have called here the definitions of functors. We would then have to deal with various problems concerning the provability of formulae in ZF. The author tried this way of exposition and found that it tends to be unbearably lengthy. Its advantage would be the possibility of including in our theory not only the transitive models of ZF but also quite arbitrary ones.

It should be noted that in our presentation we have not completelt avoided the notion of provability of formulae, either; this is apparen- from examples 5–7 and 17, given in Section 3.

However, all this does not yet explain why Gödel and other writers who followed him were able to avoid this discussion altogether. The reason is that Gödel guarded himself against the original sin which we have committed and used only the minimal finitary system of a metay theory. There is a price one has to pay if one wants to avoid the use of advanced set theory in meta-mathematics. One cannot prove, for instance, that the theory under investigation is consistent, one cannot prove that its models exist, etc. If the theory under investigation is ZF and the meta-theory is of comparable strength, one can prove only that every finitely axiomatisable subsystem of ZF has a model. Thus, if one decides to use the finitary meta-theory, one usually replaces models by nterpretations. An interpretation of a theory T in a theory T* is defined as a finite sequence of formulae of T*; each formula corresponds to exactly one of the undefined relations of the theory T and has as many free variables as there are arguments in the relation. We assumed for simplicity that all primitive notions of T are relations. If the atomic formulae of T are replaced by the corresponding formulae of the interpretation, then the axioms of T have to become theorems of T*.

All this can be explained very easily and correctly in the finitary meta-mathematics under the assumption that the axioms of the theory one wants to discuss are finite in number. For infinite systems of axioms even the definition of an interpretation requires a relatively strong meta-theory, roughly speaking of a strength comparable to that of the arithmetic of integers.

It is apparent from what was said above that the enormous simplicity of Gödel's presentation of his results was due to the fact that he discussed a finitely axiomatisable system of set theory, the so called Gödel–Bernays system. In his book he was dealing not with models of that system but with its interpretation in itself.

The reason why we committed our original sin is thus seen to be caused by our decision to discuss the infinite system of axioms ZF. Many mathematicians would doubtlessly criticize this decision from the start. The Gödel–Bernays set theory is regarded by many set-theorists as the system of set theory and systems like ZF as relics which should not be used any more as a basis for set theory.

The author of this book does not share this view. The failure in the Gödel–Bernays system of the principle according to which every formula, whose unique free variable ranges over a set a, determines a set consisting of all those elements of a which satisfy the formula, is a serious shortcoming of the system. It leads to several undesirable phenomena like for instance the following:

1) There is a formula A for which the sentences

$$A(0), \quad \textit{for every integer } x, \textit{ if } A(x), \textit{ then } A(x+1)$$

are provable but the formula

$$\textit{for every integer } x, A(x)$$

is not provable.

2) There is a formula A for which the sentences $A(0)$ and $\neg A(1)$ are provable but the sentence

there is a real number z $(0 \leqslant z \leqslant 1)$ *such that* $A(x)$ *for each* x *in the interval* $(0, z)$ *and* $\neg A(z)$

is not provable.

For this reason we think that systems like ZF or M are much more satisfactory as a basis for set theory in spite of their essentially non-finitary character. Bernays himself seems to share this point of view since he has excluded the use of bound class variables in his book [3].

Having decided to make ZF the object of our study and being thus forced to abandon from the start the completely finitary meta-theory it is psychologically understandable that we were led to the choice of a very strong meta-theory. All the resulting complications, which we described at the beginning of this section, were the natural outcome of this decision. A certain consolation is the fact that we can prove in our exposition theorems, like the one on the consistency and existence of models of ZF, which cannot be included in presentations based on the finitary meta-theory. Another positive aspect of our approach can be seen in the circumstance that we can avail ourselves of the current notions and results of model theory without being forced to redefine them for interpretations.

CHAPTER V

CONSTRUCTIBLE SETS AS VALUES OF A FUNCTOR

The aim of this chapter is to show that, under suitable assumptions concerning the function B, the set $C^B_{\pi(A)}(a)$ is a value of a strongly definable functor.

1. Uniformly definable functions

Let X be a function of, say, n arguments, i.e., a subclass of V^{n+1} such that for arbitrary $x_1, \ldots, x_n$ in V there is exactly one $y = X(x_1, \ldots, x_n)$ in V for which $\langle x_1, \ldots, x_n, y\rangle \in X$. We shall say that X *is uniformly definable* if there is a strongly definable functor f of the second kind with $n+1$ arguments such that for almost all A and for every $x_1, \ldots, x_n$ in A

$$f(A, x_1, \ldots, x_n) = X(x_1, \ldots, x_n).$$

An equivalent formulation is that there is a formula H with $n+1$ free variables such that for almost all A and arbitrary $x_1, \ldots, x_n, y$ in A

$$X(x_1, \ldots, x_n) \in A,$$

$$y = X(x_1, \ldots, x_n) \equiv \vdash_A H[y, x_1, \ldots, x_n].$$

We assume a similar definition for relations: a *relation* $\varrho \subseteq V^n$ *is uniformly definable* if there is a strongly definable relation R with $n+1$ arguments such that for almost all A and all $x_1, \ldots, x_n$ in A

$$\langle x_1, \ldots, x_n\rangle \in \varrho \equiv R(A, x_1, \ldots, x_n).$$

For $n = 1$ we obtain *uniformly definable classes.*

We can phrase the definition thus: a *class* $C \subseteq V$ *is uniformly definable* if there is a strongly definable functor F with one argument such that for almost all A

$$A \cap C = F(A).$$

Using theorems on transfinite induction we shall establish the following result:

1.1. *Let* ϱ *be a uniformly definable well founded partial ordering of a uniformly definable class* C *such that the function* $\Omega(a) = O_\varrho(a)$ *is uniformly definable. If* Y *is a uniformly definable function with domain* $V \times C$, *then the unique function* X *with domain* V *which satisfies for each* a *in* C *the equation* (cf. I.3.1):

$$(1) \qquad X(a) = Y(X|O_\varrho(a), a)$$

and is equal to 0 *outside* C *is uniformly definable.*

PROOF. Put $S(A) = C \cap A$, $R(A) = \varrho \cap A^2$ and $f(A, x, a) = Y(x, a)$ for a, x in A.

Functors S, R and f are strongly definable by our assumptions and $R(A)$ is a partial well-ordering of $S(A)$. Moreover,

$$O_A(a) = \{x \in S(A): (\langle x, a\rangle \in R(A)) \wedge (x \neq y)\}$$

is an element of A for almost all A and for arbitrary a in $S(A)$ because $O_A(a) = \Omega(a)$ and Ω is uniformly definable by assumption.

By theorem IV.4.2 there exists a uniformly definable functor In(A) such that for almost all A its value $\varphi = \text{In}(A)$ is a function with domain $S(A)$ which satisfies for each a in A the equation

$$\varphi(a) = f(A, \varphi|O_{R(A)}(a), a).$$

In view of the definability of φ we obtain $\varphi|O_{R(A)}(a) \in A$. It follows that

$$\varphi(a) = Y(\varphi|O_{R(A)}(a), a) = Y(\varphi|O_\varrho(a), a).$$

Comparing this equation with (1) we find by transfinite induction that $X(a) = [\text{In}(A)](a)$ for all a in $C \cap A$. The function X has thus the same values as In(A) for the arguments a in $A \cap C$ and the value 0 for $a \in A - C$. This proves that X is uniformly definable.

Theorem 1.1 corresponds to induction without parameters. We can formulate a similar theorem for the case of induction with fixed parameters. This form of induction is slightly less general than the one described in I.3.2 but suffices in most applications.

1.2. *Let* ϱ *and* C *be as in* 1.1 *and let* Y *be a uniformly definable function with domain* $V^k \times V \times C$. *There is then a unique function* X *with domain* $V^k \times C$ *which satisfies for each a in C and arbitrary* $q_1, \ldots, q_k$ *in V the equations*

$$(2) \qquad X(q_1, \ldots, q_k, a) = Y\big(q_1, \ldots, q_k, X|(\{q_1\}\times\ldots\times\{q_k\}\times O_\varrho(a)),\ a\big);$$

this unique function is uniformly definable.

Proof. In order to simplify the formulae we limit ourselves to the case of one parameter. The uniqueness and existence of X result easily from I.3.2, in which we put $p = \{q\}$, $h_1(q, u, v, a) = h_2(q, u, v, a) = Y(q, u, a)$. The functions e_1, e_2 whose existence and uniqueness are stated in I.3.2 are then equal and satisfy equation (2).

In order to prove that X is uniformly definable we proceed as in the proof of 1.1. We retain the same definitions of the functors R and S and put $f(A, x, a, q) = Y(q, x, a)$ for arbitrary q, x, a in A. By IV.4.1 there is a strongly definable functor In such that for almost all A and arbitrary q in A the set $\varphi = \mathrm{In}(A, q)$ is a function with domain $S(A) = C \cap A$ and satisfies the conditions:

$$O_{R(A)}(a) \in A,$$

$$\varphi(a) = f(A, \varphi|O_{R(A)}(a), a, q) = Y(q, \varphi|O_\varrho(a), a).$$

By comparing this equation with (2) we see that $X(q, a) = \varphi(a) = [\mathrm{In}(A, q)](a)$ for $a \in C \cap A$. The proof is completed as in 1.1.

In theorems 1.1 and 1.2 neither ϱ nor C depend on parameters but we shall also need a theorem on the uniform definability of a function satisfying an inductive equation whose domain is a set depending on parameters and ordered by a relation depending on parameters. This result is stated in the following theorem.

1.3. *Let* σ *and* ϱ *be uniformly definable functions with n variables such that for every* $p_1, \ldots, p_n$ *in the universal class* $\sigma(p_1, \ldots, p_n)$ *is a set and* $\varrho(p_1, \ldots, p_n)$ *a well founded partial ordering of this set. Let Y be a uniformly definable function of* $n+2$ *variables. Under these assumptions there is a unique function X with domain* V^{n+1} *which satisfies the equation*

$$(3) \qquad X(p_1, \ldots, p_n, a)$$
$$= Y\big(p_1, \ldots, p_n, X|\{p_1\}\times\{p_2\}\times\ldots\times\{p_n\}\times O_{\varrho(p_1,\ldots,p_n)}(a), a\big)$$

for arbitrary $p_1, \ldots, p_n$ *in* V *and* a *in* $\sigma(p_1, \ldots, p_n)$. *This unique function is uniformly definable.*

PROOF. The uniqueness and existence of X are obvious. Now we prove the uniform definability of X and assume for simplicity that there is just one parameter p. Let S, R, and f be strongly definable functors of the second kind such that the equations

$$\{p\}\times\sigma(p) = S(A,p), \quad \{\langle\langle p,x\rangle,\langle p,y\rangle\rangle : \langle x,y\rangle \in \varrho(p)\} = R(A,p),$$
$$Y(p,x,y) = f(A,x,y,p)$$

hold for almost all A and for arbitrary p, x, y in A.

Since $\sigma(p)$ and $\varrho(p)$ belong to A for almost all A and for arbitrary p in A, we can easily prove that for almost all A and arbitrary p in A and a in $\sigma(p)$ the set $O_{\varrho(p)}(a)$ belongs to A. This results from the remark that the existence of a segment $O_\varrho(a)$ can be proved on the basis of finitely many axioms of ZF.

It follows that for almost all A and for every pair $\langle p,a\rangle \in S(A,p)$ the segment $O_{R(A,p)} = \{p\}\times O_{\varrho(p)}(a)$ belongs to A. Thus the assumptions of theorem IV.4.2 are satisfied and there is a strongly definable functor In such that for almost all A and for each p in A the set $\mathrm{In}(A,p) = X$ is a function with domain $\{p\}\times\sigma(p)$ satisfying the inductive equation

$$X(\langle p,a\rangle) = f\big(A, X|\{p\}\times O_{\varrho(p)}(a), a, p\big)$$

for each a in $\sigma(p)$. This proves that the function X is strongly definable and satisfies the inductive equation stated in the theorem.

We shall also need the following easy theorems:

1.4. *Let* R *be a uniformly definable* $(n+1)$*-ary relation such that for arbitrary* $a_1, \ldots, a_n \in V$ *there is exactly one* $a_0 = \varphi(a_1, \ldots, a_n)$ *satisfying* $R(a_0, \ldots, a_n)$. *If* $\varphi(a_1, \ldots, a_n) \in A$ *for almost all* A *and for arbitrary* $a_1, \ldots, a_n$ *in* A, *then* φ *is uniformly definable.*

PROOF. If $\boldsymbol{R}$ is a definition of R, then this formula is a definition of the functor $f(A, a_1, \ldots, a_n) = \varphi(a_1, \ldots, a_n)$.

Theorem 1.4 can be generalized as follows:

1.5. *Let* R *be a uniformly definable* $(n+1)$*-ary relation,* $k \leqslant n$ *and assume that for arbitrary* $a_k, \ldots, a_n$ *in* V *there is exactly one* k*-tuple*

$$\langle a_0, \ldots, a_{k-1}\rangle = \langle \varphi_0(a_k, \ldots, a_n), \ldots, \varphi_{k-1}(a_k, \ldots, a_n)\rangle$$

such that $R(a_0, \ldots, a_n)$. *If for almost all* A, *for all* $j < k$ *and arbitrary* $a_k, \ldots, a_n$ *in* A

$$\varphi_j(a_k, \ldots, a_n) \in A,$$

then the functions φ_j *are uniformly definable.*

PROOF. If $\boldsymbol{R}$ is a definition of R, then the formula $(Ex_0, \ldots, x_j, x_{j+1}, \ldots, x_{k-1})\boldsymbol{R}$ is a definition of the functor $f(A, a_k, \ldots, a_n) = \varphi_j(a_k, \ldots, a_n)$.

2. Examples of uniformly definable functions

We list in this section several examples of uniformly definable functions:

1. *The function*

$$s(\xi, \eta) = \begin{cases} \xi+\eta & \textit{if} \quad \xi, \eta \in On, \\ 0 & \textit{otherwise} \end{cases}$$

is uniformly definable.

To establish this we take in 1.2

$$C = On, \quad \varrho = \{\langle \xi, \eta \rangle \in On^2 \colon \xi \leqslant \eta\}$$

and

$$Y(q, x) = \begin{cases} 0 \text{ if } & (x \notin \mathrm{Fnc}) \vee (q \notin On) \vee (\mathrm{Dom}(x) \notin \{\{q\}\times\zeta\colon \zeta \in On\}), \\ q \text{ if } & \mathrm{Dom}(x) = 0, \\ x(q, \zeta) \cup \{x(q, \zeta)\} & \text{if} \quad \mathrm{Dom}(x) = \{q\}\times(\zeta+1), \\ \bigcup \mathrm{Rg}(x) & \text{if} \quad \mathrm{Dom}(x) = \{q\}\times\lambda \text{ where } \lambda \text{ is a limit number.} \end{cases}$$

The assumptions of 1.2 are satisfied; the uniform definability of C follows from IV.3, example 11, that of ϱ follows from IV.2.5 and that of Y from IV.2.10, IV.3, examples 4, 5, 10, 15. Since

$$s(\xi, \eta) = Y(\xi, s|(\{\xi\}\times\eta))$$

we infer that s is uniformly definable.

2. *The function* p *defined as follows*:

$$p(\xi, \eta) = \begin{cases} \xi\eta & \textit{if} \quad \xi, \eta \in On, \\ 0 & \textit{otherwise} \end{cases}$$

is uniformly definable.

This is proved by considering the same class C and relation ϱ as above and changing the second and third equations in the definition of Y to read

$$Y(q, x) = 0 \quad \text{if} \quad x = 0,$$

$$Y(q, x) = x(q, \zeta)+q \quad \text{if} \quad \mathrm{Dom}(x) = \{q\}\times(\zeta+1).$$

3. *The function defined as* $\delta(r, \xi)$ *if* $r, \xi \in On$ *and as* 0 *otherwise is uniformly definable.*

The proof is obtained in the same way as before.

Notice that we have proved at the same time that for almost all A the ordinal $\pi(A)$ is closed under the operations $\xi+\eta$, $\xi\eta$ and $\delta(r, \xi)$.

4. *The functions which coincide with* I, K, L, M *on* $\omega\times On$ *and are equal to* 0 *for other values of the arguments are uniformly definable.*

This example is more complicated than the former ones. We shall proceed as follows. For $\xi \in On$ and $r \in \omega$ we denote by $S(\xi, r)$ the set of quadruples $\langle i, \alpha, \beta, \gamma\rangle$ with $1 \leqslant i \leqslant r$ and $\alpha, \beta, \gamma < \delta(r, \xi)$. By $R(\xi, r)$ we denote the antilexicographical ordering of $S(\xi, r)$ and by $\nu_r(i, \alpha, \beta, \gamma)$ the order type of the quadruples which precede $\langle i, \alpha, \beta, \gamma\rangle$ in this ordering. Outside $\omega\times On$ we put $S(x, y) = R(x, y) = 0$. Now we notice that if $r \in \omega$, $\eta \in On$ and if $\iota(r, \eta)$ is the unique ordinal such that $\delta(r, \iota(r, \eta)) \leqslant \eta < \delta(r, \iota(r, \eta)+1)$, then $I\eta$, $K\eta$, $L\eta$, $M\eta$ either are 0 (if $\delta(r, \iota(r, \eta)) = \eta$) or can be characterized as unique ordinals i, α, β, γ for which $\delta(r, \iota(r, \eta))+\nu_r(i, \alpha, \beta, \gamma) = \eta$.

Function $\iota(r, \eta)$ [1]) is uniformly definable because $\iota(r, \eta)$ is uniquely determined by a uniformly definable relation (cf. theorem 1.4) and, moreover, $\iota(r, \eta) \leqslant \eta$. Using theorem 1.5 we infer in the same way from the remark made above that $I\eta$, $K\eta$, $L\eta$, $M\eta$ are uniformly definable provided that ν_r is so definable. Thus all that remains to be shown is the uniform definability of ν_r. We see at once that the functions σ: $(\xi, r) \to S(\xi, r)$ and ϱ: $(\xi, r) \to R(\xi, r)$ are uniformly definable. We are thus entitled to use theorem 1.3 on transfinite induction. We select as Y the function $Y(\xi, r, x)$, which is equal to 0 if x is not a transfinite sequence and is equal to $\min\{\eta\colon \eta \notin \mathrm{Rg}(x)\}$ otherwise. In this

[1]) We assume that $\iota(r, \eta) = 0$ if $(r, \eta) \notin \omega\times On$.

way we obtain a uniformly definable function X such that for each a in $S(\xi, r)$ the value $X(\xi, r, a)$ is equal to the order type of $O_{R(\xi, r)}(a)$. Hence $X(\xi, r, \langle i, \alpha, \beta, \gamma\rangle)$ is the required function ν_r.

5. *The functions which coincide with* pl_k *and* $\overline{\mathrm{pl}}_k$ *on On and which are equal to* 0 *outside On are uniformly definable.*

PROOF. The function pl_k satisfies the inductive equation

$$\varphi(\xi) = F(r, k, \varphi|\xi)$$

where

$$F(r, k, x) = \min\{\zeta \colon (I(r, \zeta) = k) \wedge (\zeta \supset \bigcup \mathrm{Rg}(x))\}$$

(see III.1). The relation $(I(r, \zeta) = k) \wedge (\zeta \supset \bigcup \mathrm{Rg}(x))$ is uniformly definable and, since for almost all A and arbitrary r, k in ω and x in A there is a uniquely determined minimal ζ which belongs to A and satisfies this relation, we infer by 1.4 that the function $F(r, k, x)$ is uniformly definable. This proves that $\varphi = \mathrm{pl}_k$ is uniformly definable.

For function $\overline{\mathrm{pl}}_k$ the proof is still simpler because $\overline{\mathrm{pl}}_k(r, \xi)$ is the least ordinal η for which $\mathrm{pl}_k(r, \eta) \geqslant \xi$. Thus η is the unique element which satisfies a uniformly definable relation and η belongs to A for almost all A and arbitrary r in ω, ξ in A because $\eta \leqslant \xi$.

Our last example is concerned not with uniformly definable functions but rather with a strongly definable functor:

6. *The functor* rk *defined as*

$$\mathrm{rk}(A, \xi) = \begin{cases} A \cap R_\xi & \text{if } \xi \in \pi(A), \\ 0 & \text{otherwise} \end{cases}$$

is strongly definable.

PROOF (see I.3.3 for the definition of R_ξ). The sets $\mathrm{rk}(A, \xi)$ satisfy for each transitive set A the recursive equations:

$$\mathrm{rk}(A, 0) = 0, \quad \mathrm{rk}(A, \xi+1) = A \cap P(\mathrm{rk}(A, \xi)),$$

$$\mathrm{rk}(A, \lambda) = \bigcup\{\mathrm{rk}(A, \xi) \colon \xi < \lambda\} \quad \text{for} \quad \lambda \in \mathrm{Lim}(A).$$

Now we take in theorem IV.4.2 $S(A) = \pi(A)$, $R(A) = \{\langle u, v\rangle \in A \colon u \leqslant v \in \pi(A)\}$ and $f(A, a) = 0$ if $a \notin \mathrm{Seq}(A)$, $f(A, a) = \mathrm{un}(A, a)$ if $a \in \mathrm{Seq}(A)$ and $\mathrm{dl}(A, a) \in \mathrm{Lim}(A)$; finally we take $f(A, a)$

$= P\big(A, \mathrm{val}\big(A, a, \mathrm{pred}\,(A, \mathrm{dl}\,(A, a))\big)\big) = A \cap P\big(a(\xi-1)\big)$, where $\xi = \mathrm{dl}(A, a)$ if $\mathrm{dl}(A, a) \in \pi(A) - \mathrm{Lim}(A)$. The assumptions of IV.4.2 are satisfied and hence we obtain a strongly definable functor such that for almost every A and every $\xi \in \pi(A)$

$$\varphi(A, \xi) = \bigcup_{\eta<\xi} \varphi(A, \eta) \quad \text{if} \quad \xi \text{ is a limit number,}$$

$$\varphi(A, \xi+1) = A \cap P\big(\varphi(A, \xi)\big).$$

It follows by induction on ξ that $\varphi(A, \xi) = \mathrm{rk}(A, \xi)$ and the theorem follows by IV.4.2.

As a corollary we infer that:

For almost all A and all ξ in $\pi(A)$, $A \cap R_\xi \in A$.

Remark. The function $R\colon\ \xi \to R_\xi$ is not uniformly definable because it is not true that $R_\xi \in A$ for almost all A and for $\xi \in \pi(A)$.

3. Uniform definability of the function $C_\xi^B(a)$

Let B be a function of two variables ranging over transfinite sequences. We assume that B satisfies conditions (B.0)–(B.4) of III.2. We know from III.2 that B determines a function $C_\xi^B(a)$ of two variables: a, ranging over transfinite sequences (i.e., elements of the class S, see p. 39), and ξ, ranging over ordinals. For a fixed a the function $\varphi(\xi) = C_\xi^B(a)$ satisfies the inductive equation

$$\varphi(\xi) = B(a, \varphi|\xi).$$

From theorem 1.2 we find therefore that:

3.1. *If B is uniformly definable, then so is the function of two variables, ξ and a, whose value for the arguments ξ, a in $On \times S$ is $C_\xi^B(a)$ and which is equal to* 0 *for arguments not in $On \times S$.*

The following is an immediate corollary:

3.2. *If B is uniformly definable, then for almost all A, arbitrary a in* $\mathrm{Seq}(A)$ *and arbitrary ξ in $\pi(A)$*

$$C_\xi^B(a) \in A.$$

We shall denote by Konstr^B the following functor:

$$\mathrm{Konstr}^B(A, a) = \begin{cases} C_{\pi(A)}^B(a) & \text{if} \quad a \in \mathrm{Seq}(A), \\ 0 & \text{otherwise.} \end{cases}$$

3.3. *If B is a uniformly definable function, then the functor* Konstr^B *is strongly definable.*

PROOF. Let A be a transitive set in which as many axioms of ZF are satisfied as are necessary to ensure that

$$\xi < \pi(A) \to \delta(r, \xi) < \pi(A)$$

(cf. 2, example 3). Since $\pi(A)$ is a limit number, it follows by the continuity of δ that $\delta(r, \pi(A)) = \pi(A)$. Thus for any transfinite sequence a the set $C^B_{\pi(A)}(a)$ consists of elements $C_\xi^B(a)$ where $\xi < \pi(A)$. It follows that the relation $x \in \text{Konstr}^B(A, a)$ is equivalent to

$$(E\xi)_A[(\xi \in \pi(A)) \wedge (x = C_\xi^B(a))].$$

In view of IV.2.3, IV.3.11, V.3.1 this relation is strongly definable and hence the theorem is proved.

The results reached in 3.1–3.3 can also be expressed in the form of the following theorem:

3.4. *For every uniformly definable function B satisfying conditions* (B.0)–(B.4) *of* III.2 *there are finitely many axioms $K_1, \ldots, K_r$ of* ZF *and formulae* **constr**^{B} *with three free variables and* **Konstr**^{B} *with two free variables such that whenever A is a transitive class and $K_1, \ldots, K_r$ are valid in A, then for every transitive sequence a in A, every ordinal ξ in A and every x in A*

(1) $$C_\xi^B(a) \in A,$$

(2) $$x = C_\xi^B(a) \equiv\ \vdash_A \mathbf{constr}^B[x, \xi, a],$$

(3) $$x \in \{C_\xi^B(a)\colon \xi \in On \cap A\} \equiv\ \vdash_A \mathbf{Konstr}^B[x, a].$$

PROOF. We deal only with (1) and (2). Let us first assume that A is a set. Then (1) and (2) result from the uniform definability of the function $C_\xi^B(a)$. If A is a proper class, then we use the decomposition (cf. I.1.3)

$$A = \bigcup\{A \cap R_\xi\colon \xi \in On\} = \bigcup A_\xi$$

and apply the reflection theorem II.2.2, obtaining an elementary subset $A_\varkappa$ of A such that $A_\varkappa$ contains as elements a given sequence a, a given ordinal ξ and a given element x. Formulae (1)–(2) hold with A replaced by $A_\varkappa$. Since $A_\varkappa \prec A$, we can replace $A_\varkappa$ by A and the theorem is proved.

We add a comment in connection with this theorem. If a transitive model of ZF or of a suitable finitely axiomatisable subsystem of ZF is given, then according to (2) we can define within this model the property of its elements consisting in their being equal to $C_\xi^B(a)$, where ξ and a are given elements of the model. Formula (3) states similarly that we can define within the model the class of all elements of the form $C_\xi^B(a)$ with ξ ranging over the ordinals of the models provided that a is a fixed sequence which belongs to the model. The expression "within the model" means that the property and the class just mentioned are defined by means of the satisfiability in the model of an explicitly given formula. All this means that we can dispense with the use of the very strong meta-theory M when we discuss the properties of constructible sets belonging to $C_{\pi(A)}^B(a)$ provided that A is a model of ZF and a belongs to A. These sets can be investigated by means of notions definable in A by the formulae of ZF.

We shall now discuss the special cases of functions $B^{\min}$, B^0 and B^Z defined in III.6 and show that they are uniformly definable. We need the following lemma:

3.5. *The functions* $A_i(a, b) \cap c$ *are uniformly definable* ($i = 1, 2, \dots, 9$).

PROOF. Obviously $A_i(a, b) \in A$ for almost all A and arbitrary a, b in A. Since the function whose value for the arguments x, y is $x \cap y$ is uniformly definable, it will be sufficient to show the strong definability of functors whose values for arbitrary arguments A, a, b are $A_i(a, b)$. Thus all that we have to do is to represent the condition $x \in A_i(a, b)$ by means of operations of the propositional calculus and quantifiers restricted to A and applied to formulae of which we know that they define strongly definable functors. We list below the required formulae:

$i = 1.\quad x \in A_1(a, b) \equiv (Eu, v)_A[(x = \{\langle 0, u\rangle, \langle 1, v\rangle\}) \wedge (u \in v)],$

$i = 2.\quad x \in A_2(a, b) \equiv (x = a) \vee (x = b),$

$i = 3.\quad x \in A_3(a, b) \equiv (Eu)_A[(x \in u) \wedge (u \in a)],$

$i = 4.\quad x \in A_4(a, b) \equiv (Eu, v)_A[(x = \{\langle u, v\rangle\}) \wedge (u \in a) \wedge (v \in b)],$

$i = 5.\quad x \in A_5(a, b) \equiv (Eu, v)_A(t)_A\{(t \in x) \equiv [(t \in u) \vee (t \in v)]\},$

$i = 8.\quad x \in A_8(a, b) = a - b \equiv (x \in a) \wedge \neg(x \in b),$

$i = 6.\quad x \in A_6(a, b) \equiv (Eu, v)_A\{(t)_A[(t \in x) \equiv (t \in A_8(u, v))] \wedge \wedge (u \in a) \wedge (v \in b)\},$

$i = 9.\quad x \in A_9(a, b) = a \circ b \equiv (Eu, v, w)_A[(x = \langle u, v\rangle) \wedge \wedge (\langle u, w\rangle \in a) \wedge (\langle w, v\rangle \in b)],$

$i = 7.\quad x \in A_7(a, b) \equiv (Eu, v)_A\{(t)_A[(t \in x) \equiv (t \in A_9(u, v))] \wedge \wedge (u \in a) \wedge (v \in b)\}.$

We pass now to the uniform definability of the functions $B^{\min}$, B^0 and B^Z. These functions were defined in III.6 only for the arguments in $S \times S$ where S is the class of all transfinite sequences. We now extend these functions to the whole $V \times V$ by giving them the value 0 for arguments which do not belong to $S \times S$. The extended functions will be denoted by the same symbols as previously.

3.6. *The function $B^{\min}$ is uniformly definable.*

PROOF. We have to exhibit a strongly definable functor of the second kind such that $f(A, a, x) = B^{\min}(a, x)$ for almost all A and arbitrary a, x in A. We shall show that the following functor f has these properties:

$$f(A, a, x) = \begin{cases} B^{\min}(a, x) & \text{if} \quad B^{\min}(a, x) \in A, \\ 0 & \text{otherwise} \end{cases}$$

is strongly definable. First we notice that for almost all A the first case occurs because $B^{\min}(a, x)$ either is 0 or is one of the terms of a or is obtained from the terms of x by one of the operations discussed in 3.2 or finally is $= \mathrm{Rg}(x) = \mathrm{dp}(A, x)$. In order to abbreviate the formulae we shall omit the argument $r = 10$ writing the values of functions $I(r, x)$, $K(r, x)$, etc. For almost all A we have from the definitions which were previously adopted

$$f(A, a, x) = 0 \quad \text{if} \quad \text{either } x \notin \mathrm{Seq}(A) \text{ or } a \notin \mathrm{Seq}(A) \text{ or } I(\mathrm{Dom}(x)) = 10 \text{ and } \overline{\mathrm{pl}}'(\mathrm{Dom}(x)) \geqslant \mathrm{Dom}(a);$$

otherwise

$$f(A, a, x) = \begin{cases} \mathrm{val}\big(A, a, \overline{\mathrm{pl}}'(\mathrm{Dom}(x))\big) & \text{if} \quad I(\mathrm{Dom}(x)) = 10, \\ \mathrm{Rg}(x) & \text{if} \quad I(\mathrm{Dom}(x)) = 0, \\ A_i\Big(\mathrm{val}\big(A, x, K(\mathrm{Dom}(x))\big), \mathrm{val}\big(A, x, L(\mathrm{Dom}(x))\big)\Big) \cap & \\ \quad \cap \mathrm{val}\big(A, x, M(\mathrm{Dom}(x))\big) & \text{if} \quad 1 \leqslant I(\mathrm{Dom}(x)) < 10. \end{cases}$$

These equations show that the functor $f(A, a, x)$ is defined by cases like those in theorem IV.2.10; which case occurs depends on whether a strongly definable relation holds between the elements a and x; and the value of f in each case is equal to the value of a strongly definable functor. To see that this is really the case we have only to replace everywhere $\mathrm{Dom}(x)$, $\mathrm{Rg}(x)$ etc. by $\mathrm{dl}(A, x)$, $\mathrm{dp}(A, x)$ etc. and reflect that the functions I, K, L, M, $\overline{\mathrm{pl}}'$ and A_i are, as we know, uniformly definable.

Theorem 3.6 is thus proved. From 3.6, 3.1 and 3.3 we infer that:

3.7. *The function* $C_\xi^{B^{\min}}(a)$ *is uniformly definable; the functor* $\mathrm{Konstr}^{B^{\min}}$ *is strongly definable.*

We can deal in a similar way with the case where $B = B^Z$ or $B = B^0$.

3.8. *The function* $B^Z(a, x)$ *is uniformly definable.*

The proof is very similar to that of 3.6. This time we write $I(\xi)$ for what should really be noted as $I(12, \xi)$ and similarly for $K(\xi)$, $L(\xi)$ etc. We consider the functor $f(A, a, x) = B^Z(a, x)$ and notice that it satisfies the equations enumerated in 3.6 and also two additional ones:

$$f(A, x, a) = \begin{cases} \{\mathrm{val}(A, x, \xi) \colon (\xi < \mathrm{Dom}(x)) \wedge (I(\xi) = 11)\} \\ \qquad\qquad\qquad\qquad \text{if} \quad I(\mathrm{Dom}(x)) = 11, \\ \{\langle \xi, \mathrm{val}(A, x, \xi)\rangle \colon \mathrm{pl}(\xi) < K(\mathrm{Dom}(x))\} \cap \\ \cap\, \mathrm{val}\big(A, x, M(\mathrm{Dom}(x))\big) \quad \text{if} \quad I(\mathrm{Dom}(x)) = 12. \end{cases}$$

It is obvious that the right-hand sides of these equations are values of strongly definable functors; they are functors of the second kind because if A satisfies the axiom of replacement (VI_H) for suitable formulae H then A contains as elements the sets $\{\mathrm{val}(A, x, \xi) \colon \xi \in X\}$ and $\{\langle \xi, \mathrm{val}(A, x, \xi)\rangle \colon \xi \in X\}$ provided that $X \in A$. Thus the functor f is strongly definable of the second kind and 3.8 is proved.

In a similar way we show that

3.9. *The function* B^0 *is uniformly definable.*

From 3.8 and 3.9 we infer that:

3.10. *The functions* $C_\xi^{B^Z}(a)$ and $C_\xi^{B^0}(a)$ *are uniformly definable; the functors* Konstr^{B^0} and Konstr^{B^Z} *are strongly definable.*

4. A generalization

In this section we note briefly how one could generalize the result obtained in Section 3 and establish an analogous result for the case where the sequence a in $C^B_{\pi(A)}(a)$ is not an element of A but a sequence of length $\pi(A)$. This situation corresponds to the one described in III.7, the set A playing the role which in III.7 was played by the universal class.

Let T be a functor of the first kind such that for almost all A and all p in A^n the set $T(A,p)$ is a transitive transfinite sequence of length $\leqslant \pi(A)$. Let B be a function satisfying conditions (B.0)–(B.4) of III.2.

We define

$$\text{constr}_{B,T}(A, \xi, p) = C^B_\xi(T(A,p)).$$

4.1. *If T is strongly definable and there is a strongly definable functor f of the first kind which satisfies the equation*

$$B(T(A,p), x) = f(A, x, p)$$

for almost all A, all x in $\text{Seq}(A)$ *and all p in A^n, then the functor* $\text{constr}_{A,T}$ *is strongly definable.*

The proof is obtained by an immediate application of theorem IV.4.2.

Repeating *mutatis mutandis* the proofs of theorems 3.4–3.7, we find that the assumptions of theorem 4.1 are satisfied for $B = B^{\min}$, $B = B^0$ and $B = B^Z$.

It follows from theorem 4.1 that if its assumptions are satisfied, then there are finitely many axioms $K_1, \ldots, K_r$ of ZF such that whenever A is a transitive set in which these axioms are valid, then A contains with each ordinal ξ and each $p \in A^n$ the sets $C^B_\xi(T(A,p))$, where B is one of the functions $B^{\min}$, B^0, B^Z. Moreover, there are formulae H^B such that for each ξ in $On \cap A$ and p in A^n, x in A

$$x = C^B_\xi(T(A,p)) \equiv \vdash_A H^B[x, \xi, p].$$

By analogy with the functor Konstr^B we can introduce the functor Konstr^B_T:

$$\text{Konstr}^B_T(p) = \begin{cases} C^B_{\pi(A)}(T(A,p)) \\ \quad \text{if} \quad T(A,p) \text{ is a sequence of length } \leqslant \pi(A), \\ 0 \quad \text{otherwise.} \end{cases}$$

We prove, exactly as in 3.3, that this functor is strongly definable provided that T is so definable and B is a uniformly definable function. It follows that there exists a formula $\mathbf{Konstr}_T^B$ with $n+1$ free variables (where n is the number of parameters in the sequence p) such that for almost all A and arbitrary p in A^n, and x in A the following equivalence holds:

$$x \in \mathrm{Konstr}_T^B(p) \equiv \vdash_A \mathbf{Konstr}_T^B[x, p].$$

5. Further properties of constructible sets

The theorems proved in Sections 2 and 3 allow us to establish certain properties of constructible sets which cannot be derived directly from the definitions given in Chapter III. We must limit ourselves to the cases where the function B which determines the type of constructibility is uniformly definable.

In all the theorems of this section we assume that B is a uniformly definable function which satisfies conditions (B.0)–(B.4) of III.2.

Let us call a set *B-constructible in a transitive sequence a* if it belongs to the class $K^B(a)$. We want to investigate the transitivity and the reflexivity of this relation.

5.1. *If a, b, c are transitive sequences, then $a \in K^B(b)$ and $b \in K^B(c)$ imply that $a \in K^B(c)$.*

PROOF. Let $a = C_\alpha^B(b)$. We select according to III.3.7 a transitive subset A of $K^B(c)$ which contains b and α as elements and is an elementary submodel of $K^B(c)$. Since A is a model of ZF, we can apply theorem 3.1 and obtain $C_\alpha^B(b) \in \mathrm{Konstr}^B(A, c)$. Hence $a \in \mathrm{Konstr}^B(A, c) \subseteq A \subseteq K^B(c)$.

Theorem 5.1 states that the relation of "B-constructibility in" is transitive. As a corollary we find that:

5.2. *If b is B-constructible in c, then $K^B(b) \subseteq K^B(c)$; if, moreover, c is B-constructible in b, then $K^B(b) = K^B(c)$.*

Of special importance for our subsequent discussion is the question whether the relation of B-constructibility is reflexive. This, in general, is not the case but in some special cases the relation $a \in K^B(a)$ does hold:

5.3. *If $a \in K^B(0)$, then $a \in K^B(a)$.*

This follows immediately from 5.1 and the remark that 0 is obviously B-constructible in an arbitrary a.

5.4. *If a transitive sequence a is obtained by adding a finite number of terms $a_1, \ldots, a_k$ to a sequence Q which is B-constructible in* 0, *then* $a \in K^B(a)$.

PROOF. All terms of a and in particular the terms $a_1, \ldots, a_k$ are B-constructible in a; also all ordinals are so constructible and finally Q according to our assumptions. Hence the union

$$a = Q \cup \{\langle \xi_1, a_1 \rangle, \langle \xi_2, a_2 \rangle, \ldots, \langle \xi_k, a_k \rangle\}$$

is B-constructible in a.

If B satisfies the additional conditions (B.5) and (B.6) of III.5, we can prove that the relation of B-constructibility is reflexive:

5.5. *If B satisfies* (B.0)–(B.6), *then* $a \in K^B(a)$ *for all transitive sequences* a.

PROOF. For an arbitrary transitive sequence a denote by α the minimal ordinal which is greater than $\mathrm{pl}'(\xi)$ for every ξ in the domain of a. Thus all the terms a_ξ of a occur in the transfinite sequence of constructible sets with indices $\mathrm{pl}'(\xi) < \alpha$. By III.5.2 the sequence $C^B_\zeta(a)$ limited to indices $\zeta < \alpha$ belongs to $K^B(a)$. Let us denote this sequence by f; thus

$$f = \{\langle \zeta, C^B_\zeta(a) \rangle : \zeta < \alpha\}.$$

We must now select from f those pairs in which the first member has the form $\mathrm{pl}'(\xi)$ and replace this term by ξ. To achieve this we notice that from the uniform definability of the function pl′(cf. 2.5) it easily follows that also the function g defined by the equation

$$g(\zeta) = \langle \zeta, \mathrm{pl}'(\zeta) \rangle$$

is uniformly definable. Hence the set $s = \{g(\zeta) : \zeta < \alpha\}$ belongs to every transitive model A of ZF provided that $\alpha \in A$ [1]). In particular $s \in K^B(a)$.

We claim that $a = s \circ f$. To see this we notice that a pair $\langle u, v \rangle$ belongs to $s \circ f$ if and only if there is a w such that $\langle u, w \rangle \in s$ and

[1]) It is immaterial whether A is a set or a (proper) class because a proper class contains a subset which is elementarily equivalent to it and is transitive if the class is transitive.

$\langle w, v\rangle \in f$. Hence $\langle u, w\rangle = \langle \zeta, \mathrm{pl}'(\zeta)\rangle$ for a $\zeta < \alpha$ and $\langle w, v\rangle = \langle \xi, C^B_\xi(a)\rangle$ for a $\xi < \alpha$. Hence $\langle u, v\rangle = \langle \xi, C^B_{\mathrm{pl}'(\xi)}(a)\rangle = \langle \xi, a_\xi\rangle$ and therefore $a = s \circ f$. This proves that $a \in K^B(a)$.

The proof given above remains valid if we replace $K^B(a)$ by $C^B_\varkappa(a)$ provided that $C^B_\varkappa(a)$ is a model of ZF and $\mathrm{Dom}(a) \in \varkappa$. In this way we find that:

5.6. *If B satisfies conditions* (B.0)–(B.6) *and is uniformly definable, $\varkappa$ is an ordinal such that $C^B_\varkappa(a)$ is a model of* ZF *and a is a transitive sequence with* $\mathrm{Dom}(a) \in \varkappa$, *then $a \in C^B_\varkappa(a)$.*

Theorem 5.6 can be strengthened, and we shall use this stronger form in Chapter XII.6: under the assumptions of 5.6 there is an ordinal α depending only on $\varkappa$ and $\mathrm{Dom}(a)$ such that $a = C^B_\alpha(a)$.

The proof of this stronger theorem can be obtained by an easy analysis of the proof of 5.5.

CHAPTER VI

$C_{\pi(A)}(a)$ AS A MODEL

We shall discuss in this chapter the problem whether the set $C_{\pi(A)}(a)$ is a model for ZF and we shall prove that any finite collection of axioms of ZF is true in $C_{\pi(A)}(a)$ for almost every A and arbitrary transitive sequence a in A. In order to obtain this result we must discuss the strong definability of functions which were introduced in the proof of the reflection theorem. In the final sections of the chapter we shall use these results to establish the existence of various models of ZF.

1. The reflection theorem again

We consider a strongly definable functor f of the second kind with the following properties: For almost every A and for $\xi, \eta < \pi(A)$, $p \in A^n$

(1) $$\xi < \eta \rightarrow f(A, \xi, p) \subseteq f(A, \eta, p),$$

(2) $$\xi \in \operatorname{Lim}(A) \rightarrow f(A, \xi, p) = \bigcup_{\eta<\xi} f(A, \eta, p).$$

We put $M(A, p) = \bigcup_{\xi<\pi(A)} f(A, \xi, p)$. It is easy to show that M is a strongly definable functor. We choose a fixed formula $\boldsymbol{M}$ which defines M and denote its free variables by $x_0, x_{i_1}, \ldots, x_{i_n}$. Thus for almost all A and for $p \in A^{\{i_1,\ldots,i_n\}}$, $x \in A$ we have the equivalence

$$\vdash_A \boldsymbol{M}[p^\frown x] \equiv x \in M(A, p)\,[1].$$

[1]) The right hand side of this formula should really be written as $x \in M(A, p_{i_1}, \ldots$ $\ldots, p_{i_n})$ because M is a function with $n+1$ arguments. In order to simplify the notation we shall use the letter p somewhat ambiguously to denote a sequence with domain $\{i_1, \ldots, i_n\}$ and a complex of arguments of the function M, i.e., a sequence with domain $\{1, \ldots, n\}$.

1.1. *For every formula H there is a strongly definable functor h of the second kind such that for almost all A*

(3) *if $p \in A^n$, then the mapping $\xi \to h(A, p, \xi)$ is an increasing and continuous mapping of $\pi(A)$ into $\pi(A)$,*

(4) *if $\lambda \in \mathrm{Lim}(A)$ and $h(A, p, \lambda) = \lambda > 0$, then for arbitrary $a \in f(A, \lambda, p)^{\mathrm{Fr}(H)}$*

$$\vdash_{M(A,p)} H[a] \equiv \vdash_{f(A,\lambda,p)} H[a].$$

The proof is practically the same as in II.2.1; we must only make sure at each step that the functions with which we are dealing are values of strongly definable functors.

If H has no quantifiers, then we take as h the functor $h(A, p, \xi) = \xi$. If H is the formula $\neg H_1$ and h_1 the functor corresponding to H, then we take as h the functor h_1.

If H is $H_1 \wedge H_2$, then we take $h = h_1 \circ h_2$, i.e.,

$$h(A, p, \xi) = h_1(A, p, h_2(A, p, \xi)).$$

Hence h is strongly definable and satisfies (3) and (4).

It remains to consider the case where H is the formula $(x_0)H_1$. We can assume that x_0 is a free variable of H_1 because otherwise we can take as h the same functor as was correlated with H. We shall use the abbreviation $p^\frown x$ for $p \cup \{\langle 0, x\rangle\}$, cf. p. 12.

Define functors rho and sigma as follows

$$\mathrm{rho}(A, a, p) = \begin{cases} 0 & \text{if} \quad a \notin A^{\mathrm{Fr}(H)}, \\ \min\{\eta \in A\colon (Ex_0)_{f(A,\eta,p)} \vdash_{M(A,p)} \neg H_1[a^\frown x_0]\} & \text{otherwise,} \end{cases}$$

$$(5) \quad \mathrm{sigma}(A, \xi, p) = \begin{cases} 0 \text{ if } \xi \notin \pi(A) \text{ or the sup defined below is not in } A, \\ \sup\{\mathrm{rho}(A, a, p)\colon a \in f(A, \xi, p)^{\mathrm{Fr}(H)}\} \text{ otherwise.} \end{cases}$$

We must first prove that rho and sigma are strongly definable functors. In order to achieve this we relativize all quantifiers in H_1 to $\boldsymbol{M}$, i.e. we change the bound variables of H_1 so that none of the quantified variables is in $\boldsymbol{M}$ and then replace each $(x_i) \ldots$ by $(x_i)[\boldsymbol{M}(x_i, \ldots) \to \ldots]$. If the resulting formula is $\boldsymbol{Q}$ then for almost all A and arbitrary $x_0 \in A$, $p \in A^{\mathrm{Fr}(M)-\{0\}}$, $a \in A^{\mathrm{Fr}(H)}$

$$\vdash_{M(A,p)} H_1[a^\frown x_0] \equiv \vdash_A \boldsymbol{Q}[a^\frown(p^\frown x_0)].$$

Thus the functor Q defined by the formula $\neg Q$ has the property that for almost all A and all $p \in A^{\{i_1 \dots i_n\}}$, $a \in A^{\mathrm{Fr}(H)}$ and all x_0 in A

$$x_0 \in Q(A, a, p) \equiv \vdash_{M(A,p)} \neg H_1[a^\frown x_0].$$

Now we can redefine rho as

$$\mathrm{rho}(A, a, p) = \begin{cases} 0 & \text{if} \quad a \notin A^{\mathrm{Fr}(H)} \text{ or } p \notin A^{\mathrm{Fr}(M)-\{0\}} \text{ or} \\ & \quad \neg(Ex_0)_A(E\eta)_{\pi(A)}[x_0 \in f(A, \eta, p) \cap Q(A, a, p)]; \\ \min\{\eta < \pi(A)\colon (Ex_0)_A[x_0 \in f(A, \eta, p) \cap Q(A, a, p)]\} & \\ & \text{otherwise.} \end{cases}$$

From this it follows that rho is strongly definable (cf. IV.2.10 and IV.3.19). The strong definability of sigma easily results from the strong definability of rho by means of the theorems established in IV.2 and IV.3. Note that from IV.3.18 it follows that for almost all A we have the second formula (5) provided that $\xi < \pi(A)$ and $p \in A^{\mathrm{Fr}(H)}$.

We take in IV.4.2 for $S(A)$ the set $\pi(A)$ and for $R(A)$ the relation $\leqslant$ limited to $\pi(A)$. Let the functor $t(A, x, p)$ be defined thus:

$$t(A, 0, p) = \mathrm{sigma}\,(A, 0, p),$$

$$t(A, x, p) = \begin{cases} \max\big(x(\mathrm{Dom}(x) - 1), \mathrm{sigma}(A, \mathrm{Dom}(x), p)\big) + 1 & \\ \qquad\qquad \text{if } x \text{ is a function and } \mathrm{Dom}(x) \notin \mathrm{Lim}(A), & \\ \bigcup \mathrm{Rg}(x) \quad \text{if } x \text{ is a function and } 0 \in \mathrm{Dom}(x) \in \mathrm{Lim}(A), & \\ 0 \quad \text{in all the remaining cases.} & \end{cases}$$

Since t is strongly definable, we can apply theorem IV.4.2 and obtain a strongly definable functor ge of the second kind such that for almost all A and arbitrary ξ in $\pi(A)$ and p in A^n

$$\mathrm{ge}(A, 0, p) = \mathrm{sigma}(A, 0, p),$$

$$\mathrm{ge}(A, \xi+1, p) = \max\big(\mathrm{ge}(A, \xi, p), \mathrm{sigma}(A, \xi+1, p), p\big) + 1,$$

$$\begin{aligned} \mathrm{ge}(A, \xi, p) &= \bigcup\{\mathrm{ge}(A, \eta, p)\colon \eta < \xi\} \\ &= \sup\{\mathrm{ge}(A, \eta, p)\colon \eta < \xi\} \quad \text{if} \quad \xi \in \mathrm{Lim}(A) - \{0\}. \end{aligned}$$

We now define h by the formula

$$h(A, \xi, p) = h'\big(A, \mathrm{ge}(A, \xi, p), p\big),$$

where h' is the functor correlated with H_1. The functor h is obviously a strongly definable one and we can prove exactly as in II.2.1 that it satisfies (3) and (4).

The applicability of the reflection theorem is due to the following result:

1.2. *If f is a strongly definable functor of the second kind such that for almost all A and all $\xi, \eta < \pi(A)$, all p in A^n*

$$f(A, \xi, p) < \pi(A),$$

$$\xi < \eta \rightarrow f(A, \xi, p) < f(A, \eta, p),$$

$$0 \in \eta \in \mathrm{Lim}(A) \rightarrow f(A, \eta, p) = \sup\{f(A, \xi, p) \colon \xi < \eta\},$$

then for almost every A and all $\xi < \pi(A)$, $p \in A^n$ there is an ordinal $\varkappa < \pi(A)$ such that $\xi < \varkappa$ and $f(A, \varkappa, p) = \varkappa$.

PROOF. We use theorem IV.4.2, in which we take $S(A) = \omega$ and $R(A) =$ the relation $\leqslant$ limited to integers. The functor which in IV.4.2 was called f is replaced by the functor g defined as follows:

$$g(A, x, \xi, p) = \begin{cases} 0 & \text{if} \quad x \notin \mathrm{Fn}(A) \text{ or if } \mathrm{Dom}(x) \notin \omega, \\ \xi & \text{if} \quad x = 0, \\ f\big(A, x(\mathrm{Dom}(x) - 1), p\big) & \text{if} \quad x \in \mathrm{Fn}(A) \\ & \qquad \text{and } \mathrm{Dom}(x) \in \omega - \{0\}. \end{cases}$$

The resulting strongly definable functor h of the second kind satisfies for almost all A and arbitrary ξ in $\pi(A)$, p in A^n, s in ω the equations

$$h(A, 0, \xi, p) = \xi,$$

$$h(A, s+1, \xi, p) = f\big(A, h(A, s, \xi, p), p\big).$$

By IV.3.18 the supremum of $h(A, s, \xi, p)$ for $s < \omega$ belongs to A for almost all A and for arbitrary ξ in $\pi(A)$ and p in A^n. This supremum is the required critical number.

2. Satisfiability of the power set axiom and of the axiom of substitution

Throughout this section we assume that B is a uniformly definable function satisfying the conditions (B.0)–(B.4) of III.2. r is the integer determined by B. We shall omit the superscript B wherever possible and shall write, say, $C_\xi(a)$ for what should properly be denoted by $C_\xi^B(a)$.

We want to show that any finite collection of axioms of ZF is valid in $C_{\pi(A)}(a)$ for almost all A and arbitrary a in Str(A) [1]).

2.1. *For almost all A and all a in* Str(A) *the power set axiom is valid in* $C_{\pi(A)}(a)$.

PROOF. Define a functor by the formula

$$f(A, a, y) = \min\{\eta < \pi(A): y = C_\eta(a)\}.$$

By IV.3.19 and V.3.1 this functor is strongly definable. It follows by the use of IV.3.18 that for almost all A and arbitrary a in Str(A), x in A the supremum $\sup\{f(A, a, y): y \in x\}$ belongs to A. Now we take as x the set $P(C_\xi(a)) \cap A$, which belongs to A for almost all A and arbitrary ξ in $\pi(A)$ and a in Str(A). We obtain thus an ordinal $\gamma < \pi(A)$ such that whenever $\xi, \eta < \pi(A)$ and $C_\eta(a) \subseteq C_\xi(a)$, then there is an ordinal $\eta' < \gamma$ for which $C_\eta(a) = C_{\eta'}(a)$.

It follows that the set $Z = P(C_\xi(a)) \cap C_{\pi(A)}(a)$ is contained in $C_{\delta(\gamma)}(a)$.

We can now complete the proof using the technique developed in II.3. Denoting by H_1 the formula $(x_2)\ [(x_2 \in x_1) \to (x_2 \in x_0)]$, we can represent Z in the form

$$\{y \in C_{\delta(\gamma)}(a): \ \vdash_{C_{\delta(\gamma)}} H_1[y, C_\xi(a)]\}.$$

Thus Z is the section

$$S_{H_1}(C_{\delta(\gamma)}(a), \{\langle 0, C_\xi(a)\rangle\}).$$

We now select a limit ordinal λ between $\delta(\gamma)$ and $\pi(A)$. Since the set $C_{\delta(\lambda)}(a)$ is predicatively closed and contains as elements the sets $C_{\delta(\gamma)}(a)$ and $C_\xi(a)$, it also contains the section Z. Thus Z is an element of $C_{\pi(A)}(a)$ and theorem 2.1 is proved.

2.2. *Let H be a formula such that* $0, 1 \in \mathrm{Fr}(H)$; *for almost all A and arbitrary a in* Str(A) *the axiom of substitution* (VI_H) *corresponding to H is valid in* $C_{\pi(A)}(a)$.

The proof of this theorem is based on the same idea as the proof of II.3.1. Since the result stated in 2.2 is one of the most important tools for our further theory, we shall present the proof in detail. First we outline the main ideas: there will be three essential steps to be taken.

[1]) Str(A) is the set of (finite or transfinite) transitive sequences which belong to A; cf. IV.2, example 13.

In the first part of the proof we shall show that for almost all A, for all a in Str(A) and any ordinal $\alpha < \pi(A)$ there is an ordinal $\gamma < \pi(A)$ such that if $\xi < \alpha$ and there is an element η of $\pi(A)$ which satisfies the condition

(*) $$\vdash_{C_{\pi(A)}(a)} H[C_\xi(a), C_\eta(a)],$$

then there also is an $\eta < \gamma$ satisfying the same condition.

In the second part we assume that $\xi, \eta < \gamma$ and transform the condition (*) into

$$\vdash_{C_\lambda(a)} H[C_\xi(a), C_\eta(a)],$$

where λ is an ordinal in $\pi(A)$ which depends on A, a, γ, and H but not on ξ and η. This transformation allows us to represent the set which is the image of $C_\alpha(a)$ under the function defined in $C_{\pi(A)}(a)$ by H and possibly by some parameters as a section in a suitable $C_\lambda(a)$ (see II.3 for the definition of a section).

In the last part of the proof we use the predicative closure of $C_{\delta(\lambda+\omega)}(a)$ to infer that the image mentioned above belongs to $C_{\pi(A)}(a)$.

It is clear that this proof is almost a repetition of the one given in II.3.1 but with the universe V replaced by A. The main emphasis is of course not on the mere existence of the ordinals γ and λ but on the inequalities $\gamma < \pi(A)$ and $\lambda < \pi(A)$, which ensure that we remain within the universe A.

We now give the details of the proof. We first define a functor f:

$$f(A, a, \xi, p)$$
$$= \min\left\{\eta < \pi(A) : \vdash_{C_{\pi(A)}(a)} H[\{\langle 0, C_\xi(a)\rangle, \langle 1, C_\eta(a)\rangle\} \cup p]\right\}.$$

Here and below p is a sequence with domain $\mathrm{Fr}(H) - \{0, 1\} = Z$ and with values in A.

For each transitive A and arbitrary ξ in $\pi(A)$, p in A^Z we obviously have $f(A, a, \xi, p) \in A$. We want to show that the functor f is strongly definable. For this purpose it is sufficient to represent the condition $\eta = f(A, a, \xi, p)$ in the form

(1) $$\vdash_A K[\{\langle s, \eta\rangle, \langle t, \xi\rangle, \langle q, a\rangle\} \cup p]$$

where K is a formula with the free variables x_s, x_t, x_q and x_i, $i \in Z$.

From V.3.3 we know that for almost all A and arbitrary x in A, a in $\mathrm{Str}(A)$

(2) $$x \in C_{\pi(A)}(a) \equiv \vdash_A \mathbf{Konstr}[x, a].$$

We can assume that the free variables of the formula **Konstr** are x_v, x_q and that none of the variables which occur in H occur also in **Konstr**. We now relativize all quantifiers in H in the following way: a quantifier $(x_j)[\dots x_j \dots]$ is replaced by $(x_j)\{\mathbf{Konstr}(x_j, x_q) \to [\dots x_j \dots]\}$ where the formula $\mathbf{Konstr}(x_j, x_q)$ is obtained from **Konstr** by substituting the variable x_j for x_v wherever x_v occurs freely in the formula **Konstr**.

The formula H' obtained from H by this process has one more free variable than H. In view of (2) we easily find that for almost all A and arbitrary a in $\mathrm{Str}(A)$, p in $[C_{\pi(A)}(a)]^Z$, ξ, η in $\pi(A)$ the following equivalence is true:

(3) $$\vdash_A H'[\{\langle 0, C_\xi(a)\rangle, \langle 1, C_\eta(a)\rangle, \langle q, a\rangle\} \cup p]$$
$$\equiv \vdash_{C_{\pi(A)}(a)} H[\{\langle 0, C_\xi(a)\rangle, \langle 1, C_\eta(a)\rangle\} \cup p].$$

We now notice that the function $C_\xi(a)$ is uniformly definable and hence there exists a formula F with three free variables, say x_w, x_s, x_q, such that

(4) $$\vdash_A F[\{\langle w, x\rangle, \langle s, \xi\rangle, \langle q, a\rangle\}] \equiv x = C_\xi(a)$$

for almost all A and arbitrary x in A, ξ in $\pi(A)$ and a in $\mathrm{Str}(A)$.

We can assume that F and H have no common variables. We select integers m, t, u such that neither x_t nor x_u nor x_m occurs in either of the formulae F and H'. The required formula K is now

$$\mathbf{Ord}(x_s) \wedge (Ex_0)(Ex_1)\{F(x_1, x_s, x_q) \wedge F(x_0, x_t, x_q) \wedge H'(x_0, x_1) \wedge$$
$$\wedge (x_m)(x_u)[(x_u \in x_s) \wedge F(x_m, x_u, x_q) \to \neg H'(x_0, x_m)]\}.$$

Writing this formula we used the customary way of indicating substitutions to be performed in formulae. For instance $H'(x_0, x_m)$ denotes the formula obtained from H' by substituting x_m for x_1 throughout H'. The free variables of K are x_q, x_s, x_t and the variables x_j with j in Z.

From (3) and (4) we easily see that for almost all A and for a in $\mathrm{Str}(A)$, ξ, η in $\pi(A)$ and p in $[C_{\pi(A)}(a)]^Z$ formula (1) is equivalent to the equation $\eta = f(A, \xi, p)$. The strong definability of f is thus established.

We now use theorem IV.3.18 and find that for almost all A and arbitrary p in $[C_{\pi(A)}(a)]^Z$, a in $\mathrm{Str}(A)$, α in $\pi(A)$ the supremum $\beta = \sup\{f(A, \xi, a, p)\colon \xi < \alpha\}$ belongs to A. Hence also $\gamma = \delta(\beta)$ belongs to A for almost all A and $\gamma = \gamma(A, a, \alpha, p)$ is a strongly definable functor of the second kind (we put $\gamma = 0$ if any of the conditions $\alpha \in \pi(A)$, $a \in \mathrm{Str}(A)$, $p \in [C_{\pi(A)}(a)]^Z$ is not satisfied).

Let us now assume that as many axioms of ZF are valid in A as to ensure that the values of the functor γ belong to A. Call the conjunction of these axioms X_0. It is then obvious from the definition of f that if $a \in \mathrm{Str}(A)$, $\alpha \in \pi(A)$, $p \in [C_{\pi(A)}(a)]^Z$, $\xi < \alpha$ and there is an ordinal satisfying the conditions $\eta < \pi(A)$ and

(5) $$\vdash_{C_{\pi(A)}(a)} H[\{\langle 0, C_\xi(a)\rangle, \langle 1, C_\eta(a)\rangle\} \cup p],$$

then there is also an $\eta' < \gamma$ satisfying the same conditions.

Thus the first part of the proof is complete.

The proof of the second part is based on the reflection theorem 1.1. We specialize the assumptions of 1.1 by taking for M the functor $C_{\pi(A)}(a)$ and for f (in the notation of 1.1) the functor whose value is $C_{\delta(\xi)}(a)$. The assumptions of 1.1 are thus satisfied and we obtain a functor h such that for almost all A and for a in $\mathrm{Str}(A)$ the function $\xi \to h(A, a, \xi)$ is an increasing and continuous mapping of $\pi(A)$ into $\pi(A)$; moreover, if $\lambda = h(A, a, \lambda) > 0$ and $\xi, \eta < \lambda$, $p \in [C_{\delta(\lambda)}(a)]^Z$, then (5) is equivalent to

(6) $$\vdash_{C_{\delta(\lambda)}(a)} H[\{\langle 0, C_\xi(a)\rangle, \langle 1, C_\eta(a)\rangle\} \cup p].$$

We call X_1 the conjunction of finitely many axioms of ZF whose validity in A ensures that h has the above two properties.

We shall now complete the proof. Let us assume that A is a transitive set and that axioms X_0 and X_1 are valid in A. Let $a \in \mathrm{Str}(A)$ and $p \in [C_{\pi(A)}(a)]^Z$. We have to prove that the formula

$$(x_0)(E!x_1)H \to (c)(Eb)(x_1)\{(x_1 \in b) \equiv (Ex_0)[(x_0 \in c) \wedge H]\}$$

is satisfied in $C_{\pi(A)}(a)$ by p. We can obviously assume that the antecedent is so satisfied and hence that for each ξ in $\pi(A)$ there is exactly one $\eta < \pi(A)$ such that (5) is true. Let $c = C_\alpha(a)$; thus for each $\xi < \alpha$ there is an $\eta < \gamma(A, a, \alpha, p)$ for which (5) is true.

We now choose an ordinal λ satisfying the conditions

$$\alpha < \lambda = h(A, a, \lambda), \quad p \in [C_{\delta(\lambda)}(a)]^Z, \quad \gamma(A, a, \alpha, p) < \lambda;$$

the existence of λ follows from 1.2: there are arbitrarily high critical numbers for h.

For each $\xi < \alpha$ the unique $C_\eta(a)$ satisfying (5) can now be characterized as the unique $C_\eta(a)$ satisfying (6) and the inequality $\eta < \lambda$. It follows that the set

$$b = \{C_\eta(a) \colon (Ex)((x \in c) \wedge \vdash_{C_{\pi(A)}(a)} H[\{\langle 0\ x\rangle, \langle 1, C_\eta(a)\rangle\} \cup p])\}$$

is equal to the set

$$\{y \in C_{\delta(\lambda)}(a) \colon \vdash_{C_{\delta(\lambda)}(a)} H^*[\{\langle 1, y\rangle, \langle n, c\rangle\} \cup p]\}$$

where x_n is a variable which does not occur in H and where H^* is the formula $(Ex_0)[(x_0 \in x_n) \wedge H]$. This last set is the section of $D_{H^*}(C_{\delta(\lambda)}(a))$ determined by the sequence $\{\langle n, c\rangle\} \cup p$ (see II.3) [1]). Since all sections of the form $S_F(C_{\delta(\lambda)}(a), s)$, where F is any formula and s a sequence whose terms belong to $C_{\delta(\lambda)}(a)$, are elements of $C_{\delta(\lambda+\omega)}(a)$ (see II.4.12), we infer that b is an element of $C_{\delta(\lambda+\omega)}(a)$ and thus of $C_{\pi(A)}(a)$. Hence axiom (VI_H) is valid in A. Theorem 2.2 is thus proved.

By introducing minor changes in the proofs of theorems 2.1 and 2.2 we obtain similar results for sets $C_{\pi(A)}(T(A, p))$ (cf. V.4). We formulate these results as theorem 2.3.

2.3. *If T is a strongly definable functor such that for almost all A and all p in A^n the set $T(A, p)$ is a transitive sequence of length $\leqslant \pi(A)$, then the power-set axiom is valid in $C_{\pi(A)}(T(A, p))$ for almost all A and all p in A^n.*

If H is a formula and $\{0, 1\} \subseteq \mathrm{Fr}(H)$, then the axiom of substitution corresponding to H is valid in $C_{\pi(A)}(T(A, p))$ for almost all A and all p in A^n.

3. Existence of models

From the theorems proved in Section 2 we obtain several corollaries concerning the existence of various types of models.

[1]) In II.3 we assumed that formulae which determine sections have the free variable x_0. This variable is here replaced by x_1.

3.1. *If B is a uniformly definable function which satisfies* (B.0)–(B.4) *of* III.2 (p. 39) *and if A is a model of* ZF, *then so is $C^B_{\pi(A)}(a)$ for any $a \in \mathrm{Str}(A)$; similarly $C^B_{\pi(A)}(T(A, p))$ is a model of* ZF *provided that T is a strongly definable functor whose values are transitive sequences of length $\leqslant \pi(A)$.*

PROOF. Axioms (I)–(IV) are valid in $C^B_{\pi(A)}(a)$ in view of theorems II.1.1–1.4 and III.3.3–3.4. Axioms (V) and (VI) are valid in $C^B_{\pi(A)}(a)$ in view of 2.1 and 2.2. The second part results in the same way from 2.3.

3.2. *If K is a conjunction of finitely many axioms of* ZF *and if B is a uniformly definable function which satisfies* (B.0)–(B.4), *then the conjunction K is valid in $C^B_{\pi(A)}(a)$ for almost all A and all a in* $\mathrm{Str}(A)$. *The same is true for $C^B_{\pi(A)}(T(A, p))$ provided that T is strongly definable and its values are transitive sequences of length $\leqslant \pi(A)$.*

The proof is the same as for 3.1.

The point of theorem 3.2 is that with each finite set of axioms of ZF we can associate another, possibly larger, finite set of axioms of ZF such that for each transitive set A and each sequence a in $\mathrm{Str}(A)$ the former axioms are valid in $C_{\pi(A)}(a)$ (i.e., in $\mathrm{Konstr}(A, a)$) whenever the latter are valid in A.

In III.3.8 we proved the existence of models of ZF which have any prescribed cardinality $\geqslant \aleph_0$ and in III.3.7 we proved that for any B satisfying (B.0)–(B.4) there are arbitrarily high $\varkappa$ such that $C^B_{\varkappa}(a)$ is a model of ZF.

With the means which we had at our disposal in Chapter III we could not answer the question whether for a given function B there are models of the form $C^B_{\varkappa}(a)$ where a is any transitive sequence and $\varkappa$ an ordinal with a prescribed cardinality. This question will be answered now. We need the following lemma, which is of independent interest:

3.3. *If B is a uniformly definable function which satisfies conditions* (B.0)–(B.4) (cf. III.2) *and if a is a transitive sequence such that $a \in K^B(a)$, then*

$$x \in K^B(a) \rightarrow \vdash_{K^B(a)} \mathbf{Konstr}^B[x, a]$$

for each formula $\mathbf{Konstr}^B$ *which defines the functor* Konstr^B.

PROOF. Let x be an element of $K^B(a)$. Thus $x = C^B_\xi(a)$ where ξ is an ordinal. In III.3.7 we proved that there is a transitive subset A of $K^B(a)$ such that a and ξ belong to A and A is an elementary submodel of $K^B(a)$. Since the function Konstr^B is uniformly definable and ξ, a are elements of A, we infer that $x = C^B_\xi(a) \in \text{Konstr}^B(A, a)$ and hence $\vdash_A \mathbf{Konstr}^B[x, a]$. Now we use the fact that A is an elementary submodel of $K^B(a)$ and obtain $\vdash_{K^B(a)} \mathbf{Konstr}^B[x, a]$.

Lemma 3.3 corresponds to what Gödel [13] called the "absoluteness of L". A property of x which consists in its being an element of $K^B(a)$ can be expressed by the formula $\vdash_V \mathbf{Konstr}^B[x, a]$; lemma 3.3 shows that it can also be expressed by the formula $\vdash_{K^B(a)} \mathbf{Konstr}^B[x, a]$. Thus the property remains unaffected by the limitation of the universe V to a possibly smaller universe $K^B(a)$.

We can now prove the following theorem:

3.4. *Let B be a uniformly definable function satisfying the conditions* (B.0)–(B.4) *of* III.2. *If a is a transitive sequence and $a \in K^B(a)$, then for every aleph $\nu \geqslant \text{Dom}(a)$ there is an ordinal $\varkappa$ such that $|C^B_\varkappa(a)| = \nu$ and $C^B_\varkappa(a) \equiv K^B(a)$; thus in particular $C^B_\varkappa(a)$ is a model of* ZF. *The construction can be arranged so that $a \in C^B_\varkappa(a)$.*

PROOF. By III.4.6 the cardinal of the set $\nu \cup \bigcup \text{Rg}(a) \cup \{a\}$ is ν. Since this set is contained in $K^B(a)$, we can apply the Skolem–Löwenheim theorem I.5.1 and obtain a set M of power ν such that

$$\nu \cup \bigcup \text{Rg}(a) \cup \{a\} \subseteq M \prec K^B(a).$$

From 3.3 and the basic properties of elementary submodels we obtain

(1) $$\vdash_M \mathbf{Konstr}^B[x, a] \quad \text{for all } x \text{ in } M.$$

Let h be the contraction function which maps M onto a transitive set A (cf. I.6.1). From I.6.3 we know that h transforms each ξ into itself and also each a_ξ into itself; hence $h(\langle \xi, a_\xi \rangle) = \langle \xi, a_\xi \rangle$ for each ξ in Dom(a) and thus $h(a) = a$.

Transforming (1) by the isomorphism h we find that for all x in A

$$\vdash_A \mathbf{Konstr}^B[x, a],$$

whence $x \in \text{Konstr}^B(A, a) = C^B_{\pi(A)}(a)$. This proves that $A \subseteq C^B_{\pi(A)}(a)$.

On the other hand, each $C^B_\xi(a)$ with $\xi < \pi(A)$ is an element of A because the function $C^B_\xi(a)$ is uniformly definable. This proves that $C^B_{\delta(\pi(A))}(a) = C^B_{\pi(A)}(a) \subseteq A$. Hence $A = C^B_{\pi(A)}(a)$. Thus A is the required model because its cardinality is $= |M| = \nu$ and $a \in A$.

Theorem 3.4, though interesting, is not suitable as a basis for independence proofs because the model $C^B_\varkappa(a)$ constructed in 3.4 is elementarily equivalent to $K^B(a)$. If for instance $a \in K^B(0)$, then the model constructed in 3.4 satisfies $C^B_\varkappa(a) \equiv K^B(0)$ (cf. V.5.2). Thus in order to obtain from 3.4 a model which is not elementarily equivalent to $K^B(0)$ we have first to solve the problem whether the existence of an a which does not belong to $K^B(0)$ can be proved or at least shown to be consistent with the axioms on which our whole discussion is based. Later on we shall learn a different method of constructing models of the form $C^B_\varkappa(a)$ which are not elementarily equivalent to $K^B(0)$.

4. Minimal models

According to 3.4 for any transitive sequence a there exists a minimal ordinal $\mu(a) = \alpha > \mathrm{Dom}(a)$ such that the family $C^{B^Z}_\alpha(a)$ is a model of ZF. For brevity we shall denote this family by $M(a)$. We want to establish the following fact:

4.1. *If a is a transitive sequence, then $M(a)$ is the minimal (transitive) model of* ZF *which contains a as an element.*

PROOF. It follows from the definition that $M(a)$ is a model of ZF and from V.5.6 that $a \in M(a)$. Now let X be any (transitive) model of ZF such that $a \in X$. From 3.1 we find that $C^{B^Z}_{\pi(X)}(a)$ is a model of ZF which—again by V.5.6—contains a as an element. Hence $\mu(a) \leqslant \pi(X)$ and therefore

$$M(a) = C^{B^Z}_{\mu(a)}(a) \subseteq C^{B^Z}_{\pi(X)}(a) \subseteq X.$$

This proves the theorem.

One can ask whether the use of the function B^Z is essential for the construction of minimal models containing the given sequence a. We shall see in Chapter XIV that there are sequences a such that

$\mu(a) = \mu(0)$ but $C^{B0}_{\mu(0)}(a)$ does not contain a. Thus for arbitrary a we do not obtain a minimal model containing a if we replace the operation B^Z by B^0. However, in the particular case $a = 0$ we can replace B^Z by an arbitrary uniformly definable function satisfying (B.0)–(B.4).

4.2. *If* B *is uniformly definable and satisfies* (B.0)–(B.4), *then* $C^{B}_{\mu(0)}(0) = M(0)$.

PROOF. Since $M(0)$ is a model, it contains all ordinals up to $\mu(0)$ (cf. III.4.4). Using 3.1 for $A = M$ we thus find that $C^{B}_{\mu(0)}(0)$ is a model of ZF. By the minimality of $M(0)$ this model is equal to $M(0)$.

Theorem 4.2 shows that $M(0)$ is the absolutely minimal model in the sense that it is contained in any transitive model of ZF; for such a model must obviously contain 0 and hence $M(0)$ [1]).

Several interesting properties of the minimal model $M(0)$ were discovered by Cohen [5], who showed for instance that the generalized continuum hypothesis is valid in $M(0)$. Later he showed that this need not be the case for models of the form $M(a)$ where a is a suitable transitive sequence. We shall learn this proof in Chapter XIII.

Starting with the absolutely minimal model $M(0)$ we can define an increasing transfinite sequence of models of ZF. To obtain it we take $M_0 = M(0)$ and $M_\alpha = C^{B^Z}_{\varphi(\alpha)}(0)$ where $\varphi(\alpha)$ is the least ordinal λ such that $C^{B^Z}_{\lambda}(0)$ is a model of ZF and is different from all previous M_ξ. The existence of an ordinal λ with these properties results from 3.4 because this theorem implies the existence of models of ZF which have the form $C^{B^Z}_{\lambda}(0)$ and which properly contain the union of all M_ξ with $\xi < \alpha$.

We can also built a similar sequence consisting of models which contain a given sequence a as an element.

It is well to notice that these sequences are ordered by the ordinary inclusion relation and not by the relation $\prec$ of elementary extension.

[1]) The minimal model $M(0)$ was first constructed by Cohen [5], who established its properties and applied them to a proof that a large class of models cannot be used for the proof of independence of the axiom of choice. In this connection compare also Shepherdson [30]. Marek and Onyszkiewicz showed in [22] that there is no smallest model for the axioms obtained from ZF by adding, say, the negation of the axiom of choice. They also investigated several other extensions of ZF which do not have minimal models.

The above observations can be made more perspicuous by the use of a suggestive language due to Takeuti [33], who defined for each transitive model of ZF its *height* and its *width*. The height of a model M is simply $\pi(M)$, i.e., the first ordinal not belonging to M. Models $M_\alpha(0)$ are thus of increasing heights.

Not so immediate is the definition of the width of a model. To formulate it we notice that each (transitive) model M of ZF can be decomposed into "layers" $M \cap R_\xi$ where ξ ranges over ordinals less than the height of M. We take the family $M \cap R_\xi$ as the measure of the width of M at the ξth layer. Thus the natural models R_α (see. II.2.4) have the maximal possible width at each layer. The absolutely minimal model has a minimal width at each layer. Of all the models of a given height χ the model $C_\chi^{B^Z}(0)$ has the smallest possible width at each layer.

The width of a model at a given layer is not independent of its height. Thus for instance if $M_0(0)$ is the absolutely minimal model and $M_1(0)$ the next one in the sequence $M_\alpha(0)$ constructed above, then the width of $M_1(0)$ at the layer $\omega+1$ is larger than the width of $M_0(0)$ at the same layer. Also the width of $M_2(0)$ is larger than the width of $M_1(0)$, etc. Where exactly this increase of widths at the layer $\omega+1$ in our sequence of models stops is a delicate problem which we shall not discuss here.

In Chapters VIII–XII we shall deal with another question of a similar character: how to increase the width of a model at a given layer without increasing its height. This question is of crucial importance for several problems of independence.

CHAPTER VII

CONSISTENCY OF THE AXIOM OF CHOICE AND OF THE CONTINUUM HYPOTHESIS

In the present chapter we shall prove two celebrated results due to Gödel [11]. They are stated in the heading. The proof will be obtained in the same way as in Gödel's book [13]: we shall make sure that the axiom of choice and the generalized continuum hypothesis are valid in suitable models $K^B(a)$.

1. Axiom of choice

We shall first express this axiom in the language of ZF and for this purpose we first introduce some abbreviations, which will enable us to avoid too long formulae.

Let $\mathbf{Dis}(x)$ and $\mathbf{Sel}(x, w)$ be the formulae:

$$\mathbf{Dis}(x)\colon\ (Ey)(y \in x) \wedge (z)[(z \in x) \to (Ey)(y \in z)] \wedge \\ \wedge (z)(t)\{[(z \in x) \wedge (t \in x) \wedge (z \neq t)] \to \neg(Ey)[(y \in z) \wedge (y \in t)]\},$$

$$\mathbf{Sel}(x, w)\colon\ (z)\big((z \in x) \to (Ey)(t)\{[(t \in z) \wedge (t \in w)] \equiv (t = y)\}\big).$$

The meaning of these formulae is given in the following lemma:

1.1. *If A is a transitive class and a, $b \in A$, then*

(i) $\vdash_A \mathbf{Dis}[a] \equiv$ (*a is a non-void set consisting of non-void disjoint sets*),

(ii) $\vdash_A \mathbf{Sel}[a, b] \equiv$ (*for every c in a the intersection $c \cap b$ consists of just one element*).

We shall call a set b satisfying the right-hand side of (ii) a *selector of a*. The *axiom of choice* can be formulated thus:

$$\mathrm{AC}\colon\ (x)[\mathbf{Dis}(x) \to (Ew)\mathbf{Sel}(x, w)].$$

From this and 1.1 we infer that:

1.2. *If A is a transitive class, then* $\vdash_A$ AC *if and only if for every $a \in A$ which is a non-void set of mutually disjoint non-void sets there is a selector b of a such that $b \in A$.*

We can now prove the result referred to in III.5.

1.3. *If a model A of* ZF *has the property that for each s in A there is a function $f \in A$ which maps a set of ordinals onto a set $s' \supseteq s$, then* $\vdash_A$ AC.

PROOF. Let a be a non-void set which belongs to A and consists of mutually disjoint non-void sets. The union $s = \bigcup a$ belongs to A (cf. II.1.2). Hence there are in A a set $s' \supseteq s$ and a function f which maps a set of ordinals onto s'. The set

$$g = \{\langle x, u\rangle \in a \times s\colon\ (u \in x) \wedge (v)_x(f^{-1}(u) \leqslant f^{-1}(v))\}$$

belongs to A because the binary relation which an element x in A bears to an element u in A if and only if $(u \in x) \wedge (v)_x(f^{-1}(u) \leqslant f^{-1}(v))$ is parametrically definable in A. For every x in a there is exactly one element $u \in x$ such that $f^{-1}(u)$ is the least ordinal in the set $\{f^{-1}(v)\colon\ v \in x\}$. Hence g is a function and $\mathrm{Im}(g, a)$ is a selector of a. Since $\mathrm{Im}(g, a) \in A$,, the theorem is proved.

We notice the following corollary:

1.4. *If A is a model of* ZF *and F a one-to-one mapping of A into $\pi(A)$ which is parametrically definable in A, then* AC *is true in A.*

PROOF. Let s be an element of A. The following set of ordered pairs

$$f = F^{-1}|\mathrm{Im}(F, s) = \{\langle u, v\rangle \in \mathrm{Im}(F, s) \times s\colon\ F(v) = u\}$$

is obviously a mapping of the set $\mathrm{Im}(F, s)$ consisting of ordinals onto the set s. Moreover f belongs to A since F is parametrically definable in A. Hence, by 1.3, AC is true in A.

We can now construct models of ZF in which AC is true.

1.5. *If B satisfies conditions* (B.0)–(B.6) *of* III.2–III.4 *and a is any transitive sequence, then* AC *is true in $K^B(a)$; also it is true in $C_\alpha^B(a)$ provided that $C_\alpha^B(a)$ is a model of* ZF *and a is a transitive sequence whose domain is $< \alpha$.*

PROOF. We showed in III.5.3 that $K^B(a)$ and $C^B_\alpha(a)$ have the property stated in 1.3.

Remark: In theorem 1.5 we do not need any form of definability of the function B.

To give a concrete application of 1.5 we take $B = B^Z$ and $a = 0$ and obtain from theorem 1.5 an example of a model in which AC is true. Hence

1.6. AC *is consistent with* ZF.

This theorem was first proved by Gödel in [12].

If B satisfies only the conditions (B.0)–(B.5), then, as we shall see in Chapter XIV, AC need not be true in each model of the form $C^B_\alpha(a)$. Here we shall discuss conditions which ensure the validity of AC in those models.

In all subsequent theorems we assume that B is a uniformly definable function which satisfies conditions (B.0)–(B.4). For each A we define a mapping of A into $\pi(A)$:

$$\mathrm{Od}^B(A, a, x) = \min\{\xi < \pi(A)\colon x = C^B_\xi(a)\}.$$

Thus $\mathrm{Od}^B(A, a, x)$ is the smallest ordinal $\xi < \pi(A)$ such that x is the ξth constructible set.

It is clear that if A is a model of ZF and a a fixed sequence, then the function $f(x) = \mathrm{Od}^B(A, a, x)$ maps $C^B_{\pi(A)}(a)$ into $\pi(A)$ and is one-to-one. Hence if it could be shown that f is parametrically definable in $C^B_{\pi(A)}(a)$, we could infer by 1.4 that AC is valid in the model $C^B_{\pi(A)}(a)$.

1.7. *The functor* Od^B *is strongly definable.*

This is an immediate result of the strong definability of the functor π and of the uniform definability of $C^B_\xi(a)$ (cf. IV.3.11 and V.3.7).

From the definition of Od we infer that:

1.8. *For almost all A if $a \in \mathrm{Str}(A)$ and x, y are different elements of $C^B_{\pi(A)}(a)$, then $\mathrm{Od}^B(A, a, x) \neq \mathrm{Od}^B(A, a, y)$.*

From theorems 1.7 and 1.8 we can now deduce the criterion:

1.9. *If A is a model of* ZF *and a a transitive sequence which belongs to A and to $C^B_{\pi(A)}(a)$, then* AC *is true in $C^B_{\pi(A)}(a)$.*

PROOF. We put $A' = C^B_{\pi(A)}(a)$. Hence A' is a model of ZF, $a \in A'$ and therefore by 1.8 the function f defined by the equation

$$f(x) = \mathrm{Od}^B(A', a, x)$$

is a one-to-one mapping of A' into $\pi(A) = \pi(A')$. By 1.7 this mapping is parametrically definable in A'. Theorem 1.9 results thus from 1.4.

Quite similar is the proof of the following theorem:

1.10. *If a is a transitive sequence such that $a \in K^B(a)$, then* AC *is true in $K^B(a)$.*

In particular we see that AC is true in $K^B(0)$ and also in each model of the form $C^B_\alpha(0)$. Also AC is true in $K^B(a)$ and in each model of the form $C^B_\alpha(a)$ if the sequence a is obtained from a sequence Q which belongs to $K^B(0)$ or to $C^B_\alpha(0)$ by adding to Q a finite number of terms (cf. V.5.4).

2. Auxiliary functors

In the rest of this chapter we shall be concerned with the generalized continuum hypothesis. We shall formulate it and prove that it is valid in some of the models $C^B_{\pi(A)}(a)$ and $K^B(a)$.

Before approaching this subject we must introduce a number of auxiliary functors and relations.

DEFINITION 1. For an arbitrary class A and a, b in A we say that *a is A-embeddable in b* if there is in A a one-to-one function f with domain a and a range contained in b. We then write $|a| \leqslant_A |b|$.

DEFINITION 2. $\aleph(A, a) = \min\{\xi \in On\colon\ \neg(|\xi| \leqslant_A |a|)\}$.

The existence of $\aleph(A, a)$ follows from well-known theorems of set theory. We do not claim at this place that $\aleph(A, a) \in A$.

2.1. *For almost all A the relation $\leqslant_A$ is reflexive and transitive; also if $a_1 \in A$ and $a_1 \subseteq a$ and $|a| \leqslant_A |b|$, then $|a_1| \leqslant_A |b|$.*

PROOF. Almost all sets A are closed with respect to the composition of functions and contain with each a the identity mapping of a onto itself.

2.2. *For almost all A and a in A if $\eta < \xi \in \aleph(A, a)$, then $\eta \in \aleph(A, a)$.*

The proof is obtained immediately from 2.1.

DEFINITION 3. For an arbitrary relation R which totally orders a set $\subseteq a$ we denote by $\mathrm{Num}(R, a, \xi)$ the unique function such that $\mathrm{Num}(R, a, \xi)$ is the first element x of a which succeeds all elements $\mathrm{Num}(R, a, \eta)$, $\eta < \xi$, provided that such an element exists; otherwise $\mathrm{Num}(R, a, \xi) = a$ (the terms "first", "succeeds" etc. are meant relatively to the ordering R).

2.3. Num *is a uniformly definable function.*

PROOF. We apply theorem V.1.2 on transfinite induction by taking for C the class On of all ordinals, for ϱ the relation $\leqslant$ in On and for Y the function of three variables whose value $Y(R, a, x)$ is a if either R is not a total order of a subset of a or x is not a function or if there is no first element of $\mathrm{Dom}(R)$ which succeeds all the elements of $\mathrm{Rg}(x)$. Otherwise $Y(R, a, x)$ is that first element.

The uniformly definable function X which satisfies the equation

$$X(R, a, \xi) = Y\big(R, a, X|(\{R\}\times\{a\}\times\xi)\big)$$

is then the required function Num.

2.4. *The functor* $\aleph(A, a)$ *is strongly definable of the second kind.*

PROOF. For R, a in A and x in $\mathrm{Dom}(R)$ we put

$$g(A, R, a, x) = \min\{\xi < \pi(A)\colon \mathrm{Num}(R, a, \xi) = x\},$$

$$h(A, a) = \sup\big\{g(A, R, a, x)\colon \big(x \in \mathrm{Dom}(R)\big) \wedge \big(R \in A \cap P(a\times a)\big)\big\}.$$

Both these functors are strongly definable of the second kind (see IV.3 examples 18, 19). We claim that $h(A, a) = \aleph(A, a)$ for almost all A and arbitrary a in A.

To see this we notice that if $\xi \in \aleph(A, a)$, then there is a function f in A which embeds ξ in a. It follows that there is for almost all A a relation $R \subseteq a\times a$ which belongs to A and orders its field in type ξ. Hence for each $\eta < \xi$ there are elements x in the field of R for which $\mathrm{Num}(R, a, \eta) = x$ and therefore $\sup\{g(A, R, a, x)\colon x \in \mathrm{Dom}(R)\} \geqslant \xi$. It follows that $h(A, a) > \xi$ and hence $h(A, a) \geqslant \aleph(A, a)$.

If $\xi \in h(A, a)$, then there is an ordering relation R with field $a_1 \subseteq a$ such that $R \in A$ and for some x in $\mathrm{Dom}(R)$ the condition $g(A, R, a, x) \geqslant \xi$ is satisfied. It follows that there is a relation which well-orders a subset of a in order type ξ; this relation R_1 is obtained from R by restricting its field to elements which precede x. Hence $R_1 \in A$ provided that A is closed under the operation of forming a relation restricted to a set. Theorem 2.4 is thus proved.

Theorem 2.4 and its proof are just a repetition of simple facts of elementary set theory. We shall need similar reformulation of certain theorems concerning elementary properties of cardinals.

2.5. *For almost all A if $\omega \leqslant \xi \in \pi(A)$, then $|\xi \cdot 2| \leqslant_A |\xi|$ (see V.2.2).*

PROOF. Each infinite ordinal can be represented as $\omega^\eta \cdot n + \varrho$ where $\varrho < \omega^\eta$. Hence $\xi \cdot 2 = \omega^\eta \cdot 2n + \varrho$.

Now define a relation R with field $\xi \cdot 2$ such that ordinals between $\omega^\eta \cdot 2n$ and $\omega^\eta \cdot 2n+\varrho$ form an initial segment of $\xi \cdot 2$ under R and the ordinals $< \omega^\eta \cdot 2n$ its final segment. Then the function $\mathrm{Num}(R, \xi, \alpha) = \varphi(\alpha)$, $\alpha < \omega^\eta \cdot 2n$, establishes a one-to-one mapping of $\omega^\eta \cdot 2n$ onto $\xi \cdot 2$. Since R obviously belongs to A for almost all A, we find that $\varphi \in A$ and also $\varphi^{-1} \in A$. This proves that $|\xi \cdot 2| \leqslant_A |\omega^\eta \cdot 2n|$.

Using a lexicographical ordering of pairs (λ, μ) where $\lambda < \omega^\eta$, $\mu < 2n$, we prove in the same way that $|\omega^\eta \cdot 2n| \leqslant_A |\omega^\eta \cdot n|$ and hence $|\xi \cdot 2| \leqslant_A |\omega^\eta \cdot n| \leqslant_A |\xi|$.

Using similar methods we can also prove that:

2.6. *For almost all A if $r < \omega \leqslant \xi < \pi(A)$, then $|\xi^n| \leqslant_A |\xi^n \cdot r| \leqslant_A |\xi|$.*

The details of this proof are more complicated and we shall not stop to give them here because essentially the theorem (as well as the two preceding ones) is obvious: it is well known from elementary set theory that if ξ is an infinite ordinal, then ξ and $\xi^n \cdot r$ are of the same power. This fact can be deduced from a finite number of axioms and hence is valid in almost every A. Thus almost every A contains a one-to-one function which maps $\xi^n \cdot r$ onto ξ. We could have proved theorems 2.4 and 2.5 in the same way but since the direct proofs were not too long, we preferred to produce them instead.

To finish these auxiliary investigations we shall prove one more result, which we shall need in Section 5.

2.7. *If a is a transitive sequence, ξ an infinite ordinal $\geqslant \mathrm{Dom}(a) = \alpha$ and X a finite set, then for almost all A containing a, X and ξ as elements:*

$$\left|X \cup \mathrm{Dom}(a) \cup \mathrm{Rg}(a) \cup \bigcup a \cup a \cup \xi\right| \leqslant_A |\xi|.$$

PROOF. The set a consists of ordered pairs $\langle\zeta, a_\zeta\rangle$. The set $\bigcup a$ consists of unordered pairs $\{\zeta, a_\zeta\}$ and of singletons $\{\zeta\}$. Thus $\bigcup a$ can be represented as the union $V_1 \cup V_2$ where V_1 is the set of singletons and V_2 of unordered pairs.

The sequence a is a mapping of $\mathrm{Dom}(a)$ onto $\mathrm{Rg}(a)$; this mapping is not necessarily a one-to-one mapping but we can easily transform it into a one-to-one mapping of a subset of $\mathrm{Dom}(a)$ onto $\mathrm{Rg}(a)$ by omitting from a those pairs $\langle\zeta, a_\zeta\rangle$ for which there is an ordinal $\eta < \zeta$ satisfying the equation $a_\eta = a_\zeta$. The resulting function

$$a' = \{\langle u, v\rangle \in a\colon \neg(E\eta)_u(\langle\eta, v\rangle \in a)\}$$

belongs to A for almost all A. Thus we obtain

$$|\mathrm{Rg}(a)| \leqslant_A |\mathrm{Dom}(a)| \leqslant_A |\xi|.$$

Considering the functions

$$\{\langle u, \{u\}\rangle\colon u \in \mathrm{Dom}(a)\},$$

$$\{\langle u, \{u, v\}\rangle\colon \langle u, v\rangle \in a\},$$

$$\{\langle u, \langle u, v\rangle\rangle\colon \langle u, v\rangle \in a\},$$

which also belong to A for almost all A, we convince ourselves that $|a| \leqslant_A |\xi|$ and $|V_1| \leqslant_A |\xi|$ and $|V_2| \leqslant_A |\xi|$. Since obviously $|X \cup \xi| \leqslant_A |\xi|$, we finally infer that the set $s = X \cup \mathrm{Rg}(a) \cup \bigcup a \cup a \cup \xi \cup \mathrm{Dom}(a)$ satisfies the formula $|s| \leqslant_A |\xi \cdot 6|$. In view of 2.5 we obtain $|s| \leqslant_A |\xi|$ for almost all A.

3. Formulation of the generalized continuum hypothesis

As in Section 1, we start our discussion of the generalized continuum hypothesis by formulating it in the language of ZF. The formulae which one obtains here are much more involved. than those occurring in the case discussed in Section 1. Fortunately we do not need to write down all these formulae explicitly. Of many of them it is sufficient to know that they define certain strongly definable functors in the sense explained in Chapter IV. It will therefore be sufficient to select arbitrary formulae defining those functors. If the strong definability of a functor has already been proved, then the existence of its definition is ensured and we shall simply note that we select one of those definitions. It will be convenient to employ, as in Chapter IV, the notational device consisting in denoting a definition of a strongly definable functor by the same symbol as the functor but printed in bold type.

In writing the abbreviations which follow we shall assume that i, j are integers and $k = i+j+1$, $p = i+1$, $q = i+2$, $r = i+3$.

(i) $\mathbf{Fn}_1(x_i)$: $\mathbf{Fn}(x_i) \wedge (x_p)(x_q)(x_r)\{[(\langle x_p, x_q\rangle \in x_i) \wedge \wedge (\langle x_p, x_r\rangle \in x_i)] \to (x_q = x_r)\}$;

(ii) $x_i \subseteq x_j$: $(x_k)[(x_k \in x_i) \to (x_k \in x_j)]$;

(iii) $|x_i| \leqslant |x_j|$: $(Ex_k)[\mathbf{Fn}_1(x_k) \wedge (\mathbf{dl}(x_k) = x_i) \wedge (\mathbf{dp}(x_k) \subseteq x_j)]$;

(iv) $\mathbf{Sc}(x_i, x_j)$: $\mathbf{Ord}(x_j) \wedge \neg(|x_j| \leqslant |x_i|) \wedge \wedge (x_p)[(x_p \in x_j) \to (|x_p| \leqslant |x_i|)]$;

(v) $|\omega| \leqslant |x_i|$: $(Ex_p)(Ex_q)[(x_q \in x_p) \wedge \mathbf{Lim}(x_p) \wedge (|x_p| \leqslant |x_i|)]$;

(vi) $G(x_i)$: $\mathbf{Ord}(x_i) \wedge (x_p)(x_q)\{\mathbf{Sc}(x_i, x_p) \wedge \wedge (x_r)[(x_r \in x_q) \equiv (x_r \subseteq x_i)] \to (|x_q| \leqslant |x_p|)\}$.

As in Chapter I, so in the rest of this chapter we shall relax somewhat the rules of writing formulae and replace the variables x_i by arbitrary letters.

The notation in (i)–(vi) is chosen so as to make the formulae as readable as possible. From the methodical point of view, however, our choice of notation is objectionable. A formula like, say, $|x_i| \leqslant |x_j|$ is an object depending on two integers i, j and a natural symbol for such an object would be a letter with two indices, e.g., P_{ij}. Such notation, while less readable, would be much more convenient in writing meta-mathematical statements, especially the ones in which we deal with the satisfaction relation. For instance $\vdash_A P_{ij}[a, b]$ is a much more handy way of notation than

$$(*) \qquad \vdash_A (|x_i| \leqslant |x_j|)[a, b].$$

In order to improve the situation we shall agree that $(*)$ is to be written as $\vdash_A |a| \leqslant |b|$ and we shall use similar self-explanatory conventions also in the case of other formulae.

The next lemma explains the meaning of formulae (i)–(vi).

3.1. *For almost all* A *and arbitrary* a, b *in* A *the following equivalences hold*:

$$\vdash_A (a \subseteq b) \equiv (a \subseteq b);$$

$$\vdash_A \mathbf{Fn}_1[a] \equiv (a \text{ is a one-to-one function});$$

$$\vdash_A (|a| \leqslant |b|) \equiv (|a| \leqslant_A |b|);$$

$$\vdash_A \mathbf{Sc}[a, b] \equiv (b < \pi(A)) \wedge (b = \aleph(A, a));$$

$$\vdash_A \boldsymbol{G}[a] \equiv (a < \pi(A)) \wedge (b)\,[(b = \aleph(A, a)) \rightarrow (|A \cap P(a)| \leqslant_A |b|)].$$

The proof of this lemma is straightforward and need not be given in full.

By the *general continuum hypothesis* we understand the formula:

$$\text{GCH}: (x)[\mathbf{Ord}(x) \wedge (|\omega| \leqslant |x|) \rightarrow \boldsymbol{G}(x)].$$

We mention that it is also easy to formulate special cases of the continuum hypothesis. They all have the form $(x)[\boldsymbol{O}(x) \rightarrow \boldsymbol{G}(x)]$ where $\boldsymbol{O}(x)$ is a formula which describes an ordinal. For instance, if we want to formulate the ordinary continuum hypothesis we take as $\boldsymbol{O}(x)$ the formula

$$\boldsymbol{O}_0(x): (Ez)(z \in x) \wedge \mathbf{Lim}\,(x) \wedge (y)(z)\{[(z \in y) \wedge (y \in x)] \rightarrow \neg\, \mathbf{Lim}(y)\}$$

which defines ω in almost all sets A. In order to express the hypothesis which in the usual language of set theory is written as $2^{\aleph_1} = \aleph_2$ we take as $\boldsymbol{O}$ the formula $(Ey)[\boldsymbol{O}_0(y) \wedge \mathbf{Sc}(y, x)]$, etc. Since the number of formulae is denumerable, we can express in this way at most denumerably many special cases of the continuum hypothesis.

4. A sufficient condition for the validity of GCH

We assume the following model-theoretic definition:

For every class A we say that the *continuum hypothesis is valid in* A *for the ordinal* ξ if $\xi \in On \cap A$ and $\vdash_A \boldsymbol{G}[\xi]$.

Thus $\vdash_A$GCH is equivalent to the statement that the continuum hypothesis is valid in A for each infinite ordinal ξ in $On \cap A$.

We shall formulate a sufficient condition for the continuum hypothesis to be valid in A for an ordinal ξ.

4.1. *If A is a model of* ZF, $\omega \leqslant \xi < \pi(A)$ *and φ is a one-to-one mapping of A into $\pi(A)$ which is parametrically definable in A and which has the property*

$$(x \in P(\xi) \cap A) \to |\varphi(x)| \leqslant_A |\xi|,$$

then the continuum hypothesis is valid in A for ξ.

PROOF. We denote $P(\xi) \cap A$ by z and $\aleph(A, \xi)$ by η. We have to show that z is A-embeddable in η. According to the assumptions of the theorem, each element of $\text{Im}(\varphi, z)$ is an ordinal which is A-embeddable in ξ and hence $< \eta$ (cf. 2.2). Therefore $\text{Im}(\varphi, z)$ is contained in η, and since φ is one-to-one and is parametrically definable in A, we find that z is A-embeddable in η.

5. Construction of models in which the continuum hypothesis is valid

In this section we outline in general terms the method of construction of models in which the assumptions of theorem 4.1 are satisfied for all or for some ordinals. As a result of this discussion we shall formulate some auxiliary problems, upon the solution of which depend the success of our construction. These problems will be solved in Sections 6 and 7, and in Section 8 we shall be able to achieve the construction.

We assume in this section that A is a model of ZF, B is a uniformly definable function satisfying conditions (B.0)–(B.4) and a is a transitive sequence which belongs to A and to $C^B_{\pi(A)}(a)$. We abbreviate $C^B_{\pi(A)}(a)$ to A'.

We know from VI.3.1 that A' is a model of ZF and from 1.7, 1.8 that the function $\varphi(x) = \text{Od}^B(A', a, x)$ maps A' into $\pi(A)$, is one-to-one and is parametrically definable in A'. The unique parameter which occurs in the definition of φ is a; we needed the assumption that $a \in A'$ just in order to ensure that the parameter belongs to A'. It is natural to inquire whether the function φ satisfies the assumptions of 4.1, i.e., whether it maps the set $A' \cap P(\xi)$ into $\aleph(A', \xi)$. We shall show that this is the case provided that $\omega \leqslant \xi < \pi(A)$ and $|\text{Dom}(a)| \leqslant_{A'} |\xi|$.

Let us see how we could prove this statement. We take an arbitrary set b in A' which is a subset of ξ; thus $b = C^B_\beta(a)$. We have to evaluate the minimal β_0 such that $b = C^B_{\beta_0}(a)$ and to show that $|\beta_0| \leqslant_{A'} |\xi|$ or, which amounts to the same, that $\beta_0 < \aleph(A', \xi)$.

To achieve this we consider the set

$$s = \xi \cup \mathrm{Rg}(a) \cup \{a, b\} \cup a \cup \bigcup a \cup \mathrm{Dom}(a),$$

which obviously belongs to A'. We know from 2.7 that

$$|s| \leqslant_{A'} |\xi|.$$

It is easily derivable from V.3.4 that if P is the formula

$$P\colon\ (x)(Ey)[\mathbf{Ord}\,(y) \wedge \mathbf{constr}^B(ax, y, z)],$$

then

(1) $$\vdash_{A'} P[a].$$

To see this we notice that A' is a model of ZF and $a \in A'$; hence if x has the form $C^B_\xi(a)$ and $\xi < \pi(A)$, then by IV.3.11 and V.3.4 we obtain $\vdash_{A'} \mathbf{Ord}[\xi]$ and $\vdash_{A'} \mathbf{constr}^B[x, \xi, a]$. Since for every x in A' there is a $\xi < \pi(A) = \pi(A')$ such that x has the form $C^B_\xi(a)$, we obtain (1).

The main step in the proof is now to find a set m^* which satisfies the following conditions:

(2) $$s \subseteq m^* \in A',$$

(3) m^* is transitive,

(4) $$|m^*| \leqslant_{A'} |\xi|,$$

(5) $$\vdash_{m^*} P[a],$$

(6) a given finite number of axioms $K_1, \ldots, K_r$ of ZF are valid in m^*.

If a set m^* with these properties can be found for arbitrarily given axioms $K_1, \ldots, K_r$, then it is not difficult to show that φ satisfies the assumptions of 4.1 and hence that the continuum hypothesis is valid in A' for ξ. To see this we fix the axioms $K_1, \ldots, K_r$ as in V.3.4 and infer from (3), (5), (6) that for each element of m^* there is an ordinal α in m^* such that $x = C^B_\alpha(a)$. Since $b \in s$ it follows by (2) that b can be represented as $C^B_\alpha(a)$ with α in m^*. From the transitivity of m^* it follows that $\alpha \subseteq m^*$, whence, by (4), $|\alpha| \leqslant_{A'} |\xi|$. Since $\varphi(b) = \beta_0 \leqslant \alpha$ we obtain $\varphi(b) < \aleph(A', \xi)$.

What are now the chances of finding an m^* with the required properties? If we could find a set m in A' which would satisfy the conditions

(7) $$|m| \leqslant_{A'} |\xi| \quad \text{and} \quad s \subseteq m \prec A',$$

then the problem of finding the required m^* would be reducible to simple matters concerning the contracting function defined in I.6.

Let us assume for a moment that we have succeeded in finding an m in A' satisfying (7). Contracting m as described in I.6.1 we would find a set m^* which would obviously satisfy (3). Since a is not changed by a contraction of any set containing s (see I.6.3) we would also obtain (5) and (6) directly from (7). Finally (2) and (4) could also be obtained from (7) since it can be shown that the contracting function for a set m which belongs to a model of ZF is itself an element of that model.

Unfortunately the plan outlined above cannot be carried out because we cannot prove that an element of A' is its elementary sub-model.

However, the essential features of the plan can be saved. We observe that m need not be the full elementary sub-set of A'. What we really need is a set m in A' for which $s \subseteq m$, $|m| \leqslant_{A'} |\xi|$ and which satisfies the condition that for a single formula H (the conjunction of P and of the axioms $K_1, \ldots, K_r$) the equivalence

$$\vdash_m H[z] \equiv \vdash_{A'} H[z]$$

be true for each z in $m^{\mathrm{Fr}(H)}$. We shall call a set m which satisfies this condition an *H-elementary sub-set of A'*. Thus the success of our construction depends on the existence of H-elementary sub-sets of a given model A', which, moreover, are A'-embeddable in a given ordinal.

The existence of H-elementary sub-sets of a model will be proved in Section 7 essentially by repeating the proof of the Skolem–Löwenheim theorem, which we discussed in I.3. We shall have to take special care that all constructions leading to the required set be performable within the given model of ZF (in our case within A').

We devote the next section to the rather easy problem connected with the existence of the contracting function in a model of ZF. In Section 7 we return to the problem of the Skolem–Löwenheim theorem.

6. Definability of the contracting function

In Section 6 of Chapter I we proved that for every set m in which axiom (I) (of extensionality) is valid there is exactly one function f (the contracting function of m) such that $f(m_0) = 0$ if m_0 is the minimal element of m and $f(x) = \mathrm{Im}(f, x \cap m)$ for all elements of m. We now want to prove that this function f belongs to A for almost all A and arbitrary m in A.

From theorem IV.4.2 (on functors defined by transfinite induction) we infer that there is a strongly definable functor F of the second kind with three arguments which satisfies for almost all A the following inductive equations:

$$F(A, m, 0) = 0,$$

$$F(A, m, \xi+1) = F(A, m, \xi) \cup$$
$$\cup\{\langle x, \operatorname{Im}(F(A, m, \xi), m \cap x)\rangle : x \in m \cap R_{\xi+1} - R_\xi\},$$

$$F(A, m, \lambda) = \bigcup \{F(A, m, \xi) : \xi < \lambda\} \quad \text{if} \quad \lambda \in \operatorname{Lim}(A).$$

These equations hold for arbitrary m in A and ξ, λ in $\pi(A)$.

From the strong definability of F it follows that:

6.1. *For almost all A and arbitrary m in A, ξ in $\pi(A)$*

$$F(A, m, \xi) \in A.$$

Further properties of $F(A, m, \xi)$ which also hold for almost every A are the following:

6.2. $F(A, m, \xi) \subseteq F(A, m, \eta)$ *for* $\xi \leqslant \eta$. *Moreover,* $F(A, m, \xi)$ *is a function with domain* $m \cap R_\xi$.

The proof of 6.2 is obvious.

6.3. *For almost every A and all m in A, ξ in $\pi(A)$ if $x \in m \cap R_\xi$, then the value of $F(A, m, \xi)$ for the argument x is* $\operatorname{Im}(F(A, m, \xi), m \cap x)$.

PROOF. Let the rank of x be α. Hence $\alpha+1$ is the minimal index such that $x \in R_{\alpha+1}$ and therefore $F(A, m, \xi)$ is an extension of $F(A, m, \alpha+1)$. From the definition of $F(A, m, \alpha+1)$ we infer that the required value is

$$\operatorname{Im}(F(A, m, \alpha), m \cap x) = \operatorname{Im}(F(A, m, \xi), m \cap x).$$

6.4. *For almost all A and all m in A, ξ in $\pi(A)$ if $m \in A \cap R_\xi$ and axiom* (I) *is valid in m, then $F(A, m, \xi)$ is the contracting function for m.*

PROOF. Put $\varphi = F(A, m, \xi)$. From 6.3 it follows that (for almost all A) $\varphi(x) = \operatorname{Im}(\varphi, x \cap m)$ whenever $x \in m$. Since the contracting function for m satisfies the same equation and is unique, we obtain the required result.

From 6.4. and 6.1 we infer that:

6.5. *If A is a model of* ZF, *$m \in A$ and axiom* (I) *is valid in m, then the contracting function for m belongs to A.*

In I.6 we saw that if $s \subseteq m$ and s is transitive, then the contracting function of m maps every element of s onto itself. In particular we infer from this remark that:

6.6. *If a is a transitive sequence, $\xi \in On$ and $b \subseteq \xi$, then the set*

$$\{a, b\} \cup \xi \cup \mathrm{Rg}(a) \cup \bigcup a \cup a \cup \mathrm{Dom}(a)$$

is transitive and hence for each m such that $m \supseteq s$ the contracting function of m maps every element of s onto itself.

7. A refinement of the Skolem–Löwenheim theorem

We assume in this section that $R(A, p)$ is a strongly definable functor of the first kind and that for almost all A and arbitrary p in A^n the set $R(A, p)$ is a relation which orders A.

Let us repeat a definition introduced in Section 5: *A set $m \in A$ is an H-elementary sub-set of A* if for all $z \in m^{\mathrm{Fr}(H)}$

$$\vdash_m H[z] \equiv \vdash_A H[z].$$

Another definition which will be of use is as follows. Let $f(A, p, x)$ be a functor of the second kind with $1+n+k$ variables and let A be a set, $p \in A^n$. We shall say that *a set $m \in A$ is closed under $f(A, p, \cdot)$* if $f(A, p, x) \in m$ for arbitrary x in m^k.

7.1. *For each formula H there are finitely many strongly definable functors of the second kind $f_i(A, p, x)$, $i = 1, 2, \ldots, h$, such that for almost all A and arbitrary p in A and m in A the following is true: either $R(A, p)$ is not a well-ordering of A; or m is not closed under $f_j(A, p, \cdot)$, $j = 1, 2, \ldots, h$; or m is an H-elementary sub-set of A.*

Proof. If H is an atomic formula, then we take just one functor $f_1(A, p, x) = x$. If H is $\neg H_1$ or $(x_i)H_1$ where $i \notin \mathrm{Fr}(H_1)$, take as $f_1, \ldots, f_h$ the functors which were correlated with H_1. If H is $H_1 \wedge H_2$, then we take as $f_1, \ldots, f_h$ all the functors which were correlated with H_1 and those which were correlated with H_2. It remains to consider the case where H is the formula $(x_i)H_1$ and x_i is free in H_1. In this case we join to the functors correlated with H_1 one more functor, let us call it g, which has $n+1+q$ arguments where q is the number of free variables of H. If $x \in A^{\mathrm{Fr}(H)}$, then we take as $g(A, p, x)$ the first element y of A such that $\vdash_A \neg H_1[\{\langle i, y\rangle\} \cup x]$ provided that $R(A, p)$ orders A and the first element y of the indicated kind exists; otherwise we put $g(A, p, x) = 0$. It is obvious from this definition that g is a strongly definable functor of the second kind. For almost all A and for all p such that $R(A, p)$ is a well-ordering of A we infer that if $m \in A$, m is closed under $g(A, p, \cdot)$ and $z \in m^{\mathrm{Fr}(H)}$, then

$$\vdash_A H[z] \equiv (y)_m \vdash_A H_1[\{\langle i, y\rangle\} \cup z].$$

By the inductive assumption it follows that the right-hand side is equivalent to $\vdash_m H[z]$ provided that m is also closed under functors correlated with H_1. Theorem 7.1 is thus proved.

7.2. *Let f_j, $j = 1, 2, \ldots, h$, be strongly definable functors of the second kind with $1+n+r$ arguments. For almost all A and for all $p \in A^n$, $s \in A$, $\xi \in \pi(A)$ there is in A a set $m \supseteq s$ closed under the functors $f_j(A, p, \cdot)$, $j = 1, 2, \ldots, h$; moreover, if $|s| \leqslant_A |\xi|$ and $\omega \subseteq \xi$, then there exists an m closed under the $f_j(A, p, \cdot)$ and such that $|m| \leqslant_A |\xi|$.*

We can assume that one of the functors, say f_1, is defined by $f_1(A, p, x_1, \ldots, x_r) = x_1$.

We use (ordinary) induction and define a sequence ψ_k such that

$$\psi_0 = s, \qquad \psi_{k+1} = \bigcup_{1 \leqslant j \leqslant h} \{f_j(A, p, x)\colon\ x \in \psi_k^r\}. \tag{1}$$

The sequence ψ_i belongs to A for almost all A and for arbitrary p in A^n, s in A. To see this we apply the theorem IV.4.2 on transfinite induction taking as $S(A)$ the set ω, and as $R(A)$ the relation $\leqslant$ limited to ω. Let F be the function

$$F(A, p, s, y) = \begin{cases} s & \text{if } y = 0 \text{ or } y \text{ is not a sequence} \\ & \qquad \text{with } \mathrm{Dom}(y) \in \omega, \\ \bigcup\limits_{1 \leqslant j \leqslant h} \{f_j(A, p, x)\colon\ x \in y(k)^r\} & \text{if } y \text{ is a sequence} \\ & \qquad \text{with } \mathrm{Dom}(y) = k+1 \in \omega. \end{cases}$$

Since the functor F is strongly definable we infer that there is a strongly definable functor ψ such that

$$\psi(A, p, s, 0) = s,$$

$$\psi(A, p, s, k+1) = \bigcup_{1 \leqslant j \leqslant h} \{f_j(A, p, x) \colon x \in \psi(A, p, s, k)^r\}.$$

Thus in order to satisfy (1) it is sufficient to take $\psi_k = \psi(A, p, s, k)$ for $k \in \omega$. The set $m = \bigcup \{\psi_i \colon i < \omega\}$ is closed under the $f_j(A, p, \cdot)$ and belongs to A.

Note that because of our choice of f_1 we have $\psi_k \subseteq \psi_{k+1}$, which implies $s \subseteq m$.

We now prove the statement concerning the mapping of ξ onto m. To obtain this result we assume that $s \neq 0$ and $|s| \leqslant_A |\xi|$ and we consider a function which embeds s into ξ. For $\zeta < \xi$ let us denote by $\varphi_0(\zeta)$ the element of s mapped onto ζ provided that such an element exists; otherwise we put $\varphi_0(\zeta) = s_0$ where s_0 is a fixed element of s. Function φ_0 belongs to A for almost all A.

We also consider a mapping σ of ξ onto $\xi^r \cdot h$ (cf. 2.6) of which we can assume that it belongs to A. We denote the image of ζ under this mapping by $\langle \zeta^{(1)}, \ldots, \zeta^{(r)}, j_\zeta \rangle$. Functions which correlate $\zeta^{(i)}$ and j_ζ with ζ are elements of A for almost all A. Now we define by induction a sequence of mappings with domain ξ such that $\mathrm{Im}(\varphi_i, \xi) = \psi_i$, where the ψ_i are defined in (1). The mapping φ_0 was defined above; for $i \geqslant 0$ we put

$$\varphi_{i+1}(\zeta) = f_{j_\zeta+1}\big(A, p, \varphi_i(\zeta^{(1)}), \ldots, \varphi_i(\zeta^{(r)})\big).$$

By induction we prove that with ζ ranging over ξ the elements $\varphi_i(\zeta)$ range over ψ_i. From theorem IV.4.2 on transfinite induction it follows that for almost all A the sequence of functions φ_i belongs to A.

Now for $\xi \cdot i \leqslant \zeta < \xi \cdot (i+1)$ we put

$$\varphi(\zeta) = \varphi_i(\zeta - \xi i)$$

and obtain a mapping which belongs to A, has the domain $\xi\omega$ and the range $\bigcup \psi_i = m$. Hence there is in A a mapping $\bar{\varphi}$ of ξ onto m because $|\xi\omega| \leqslant_A |\xi|$ for almost all A and for ξ in A.

The mapping $\overline{\varphi}$ is not necessarily one-to-one but we may correct it slightly so as to obtain a one-to-one mapping. We simply put

$$\overline{\overline{\varphi}} = \{\langle\zeta, u\rangle \in \overline{\varphi}\colon (\varrho)_\zeta(\langle\varrho, u\rangle \notin \overline{\varphi})\}\,.$$

This function is one-to-one and has the same range as $\overline{\varphi}$. Since $\overline{\overline{\varphi}}$ and $\overline{\overline{\varphi}}^{-1}$ belong to A for almost all A we find that $|m| \leqslant_A |\xi|$.

We now apply theorems 7.1 and 7.2 to obtain a set m described in Section 5. We continue to use the symbol A' for $C^B_{\pi(A)}(a)$.

7.3. *Assume that* A_0 *is a model of* ZF, a_0 *is a transitive sequence,* $a_0 \in C^B_{\pi(A_0)}(a_0) = A_0'$, $\omega \leqslant \xi < \pi(A_0)$, $s \in A_0'$ *and* $|s| \leqslant_{A_0'} |\xi|$. *Then for every formula H there exists a set* $m \in A_0'$ *such that*

(1) $$s \subseteq m, \quad |m| \leqslant_{A_0'} |\xi|,$$

(2) *m is an H-elementary sub-set of* A_0'.

PROOF. We take in 7.1

$$S(A, a) = \mathrm{Konstr}^B(A, a) = C^B_{\pi(A)}(a)$$

and

$$R(A, a) = \{\langle u, v\rangle \in S(A, a)^2\colon \mathrm{Od}^B(A, a, u) \leqslant \mathrm{Od}^B(A, a, v)\}\,.$$

The element a plays the role of a parameter; we can assume, if we wish, that if $a \notin \mathrm{Str}(A)$, then $R(A, a) = 0$. We correlate with the given formula H the functors $f_i(A, a, x)$ according to 7.1. Now we substitute for A, which until now was undetermined, the family $A_0' = C^B_{\pi(A_0)}(a_0)$ where A_0 is a given model of ZF; we also fix the value of the parameter a by choosing for it the given transitive sequence a_0 satisfying $a_0 \in A_0'$. Since $\pi(A_0') = \pi(A_0)$, we have $S(A_0', a_0) = A_0'$; moreover, $R(A_0', a_0)$ is a well-ordering of A_0' (cf. 1.8).

Now we use theorem 7.2 and obtain a set m in A_0' satisfying (1) and closed under the $f_i(A_0, a_0, \cdot)$. Since $R(A_0', a_0)$ is a well-ordering of A_0', it follows by 7.1 that m satisfies (2).

8. Consistency of GCH

With the help of theorems proved in Sections 6 and 7 we are now able to execute the plan described in Section 5.

8.1. *Let A be a model of* ZF, *B a uniformly definable function satisfying* (B.0)–(B.4) *and* a *a transitive sequence in A such that* $a \in A' = C^B_{\pi(A)}(a)$.

If ξ is an infinite ordinal $< \pi(A)$ such that $|\mathrm{Dom}(a)| \leqslant_{A'} |\xi|$, then the continuum hypothesis is valid in A' for ξ.

PROOF. We quickly repeat the steps described in Section 5. For x in A' we put $\varphi(x) = \mathrm{Od}^B(A', a, x)$. Since φ is parametrically definable in A' (cf. 1.7) and maps A' into $\pi(A')$ in a one-to-one way (cf. 1.8), we see from 4.1 that it is sufficient to prove the implication: if $b \in P(\xi) \cap A'$, then $|\varphi(b)| \leqslant_{A'} |\xi|$.

We denote by s the transitive set

$$s = \mathrm{Rg}(a) \cup \bigcup a \cup a \cup \xi \cup \{a, b\} \cup \mathrm{Dom}(a).$$

From 2.7 we obtain $|s| \leqslant_{A'} |\xi|$. Now we denote by $K_1, \ldots, K_r$ finitely many axioms of ZF which have the following property: whenever X is a transitive set in which these axioms are valid and x is a transitive sequence, $x \in X$ and $\eta \in X \cap On$, then

$$C_\eta^B(x) \in X,$$

$$y = C_\eta^B(x) \equiv \vdash_X \mathbf{constr}^B[y, \eta, x]$$

(cf. V.3.4). We can assume that axiom (I) of extensionality is among the axioms K_j. Since A' is a transitive set in which all these axioms are valid and since each element of A' has the form $C_\eta^B(a)$ with $\eta < \pi(A')$, we obtain

$$\vdash_{A'} P[a]$$

where P is the formula $(x_2)(Ex_1)[\mathbf{Ord}(x_1) \wedge \mathbf{constr}^B(x_2, x_1, x_0)]$.

We denote by H the conjunction of P and of the axioms $K_1, \ldots, K_r$. Using theorem 7.3 we obtain a set m in A' such that

$$s \subseteq m, \quad |m| \leqslant_{A'} |\xi|$$

and

$$\vdash_m H[a] \equiv \vdash_{A'} H[a].$$

Thus

(1) $$\vdash_m H[a]$$

because H is satisfied by a in A'.

Now let F be the contracting function for m. It is evident that the set $m^* = \mathrm{Im}(F, m)$ is transitive. By 6.5 F is an element of A' and hence $m^* \in A'$. Since F is one-to-one, we obtain $|m^*| \leqslant_{A'} |\xi|$. Finally $F(a) = a$

because $a \in s$, s is transitive and hence, by 6.6, F is the identity on s. Since F is an isomorphism, we infer from (1) that $\vdash_{m*} H[a]$ and hence the axioms $K_1, \ldots, K_r$ are valid in m^* and the formula P is satisfied in m^* by a. From this we infer that each element of m^* has the form $C_\eta^B(a)$ where $\eta \in m^*$.

Now we consider the element b. Since $b \subseteq \xi$ and $b \in s$, the contracting function F maps b onto itself. Hence $b \in m^*$ and, according to the remark above, b can be represented as $C_\eta^B(a)$ with $\eta \in m^*$. Hence $\varphi(b) \leqslant \eta \subseteq m^*$ and we obtain $|\varphi(b)| \leqslant_{A'} |\xi|$.

Theorem 8.1 is thus proved.

If we take in particular $a = 0$, we obtain from 8.1

8.2. *If A is a set, B is uniformly definable and satisfies* (B.0)–(B.4) *and A is a model of* ZF, *then* GCH *is valid in* $C_{\pi(A)}^B(0)$.

In the next two corollaries we assume that B is uniformly definable and satisfies (B.0)–(B.4):

8.3. *If a set A is a model of* ZF, *Q is a transitive sequence which belongs to $C_{\pi(A)}^B(0)$ and a is a transitive sequence obtained from Q by adjunction of a finite number of elements of A, then the continuum hypothesis is valid in $A' = C_{\pi(A)}^B(a)$ for all infinite ordinals $\xi < \pi(A)$ provided that* $|\mathrm{Dom}(Q)| \leqslant_{A'} |\xi|$.

8.4. *If a set A is a model of* ZF *and B a function satisfying the conditions* (B.0)–(B.6) *of* III.2 *and* III.4, *then for every transitive sequence a which belongs to A the continuum hypothesis is valid in $A' = C_{\pi(A)}^B(a)$ for any infinite ordinal $\xi < \pi(A)$ such that* $|\mathrm{Dom}(a)| \leqslant_{A'} |\xi|$.

To prove 8.3 and 8.4 it is sufficient to notice that under the assumptions of these theorems the sequence a is an element of A' and hence theorem 8.1 is applicable. It is worthwhile to stress that in 8.3 B can be any uniformly definable function satisfying conditions (B.0)–(B.4) while in 8.4 we need the additional assumption that this function satisfies conditions (B.5) and (B.6).

In our final theorem we construct a proper class in which GCH is valid:

8.5. *If B is uniformly definable and satisfies conditions* (B.0)–(B.6) *and a is any transitive sequence, then the continuum hypothesis is valid in $K^B(a)$ for any infinite ordinal ξ such that* $\mathrm{Dom}(a)$ *is $K^B(a)$-embeddable in ξ.*

To prove this remark we notice that $K^B(a)$ contains elementary subsets of the form $C^B_{\pi(A)}(a)$ which contain a as an element. See V.5.5 and III.3.7.

The above theorems provide us with various examples of models in which the continuum hypothesis is valid for all or for sufficiently great ordinals. From the existence of these models we obtain at once the famous result of Gödel [11], [13]:

8.6. *The conjunction of* AC *and* GCH *is consistent with* ZF.

9. Axioms of constructibility. Final remarks

The axiom of choice, which we proved to be consistent in 1.6, is accepted by most mathematicians as "true". The generalized continuum hypothesis is also consistent, as we saw above, but, to say the least, it is regarded with mistrust by most mathematicians. Still more dubious but also consistent with ZF are the hypotheses known under the general name of the *axioms of constructibility.*

The *weak axiom of constructibility* is the formula

$$\mathrm{C}: \quad (Ea)(x)(Ey)[\mathbf{Ord}(y) \wedge \mathbf{Str}(a) \wedge \mathbf{constr}^B(x, y, a)].$$

It says that there is a transitive sequence a such that each set is constructible in a. We can formulate this axiom for any uniformly definable function B which satisfies (B.0)-(B.4).

The *strong axiom of constructibility* first introduced by Gödel [11] says that each set is constructible from the void sequence 0:

$$\mathrm{C}^+: \quad (Ea)(x)(Ey)[\mathbf{Ord}(y) \wedge \mathbf{constr}^B(x, y, a) \wedge (z)\neg(z \in a)].$$

It is obvious that C follows from C^+. The consistency of C^+ is proved by noticing that this formula is true in $C^B_{\pi(A)}(0)$ where A is any model of ZF.

The axiom of constructibility C^+ has many startling consequences, especially in the descriptive theory of sets (cf. for instance Gödel [11], Addison [1]). The axioms of constructibility are thus extremely valuable as tools which allow us to show that certain hypotheses cannot be proved. Gödel, who introduced these axioms, had just this aim in mind. He did not claim that his axiom represents a "true" statement which should be added to the usual axioms of set theory. On the contrary, he expressly stated that the axiom of constructibility which he formulated is "evidently false" although consistent (see Gödel [12]).

It is not easy to answer the obvious question what is meant by the words "true" and "false" in the above remarks. Representatives of an important trend in the foundations of mathematics, the so called formalists, deny the possibility of an adequate explanation of these notions. They conceive of mathematics as of an assemblage of systems whose axioms can be accepted at will with the only limitation that no inconsistency should result from them. The so called platonists insist, on the contrary, that the notion of truth is as meaningful in set theory as in any other field of knowledge. It is not clear whose opinion will eventually prevail. The reluctance of most mathematicians to include such hypotheses as C or C^+ into the axioms of set theory indicates that the mere absence of inconsistency is instinctively felt as an insufficient criterion for the acceptance of an axiom. Yet what are the positive criteria is not clear. At the present moment we do not see whether the axioms of set theory as they are formulated today will continue to serve as a basis for set theory also in the future or whether they will undergo essential modifications, which will enable the future mathematicians to disprove hypotheses which seem dubious to the present generation.

CHAPTER VIII

REDUCTION OF MODELS

In this chapter we shall discuss the principles of a method due to Cohen [4], [6] which allows one to construct a new model N of ZF from a given transitive model M. The model N is simply our familiar $C^B_{\pi(M)}(a)$ where a is a transitive sequence. If a is arbitrary, then N is, in general, not a model of ZF. We saw in Chapter VI that if $a \in M$ and if suitable assumptions concerning B are satisfied, then N is a model of ZF (see VI.3.1). We now want to discuss the case where a is not necessarily an element of M and to formulate conditions on a which ensure that N is a model of ZF.

The results obtained in this way are important because they allow us to construct models which contain entirely new elements completely unrelated to the elements of the model from which we started. The constructions form a basis for various proofs of independence.

1. A reflection lemma

Throughout the chapter we denote by M a fixed transitive model of ZF. We also fix a function B satisfying the conditions (B.0)–(B.4) of III.2 and abbreviate $C^B_\xi(a)$ as C_ξ or, if necessary, $C_\xi(a)$.

Let $\Pi \in M$ and $\Pi^* \subseteq \Pi$. Following Cohen we call elements of Π *conditions* and elements of Π^* *special conditions*. Note that Π^* is, in general, not an element of M. If ξ is a finite sequence of ordinals, $\xi \in On^s$, then by $C_\xi = C_\xi(a)$ we denote the sequence $\{\langle i, C_{\xi(i)}\rangle : i \in s\}$.

DEFINITION 1. *N is reducible to M* if there are: a finite sequence $\mathfrak{a}$ of elements of M and a function Φ whose domain consists of formulae H such that $0 \notin \mathrm{Fr}(H)$ and $\mathrm{Dom}(\mathfrak{a}) \cap \mathrm{Fr}(H) = 0$ and whose value is a formula Φ_H with $\mathrm{Fr}(\Phi_H) = \mathrm{Fr}(H) \cup \{0\} \cup \mathrm{Dom}(\mathfrak{a})$ such that for arbitrary sequences $\xi \in \pi(M)^{\mathrm{Fr}(H)}$

$$\vdash_N H[C_\xi] \equiv (E\pi)_{\Pi^*} \vdash_M \Phi_H[\{\langle 0, \pi\rangle\} \cup \xi \cup \mathfrak{a}].$$

The idea behind this definition, as Cohen expresses it, is that questions concerning the properties of N are thrown back [1]) to questions concerning M: on the left-hand side of the equivalence we have a property of N and on the right-hand side a property of M and of its elements. However, we cannot express the right-hand side of the equivalence in the form that elements $\mathfrak{a}$, ξ and Π^* satisfy in M a formula because Π^* is in general not an element of M.

The reducibility of N to M is relative to the sequence $\mathfrak{a}$ of parameters. These parameters would cause a great deal of notational burden if we had to put them always in evidence. To alleviate our symbolism we shall assume once for all that the formulae H used below are such that $0 \notin \mathrm{Fr}(H)$ and $\mathrm{Dom}(\mathfrak{a}) \cap \mathrm{Fr}(H) = 0$. In writing the relation of satisfaction for formulae Φ_H we shall tacitly understand that the sequence $\mathfrak{a}$ is included in the sequence of objects satisfying Φ_H.

We first prove two simple lemmas and then derive a theorem scheme which is similar to the reflexion theorem:

1.1. *If G is a function from $\pi(M)$ to $\pi(M)$ which is parametrically definable in M, then $\lambda < \pi(M) \to \sup\{G(\alpha)\colon \alpha < \lambda\} < \pi(M)$.*

PROOF. In ZF we can prove that there is an upper bound for every set of ordinals and hence this theorem is true in M. Since the set $\{G(\alpha)\colon \alpha < \lambda\}$ belongs to M, we obtain the theorem.

1.2. *If F is an increasing and continuous mapping of $\pi(M)$ into $\pi(M)$ which is parametrically definable in M, then for every $\alpha < \pi(M)$ there is an ordinal $\varkappa$ such that $\alpha < \varkappa < \pi(M)$ and $F(\varkappa) = \varkappa$.*

PROOF. The smallest set X of ordinals which contains α and has the property $\xi \in X \to F(\xi) \in X$ is an element of M since all axioms of ZF are valid in M. The supremum $\sup X$ is the required $\varkappa$ [2]).

[1]) See [4], part I, p. 1147. Webster's Third New International Dictionary of the English Language (Springfield, Mass. 1966) explains the phrase "throw back" as meaning "to cause to rely" or "to make dependent" or "to revert to an earlier type or phase".

[2]) Theorems 1.1 and 1.2 can also be proved by the methods which we used in IV.3.18 and VI.1.2.

1.3. (A REFLECTION LEMMA). *If N is reducible to M, then for every formula H there is an increasing and continuous function F_H: $\pi(M) \to \pi(M)$ which is parametrically definable in M and has the property that whenever $0 < \varkappa < \pi(M)$, $F_H(\varkappa) = \varkappa$ and $\xi \in \varkappa^{\mathrm{Fr}(H)}$, then*

$$\vdash_N H[C_\xi] \equiv \vdash_{C_\varkappa} H[C_\xi]. \tag{1}$$

The proof is very similar to that of II.2.1. For H without quantifiers we take $F_H(\xi) = \xi$ and we define $F_{\neg H} = F_H$, $F_{H_1 \wedge H_2} = F_{H_1} \circ F_{H_2}$. The proof that (1) is preserved when one passes from H to $\neg H$ and from H_1, H_2 to $H_1 \wedge H_2$ is the same as in II.2.1 and it is evident that F_H is parametrically definable in M if F_{H_1} and F_{H_2} were so definable. Thus the only case which we have to consider is that of the formula $(x_n)H$, which we denote by H'. We assume that $n \in \mathrm{Fr}(H)$.

For π in Π and ξ in $\alpha^{\mathrm{Fr}(H)-\{n\}}$ we denote by $\varrho(\pi, \xi)$ the smallest ordinal ϱ such that

$$\vdash_M \Phi_{\neg H}[\xi \cup \{\langle 0, \pi\rangle, \langle n, \varrho\rangle\}]$$

or 0 if there are no such ϱ.

We further put

$$\sigma(\alpha) = \sup\{\varrho(\pi, \xi) \colon \pi \in \Pi \wedge \xi \in \alpha^{\mathrm{Fr}(H)-\{n\}}\}$$

if this number is $< \pi(M)$; otherwise we take $\sigma(\alpha) = 0$. Next we define by induction the function G as follows:

$$\begin{aligned} G(0) = \sigma(0), \quad G(\alpha+1) &= \max\bigl(G(\alpha), \sigma(\alpha+1)\bigr)+1, \\ G(\lambda) &= \sup\{G(\alpha) \colon \alpha < \lambda\} \end{aligned} \tag{2}$$

where max and sup are to be replaced by 0 if the right-hand sides of the corresponding equations are $\geqslant \pi(M)$.

Finally we let $F_{H'} = F_H \circ G$.

We first discuss the definability of $F_{H'}$. Function ϱ is parametrically definable in M. To see this we notice that $\varrho = \varrho(\pi, \xi)$ if and only if $\pi \in \Pi$ and π and ϱ satisfy the formula

$$\begin{aligned} \bigl((\varrho = 0) \wedge (\varrho')_{\pi(M)} \vdash_M \neg \Phi_{\neg H}[\xi \cup \{\langle 0, \pi\rangle, \langle n, \varrho'\rangle\}]\bigr) \vee \\ \vee \bigl(\vdash_M \Phi_{\neg H}[\xi \cup \{\langle 0, \pi\rangle, \langle n, \varrho\rangle\}] \wedge \\ \wedge (\varrho')_\varrho \vdash_M \neg \Phi_{\neg H}[\xi \cup \{\langle 0, \pi\rangle, \langle n, \varrho'\rangle\}]\bigr). \end{aligned}$$

Hence σ is parametrically definable and so is G by the general theorem IV.4.2 [1]) on inductive definitions. Now since G is parametrically definable, we can apply lemma 1.2 and infer that $\sup\{G(\xi): \xi < \lambda\}$ belongs to M for each λ in M. It follows that G satisfies (2). Similarly $\sigma(\xi) = \sup\{\sigma(\alpha): \alpha < \xi\}$.

Now assume that $\xi \in \varkappa^{\mathrm{Fr}(H')}$ where $F_{H'}(\varkappa) = \varkappa > 0$ (cf. 1.2).

We shall establish equivalence (1) for the formula H'. If the left-hand side of this equivalence is true, then

$$\vdash_N H[\{\langle n, C_\varrho\rangle\} \cup C_\xi] \quad \text{for every } \varrho < \pi(M);$$

hence the same is true for all $\varrho < \varkappa$ and so we obtain the right-hand side of the equivalence using the equation $F_H(\varkappa) = \varkappa$.

Now we assume that the left-hand side of the equivalence is false. Hence there is a $\varrho < \pi(M)$ for which $\vdash_N \neg H[\{\langle n, C_\varrho\rangle\} \cup C_\xi]$. Using Definition 1 we infer that there is a special condition π in Π^* for which

$$\vdash_M \Phi_{\neg H}[\{\langle 0, \pi\rangle, \langle n, \varrho\rangle\} \cup \xi].$$

Hence, by the definition of $\varrho(\pi, \xi)$ we find that

$$(3) \qquad \vdash_M \Phi_{\neg H}[\{\langle 0, \pi\rangle, \langle n, \varrho(\pi, \xi)\rangle\} \cup \xi]$$

and $\varrho(\pi, \xi) < \sigma(\varkappa) < F_{H'}(\varkappa) = \varkappa$. From (3) we obtain

$$\vdash_N \neg H[\{\langle n, C_{\varrho(\pi,\xi)}\rangle\} \cup C_\xi]$$

and we can use the inductive assumption to infer that

$$\text{non} \vdash_{C_\varkappa} H[\{\langle n, C_{\varrho(\pi,\xi)}\rangle\} \cup C_\xi]$$

and hence

$$\text{non} \vdash_{C_\varkappa} H'[C_\xi].$$

Theorem 1.3 is thus proved.

1.4. *If N is reducible to M, then axiom* (VI_H) *is valid in N for every formula H.*

PROOF. We assume that $\varphi: N \to N$ is a function parametrically definable in N and $m \in N$. Obviously $\mathrm{Im}(\varphi, m) \subseteq N$. We first show that $\mathrm{Im}(\varphi, m) \subseteq C_\beta$ where β is an ordinal $< \pi(M)$.

[1]) See the concluding remarks in Chapter IV.4, p. 64.

Let the formula H and the sequence C_σ of parameters define φ:

$$C_\eta = \varphi(C_\xi) \equiv \vdash_N H[\{\langle 1, C_\xi\rangle, \langle 2, C_\eta\rangle\} \cup C_\sigma]$$

$$\equiv (E\pi)_{\Pi*} \vdash_M \Phi_H[\{\langle 0, \pi\rangle, \langle 1, \xi\rangle, \langle 2, \eta\rangle\} \cup \sigma].$$

We can assume that x_0 does not occur in H.

For given π, ξ, σ we denote by $\eta(\pi, \xi, \sigma)$ the least η such that

$$\vdash_M \Phi_H[\{\langle 0, \pi\rangle, \langle 1, \xi\rangle, \langle 2, \eta\rangle\} \cup \sigma]$$

or 0 if no such η exists and define

$$\gamma(\alpha, \sigma) = \sup\{\eta(\pi, \xi, \sigma)\colon \pi \in \Pi \wedge \xi < \alpha\}.$$

Since the function η is definable in M, we have $\gamma(\alpha, \sigma) < \pi(M)$.

If $m = C_\mu$ and $x \in m$, then $x = C_\xi$ where $\xi < \mu$, whence $\varphi(C_\xi) = C_\eta$ where $\eta < \gamma(\mu, \sigma)$. Thus $\mathrm{Im}(\varphi, m) \subseteq C_\beta$ whenever $\beta = \delta(\varrho) \geqslant \delta(\gamma(\mu, \sigma))$. We can fix a $\beta < \pi(M)$ satisfying this inequality such that $\mu < \beta$ and $\sigma_i < \beta$ for all terms of σ.

Now we obtain by 1.3 an ordinal $\varkappa$ such that $\beta < \varkappa < \pi(M)$ and the following equivalence holds for all x, y in C_β

$$\vdash_N H[\{\langle 1, x\rangle, \langle 2, y\rangle\} \cup C_\sigma] \equiv \vdash_{C_\varkappa} H[\{\langle 1, x\rangle, \langle 2, y\rangle\} \cup C_\sigma].$$

To accomplish the proof we put $H' = (Ex_1)[(x_1 \in x_p) \wedge H]$ where p is any integer not in $\mathrm{Fr}(H)$ and denote by H^* a formula resulting from H' by substituting x_0 for x_2 at all places where x_2 occurs freely in H'. We then obtain

$$y \in \mathrm{Im}(\varphi, m) \equiv \vdash_{C_\varkappa} H^*[\{\langle 0, y\rangle, \langle p, m\rangle\} \cup C_\sigma],$$

which proves that

$$\mathrm{Im}(\varphi, m) = S_{H^*}(C_\varkappa, \{\langle p, m\rangle\} \cup C_\sigma).$$

Since $C_\varkappa \in C_{\delta(\varkappa+\omega)}$ and the set $C_{\delta(\varkappa+\omega)}$ is predicatively closed, we obtain $\mathrm{Im}(\varphi, m) \in C_{\delta(\varkappa+\omega)} \subseteq N$.

2. The validity of the power set axiom

In this section we use a method designed by Solovay [31] for proving that the axiom (V) of power set is valid in N [1]).

[1]) The method is presented in detail in Easton [7].

In our proofs we shall use a simplified notation for sequences writing for instance π, τ, σ for $\{\langle 0, \pi\rangle, \langle 1, \tau\rangle, \langle 2, \sigma\rangle\}$; the correlation between terms of sequences occurring in the formulae and integers will always be clear from the context.

2.1. *If N is reducible to M, then the axiom* (V) *of power sets is valid in N.*

PROOF. Let $x = C_\xi \in N$. We want to show that $P(x) \cap N \in N$. The main difficulty is to show that all elements of $P(x) \cap N$ can be represented as C_ϱ where $\varrho < \gamma$ with a fixed $\gamma < \pi(M)$. We denote by H_0 and H_1 the formulae $x_1 \in x_2$ and $(x_3)[(x_3 \in x_1) \to (x_3 \in x_2)]$ and consider the set

$$S = \{\langle s, \pi_0\rangle \in M\colon\ (s \subseteq \Pi\times\xi) \wedge (\pi_0 \in \Pi) \wedge (E\sigma)_{\pi(M)} F(\sigma, \xi, \pi_0, s)\}$$

where $F(\sigma, \xi, \pi_0, s)$ is the conjunction of

$$(1) \qquad \vdash_M \Phi_{H_1}[\pi_0, \sigma, \xi],$$

$$(2) \qquad (\tau)_\xi(\pi)_\Pi\{\langle \pi, \tau\rangle \in s \equiv \vdash_M \Phi_{H_0}[\pi, \tau, \sigma]\}.$$

LEMMA. $S \in M$.

PROOF. From the definition it follows that

$$x \in S \equiv \big(x \in M \cap (P(\Pi\times\xi)\times\Pi)\big) \wedge$$

$$\wedge (E\pi_0)_\Pi (Es)_{M\cap P(\Pi\times\xi)}(x = \langle s, \pi_0\rangle) \wedge (E\sigma)_{\pi(M)} F(\sigma, \xi, \pi_0, s).$$

This equivalence shows that S is contained in the set $z = M \cap \cap [P(\Pi\times\xi)\times\Pi]$ which belongs to M and that S is a parametrically definable subset of z. Hence $S \in M$.

For $\langle s, \pi_0\rangle \in S$ we denote by $\sigma(s, \pi_0)$ the smallest ordinal σ which satisfies (1) and (2) and we put $\gamma = \sup\{\sigma(s, \pi_0)\colon \langle s, \pi_0\rangle \in S\}$. Since $\sigma(s, \pi_0)$ is the value of a parametrically definable function, we have $\gamma < \pi(M)$. We are going to prove that if $y \subseteq x$ and $y \in N$, then $y = C_\varrho$ with $\varrho < \gamma$.

Let $y \subseteq x$, $y = C_\eta$. Hence

$$\vdash_N H_1[\{\langle 1, C_\eta\rangle, \langle 2, C_\xi\rangle\}],$$

and therefore there is a π_0 in Π^* such that

$$(3) \qquad \vdash_M \Phi_{H_1}[\pi_0, \eta, \xi].$$

Let

(4) $$s = \{\langle \pi, \tau\rangle \in \Pi \times \xi : \vdash_M \Phi_{H_0}[\pi, \tau, \eta]\}.$$

Formulae (3) and (4) prove that $F(\eta, \xi, \pi_0, s)$ and hence $\langle s, \pi_0\rangle \in S$. Hence $\sigma(s, \pi_0) < \gamma$ and (1) and (2) are valid for $\sigma = \sigma(s, \pi_0)$. We shall show that $y = C_{\sigma(s,\pi_0)}$, i.e.

(i) $$(z \in y) \to (z \in C_{\sigma(s,\pi_0)}),$$

(ii) $$(z \in C_{\sigma(s,\pi_0)}) \to (z \in y).$$

P r o o f o f (i). Let $z \in y$; hence $z \in x$, $z = C_\tau$ where $\tau < \xi$ (cf. III.3.3). From $\vdash_N H_0[z, y]$ we infer that there is a π in Π^* such that $\vdash_M \Phi_{H_0}[\pi, \tau, \eta]$ and hence, by (4), $\langle \pi, \tau\rangle \in s$. Now we use (2) and obtain $\vdash_M \Phi_{H_0}[\pi, \tau, \sigma(s, \pi_0)]$ whence, in view of $\pi \in \Pi^*$, $C_\tau \in C_{\sigma(s,\pi_0)}$. Thus (i) is proved.

P r o o f o f (ii). Let $z \in C_{\sigma(s,\pi_0)}$. From (1) we obtain $C_{\sigma(s,\pi_0)} \subseteq C_\xi$ since $\pi_0 \in \Pi^*$. Thus z can be represented as C_τ with $\tau < \xi$. Since z is an element of $C_{\sigma(s,\pi_0)}$, there exists by Definition 1 a π in Π^* such that $\vdash_M \Phi_{H_0}[\pi, \tau, \sigma(s, \pi_0)]$, and from (2) we obtain $\langle \pi, \tau\rangle \in s$, whence, by (4), $\vdash_M \Phi_{H_0}[\pi, \tau, \eta]$ and $z = C_\tau \in C_\eta$.

Now we use the fact that $C_{\delta(\gamma+\omega)}$ is predicatively closed and find that

$$\begin{aligned} P(x) \cap N &= \{y \in C_{\delta(\gamma)} : \vdash_N H_1[\{\langle 1, y\rangle, \langle 2, x\rangle\}]\} \\ &= \{y \in C_{\delta(\gamma)} : \vdash_{C_{\delta(\gamma)}} H_1[\{\langle 1, y\rangle, \langle 2, x\rangle\}]\} \\ &= S_{H_1}(C_{\delta(\gamma)}, \{\langle 2, x\rangle\})\ ^{1)} \end{aligned}$$

belongs to $C_{\delta(\gamma+\omega)} \subseteq C_{\pi(M)} = N$.

[1]) Strictly speaking we should have replaced first the variable x_1 by x_0 in the formula H_1 because we used only formulae with the free variable x_0 to define sections (cf. p. 27).

CHAPTER IX

GENERIC POINTS AND FORCING; GENERAL THEORY

In this chapter we shall describe a notion introduced by P. J. Cohen [4] which allows us to construct models reducible to a given denumerable model M. The novel idea introduced by Cohen is that he considers a family of sets $N(p)$ each of which is a candidate for a model. This family is indexed by a parameter p which ranges over a topological space $\mathscr{X}$ and the Baire theorem is used to select a p such that $N(p)$ is indeed a model. The elements of $N(p)$ are obtained from p by a uniform process. Thus

$$N(p) = \{S_t(p)\colon\ t \in T\}$$

where S_t are functions and T a fixed set. Elements of T are parameters which determine the elements of $N(p)$.

The notion of forcing introduced by Cohen is a relation between open subsets of $\mathscr{X}$ and elements of T. Let H be a formula with, say, two free variables. Then we say that an open set U forces H for the values t_1, t_2 of the parameters if for almost all p in U the formula H is satisfied in $N(p)$ by sets $S_{t_1}(p)$, $S_{t_2}(p)$. The expression "almost all" is meant in the sense of category: A property holds almost everywhere if the set of points p in $\mathscr{X}$ which do not have this property is a denumerable union of nowhere dense sets, i.e. belongs to the family $I = I(\mathscr{X})$ of sets of the first category.

Cohen's ideas are susceptible of various generalizations and modifications but these will not be presented here. The approach to forcing via category theory is due to Ryll-Nardzewski, cf. [25], and Takeuti [32].

In the present section we define the notion of forcing and of generic sets in a rather general situation, which will then be more and more specialize d.

To begin with we collect for further reference the basic facts of general topology. Readers who want more details about these topics should consult [16].

1. Auxiliary topological notions

A topological space is a set $\mathscr{X}$ together with a family G of subsets of $\mathscr{X}$ which satisfies the conditions:

(i) if $G' \subseteq G$, then $\bigcup G' \in G$,

(ii) if $X, Y \in G$, then $X \cap Y \in G$,

(iii) $0, \mathscr{X} \in G$.

Elements of $\mathscr{X}$ are called *points*, elements of G *open sets*. If $\{p\} \in G$, then we call p an *isolated point of* $\mathscr{X}$. A space is *discrete* if all its points are isolated.

A family B of sets is called an (open) *basis of* $\mathscr{X}$ if $0 \notin B \subseteq G$ and each non-void open set is a union of a subfamily of B. If a basis is fixed, then its elements are called *neighbourhoods*.

Complements of open sets are called *closed*.

For $X \subseteq \mathscr{X}$ we denote by $\overline{X}$ (the closure of X) the intersection of all closed sets which contain X and by $\mathrm{Int}(X)$ (interior of X) the union of open sets contained in X.

A set X is *regular* if $X = \mathrm{Int}(\overline{X})$.

A space which has a basis consisting exclusively of regular sets is called *semi-regular*; the basis itself is called *regular*.

A set $X \subseteq \mathscr{X}$ is called *dense* if each neighbourhood contains points of X.

It is called *nowhere dense* if each neighbourhood contains a neighbourhood disjoint of X. These notions are independent of the particular basis chosen in $\mathscr{X}$.

Examples of nowhere dense sets: $\overline{X}-X$ where X is an open set; $X-\mathrm{Int}(X)$ where X is a closed set.

A set X which can be represented as a union of a denumerable family of nowhere dense sets is called a *set of the first category*. The family of those sets is denoted by $I(\mathscr{X})$ or simply by I if the space is fixed.

The family I is an *ideal*. With the help of the axiom of choice one shows that this ideal is σ-additive.

The complement of a set of the first category is called a *residual set*.

We say that a *space $\mathscr{X}$ satisfies Baire's theorem* if each residual set is dense.

A sufficient condition for a space to satisfy Baire's theorem is this: *there is a basis B such that each decreasing sequence of neighbourhoods which belong to this basis has a non-void intersection.*

A set X is said *to have Baire's property* if there is an open set A such that $X \dot{-} A \in I(\mathscr{X})$. Here $\dot{-}$ denotes the symmetric difference. The relation $X \dot{-} Y \in I$ is called a *congruence modulo sets of the first category.*

Product spaces. Let T be a set, $\mathscr{X}_t$ a family of topological spaces where $t \in T$ and B_t is a basis of $\mathscr{X}_t$ $(t \in T)$.

We denote by $\mathscr{X} = \mathbf{P}_{t \in T} \mathscr{X}_t$ the *Cartesian product* of sets $\mathscr{X}_t$, i.e., the set of functions f with $\mathrm{Dom}(f) = T$ satisfying the condition $f(t) \in \mathscr{X}_t$ for each t in T.

For an arbitrary ideal J of $P(T)$ containing all finite subsets of T we define the *J-topology* in the product space. We call a *J-box* each function b such that $\mathrm{Dom}(b) \in J$ and $b(t) \in B_t$ for $t \in \mathrm{Dom}(b)$. A J-box b determines the family U_b of points p in the product space satisfying the condition $p(t) \in b(t)$ for each t in $\mathrm{Dom}(b)$.

We define *open sets in the J-topology* as arbitrary unions of sets U_b where b ranges over J-boxes. Thus we can take the non-void sets U_b as neighbourhoods in $\mathscr{X}$.

If J is the family of finite subsets of T, then the J-topology is called the *Tichonoff topology of $\mathscr{X}$.*

Example. Let X be a discrete space and let $\mathscr{X}_t = X$ for $t \in T$. Each neighbourhood U in the product space is determined by a non-void finite function $\varphi \in X^S$ where S is finite; U consists of functions $f \in X^T$ such that $f \supseteq \varphi$.

If in particular $X = \{0, 1\}$, then each neighbourhood in the product space is determined by a pair of disjoint finite subsets S_0, S_1 of T and consists of functions f such that $f(t) = i$ for $t \in S_i$ $(i = 0, 1)$. Obviously we can identify this product space with $P(T)$; thus the neighbourhood determined by $\langle S_0, S_1\rangle$ consists of sets $S \subseteq T$ such that $S_0 \subseteq S$ and $S \cap S_1 = 0$.

A mapping of a space into another space is called *continuous* if the inverse images of open sets are open. Two spaces are *homeomorphic* if there is a continuous mapping of one onto the other such that the inverse mapping is also continuous.

A homeomorphic mapping of $\mathscr{X}$ onto itself is called an *auto-homeomorphism.*

2. Valuations

Let $\mathscr{X}$ be a topological space. Let T be a set and let T^* be the set of all finite sequences with range included in T:

$$T^* = \{f\colon (\mathrm{Dom}(f) \subset \omega) \wedge (\mathrm{Dom}(f) \text{ finite}) \wedge (\mathrm{Rg}(f) \subseteq T)\}.$$

Let $\mathscr{F}$ be a mapping of pairs (H, t), t in T^*, H a formula, into $P(\mathscr{X})$. We assume that $\mathscr{F}_{H,t}$ is defined whenever $\mathrm{Dom}(t) = \mathrm{Fr}(H)$.

The mapping $\mathscr{F}$ will be called a *valuation* (or, more exactly, a *T-valuation*) if the following conditions are satisfied:

(1) If the equivalence $H' \equiv H''$ is logically valid and $\mathrm{Dom}(t) = \mathrm{Fr}(H') \cup \mathrm{Fr}(H'')$, then

$$\mathscr{F}_{H', t|\mathrm{Fr}(H')} = \mathscr{F}_{H'', t|\mathrm{Fr}(H'')}.$$

(2) If H' arises from H by a substitution of x_i for x_j[1]) (where $j \in \mathrm{Fr}(H)$ and $i \in \mathrm{Fr}(H')$) and $\mathrm{Dom}(t) = \mathrm{Fr}(H) - \{j\}$, then

$$\mathscr{F}_{H, t\cup\{\langle j, s\rangle\}} = \mathscr{F}_{H', t\cup\{\langle i, s\rangle\}} \quad \text{for any } s \text{ in } T.$$

(3) If $H = H_1 \wedge H_2$ and $t \in T^{\mathrm{Fr}(H_1)\cup\mathrm{Fr}(H_2)}$, then

$$\mathscr{F}_{H,t} = \mathscr{F}_{H_1, t|\mathrm{Fr}(H_1)} \cap \mathscr{F}_{H_2, t|\mathrm{Fr}(H_2)}.$$

(4) If $H = \neg H'$ and $t \in T^{\mathrm{Fr}(H)}$, then

$$\mathscr{F}_{H,t} = \mathscr{X} - \mathscr{F}_{H',t}.$$

[1]) We assume that the substitution is correct, i.e., that no free occurrence o x_j in H becomes a bound occurrence of x_i in H'.

(5) If $H = (x_j)H'$, $t \in T^{\mathrm{Fr}(H')}$ and $j \notin \mathrm{Fr}(H')$, then

$$\mathscr{F}_{H,t} = \mathscr{F}_{H',t};$$

if $j \in \mathrm{Fr}(H')$, then

$$\mathscr{F}_{H,t} = \bigcap_{s \in T} \mathscr{F}_{H',t \cup \{\langle j,s \rangle\}}.$$

In the situation described in the introduction to this chapter we define $\mathscr{F}_{H,t}$ as $\{p: \vdash_{N(p)} H[S_t(p)]\}$ where $S_t(p)$ is a sequence $\{\langle j, S_{t(j)}(p)\rangle: j \in \mathrm{Fr}(H)\}$. However, several theorems can be proved for abstract valuations which have no reference to sets $S_t(p)$.

The valuation $\mathscr{F}$ will be called *adequate* if there are functions: G_H with domain T^* and N_H with domain $\omega \times T^*$ such that for every formula H, for every $t \in T^{\mathrm{Fr}(H)}$ and every n in ω

(6) $G_{H,t}$ is an open set and $N_{H,n,t}$ is a nowhere dense set.

(7) $\mathscr{F}_{H,t} \dot{-} G_{H,t} \subseteq \bigcup_{n \in \omega} N_{H,n,t}$.

Thus adequate valuations are such that the sets $\mathscr{F}_{H,t}$ satisfy the condition of Baire and an open set $G_{H,t}$ which is congruent to $\mathscr{F}_{H,t}$ modulo sets of first category and also the sequence of nowhere dense sets whose union contains $\mathscr{F}_{H,t} \dot{-} G_{H,t}$ are determined by explicitly given functions.

Remark. If we assume the axiom of choice, then we can prove that all Borel sets have the property of Baire and that if $\mathscr{F}_{H,t}$ is a Borel set, then there exist functions G, N satisfying (6) and (7). Thus from the axiom of choice it follows that every valuation such that $\mathscr{F}_{H,t}$ is a Borel set is adequate.

For adequate valuations we can introduce the notion of generic points. We precede this definition by two simple theorems:

2.1. *If the theorem of Baire is valid in* $\mathscr{X}$ *and* T *is at most denumerable, then* $\mathscr{X} - \bigcup_{H} \bigcup_{n<\omega} \bigcup_{t \in T^{\mathrm{Fr}(H)}} N_{H,n,t} \neq 0$.

PROOF. The union $\bigcup_{H}$ is taken over the denumerable set of all formulae. Since the other two unions are also taken over denumerable sets we infer that the whole union is nowhere dense and hence, by Baire's theorem does not coincide with $\mathscr{X}$.

2.2. *If* $p \in \mathscr{X} - \bigcup_H \bigcup_{n<\omega} \bigcup_{t \in T^{\mathrm{Fr}(H)}} N_{H,n,t}$ *and* $p \in \mathscr{F}_{H,t}$ *where* H *is a formula and* $t \in T^{\mathrm{Fr}(H)}$, *then there is a neighbourhood* U *of* p *such that* $U - \mathscr{F}_{H,t} \in I$.

PROOF. Since $p \notin \bigcup_n N_{H,n,t}$ we infer from (7) that $p \notin \mathscr{F}_{H,t} \dot{-} G_{H,t}$ and hence $p \in G_{H,t}$. Thus we can take as U any neighbourhood of p which is contained in $G_{H,t}$.

After these lemmata we can introduce the following

DEFINITION. A point p of $\mathscr{X}$ is *generic with respect to a given T-valuation* $\mathscr{F}$ if for every formula H and every t in $T^{\mathrm{Fr}(H)}$ the condition $p \in \mathscr{F}_{H,t}$ implies that there is a neighbourhood U of p such that $U - \mathscr{F}_{H,t} \in I$.

From 2.2 it follows that all points of the difference

$$\mathscr{X} - \bigcup_H \bigcup_{n<\omega} \bigcup_{t \in T^{\mathrm{Fr}(H)}} N_{H,n,t}$$

are generic whence we see that the following theorem holds:

2.3. *If the theorem of Baire is valid in* $\mathscr{X}$ *and* T *is at most denumerable, then for every adequate* T *valuation in* $\mathscr{X}$ *the set of points which are generic with respect to this valuation is residual and hence non void.*

3. The forcing relation

Let $\mathscr{X}$ be a topological space in which Baire's theorem is valid, let Π be a set and $\pi \to U_\pi$ a mapping of Π onto an open basis of $\mathscr{X}$. We assume that $\mathscr{F}$ is an adequate valuation and retain the notation $G_{H,t}$ and $N_{H,n,t}$ introduced in Section 2.

The forcing relation is defined thus:

$$\mathrm{Forc}_H(\pi, t) \equiv U_\pi - \mathscr{F}_{H,t} \in I.$$

Thus for every H the relation Forc_H is a binary relation between elements of Π and $T^{\mathrm{Fr}(H)}$: $\mathrm{Forc}_H \subseteq \Pi \times T^{\mathrm{Fr}(H)}$.

3.1. $\mathrm{Forc}_{H_1 \wedge H_2}(\pi, t) \equiv \mathrm{Forc}_{H_1}\big(\pi, t|\mathrm{Fr}(H_1)\big) \wedge \mathrm{Forc}_{H_2}\big(\pi, t|\mathrm{Fr}(H_2)\big)$.

This follows immediately from the additivity of I and the definition of valuations.

3.2. *If* $n \in \mathrm{Fr}(H)$, *then*

$$\mathrm{Forc}_{(x_n)H}(\pi, t) \equiv (s)_T \, \mathrm{Forc}_H(\pi, t \cup \{\langle n, s \rangle\});$$

if $n \notin \mathrm{Fr}(H)$, *then*

$$\mathrm{Forc}_{(x_n)H}(\pi, t) \equiv \mathrm{Forc}_H(\pi, t).$$

PROOF. We consider only the case where $n \in \mathrm{Fr}(H)$. We have

$$U_\pi - \mathscr{F}_{(x_n)H,t} = \bigcup_{s \in T} (U_\pi - \mathscr{F}_{H, t \cup \{\langle n, s\rangle\}})$$

by the definition of $\mathscr{F}$. Hence if the left-hand side is in I, then so is every component of the union on the right-hand side and the right-hand side of 3.2 is true. If the right-hand side of 3.2 is true, then $U_\pi - G_{H, t\cup\{\langle n, s\rangle\}} \in I$ for every s in T. In order to simplify the notation we write this formula as $U - G_s \in I$.

Since $U - \overline{G}_s$ is open and contained in $U - G_s$, we obtain $U - \overline{G}_s \in I$. Since an open non-void set is not in I, we obtain $U \subseteq \overline{G}_s$ and $U \subseteq \mathrm{Int}(\overline{G}_s)$. Taking an intersection over s we obtain $U \subseteq \bigcap_s \mathrm{Int}(\overline{G}_s)$. This proves that

$$U - \bigcap_s \mathscr{F}_s \subseteq \bigcap_s \mathrm{Int}(\overline{G}_s) - \bigcap_s \mathscr{F}_s \subseteq \bigcup_s (\mathrm{Int}(\overline{G}_s) \dot{-} \mathscr{F}_s)$$

where we abbreviated $\mathscr{F}_{H, t\cup\{\langle n, s\rangle\}}$ to $\mathscr{F}_s$.

We now use the formulae

$$\mathrm{Int}(\overline{G}_s) \dot{-} \mathscr{F}_s \subseteq (\mathrm{Int}(\overline{G}_s) \dot{-} \overline{G}_s) \cup (G_s \dot{-} \mathscr{F}_s) \cup (\overline{G}_s \dot{-} G_s),$$

which prove that $\bigcup_s (\mathrm{Int}(\overline{G}_s) \dot{-} \mathscr{F}_s) \in I$. Hence $U - \bigcap_s \mathscr{F}_s \in I$ and thus the left-hand side of 3.2 is true.

3.3. $\mathrm{Forc}_{\neg H}(\pi, t) \equiv (\varrho)[U_\varrho \subseteq U_\pi \rightarrow \neg \mathrm{Forc}_H(\varrho, t)]$.

PROOF. Since $U_\pi - \mathscr{F}_{\neg H, t} = U_\pi \cap \mathscr{F}_{H,t}$, we infer that if the left-hand side of 3.3 is satisfied, then $U_\varrho \cap \mathscr{F}_{H,t} \in I$ for every ϱ satisfying $U_\pi \supseteq U_\varrho$. It follows that $U_\varrho - \mathscr{F}_{H,t}$ is not in I since otherwise $U_\varrho = (U_\varrho \cap \mathscr{F}_{H,t}) \cup \cup (U_\varrho - \mathscr{F}_{H,t})$ would be in I.

If the left-hand side of 3.3 is false, then $U_\pi \cap G_{H,t} \notin I$. Taking ϱ such that $U_\varrho \subseteq U_\pi \cap G_{H,t}$ we obtain $U_\varrho - G_{H,t} = 0$ and hence $U_\varrho - \mathscr{F}_{H,t} \in I$.

3.4. *If* $n \in \mathrm{Fr}(H)$, *then*

$\mathrm{Forc}_{(Ex_n)H}(\pi, t)$

$$\equiv (\varrho)_\Pi\{(U_\varrho \subseteq U_\pi) \rightarrow (Es)_T(E\sigma)_\Pi[(U_\sigma \subseteq U_\varrho) \wedge \mathrm{Forc}_H(\sigma, t \cup \{\langle n, s\rangle\})]\}.$$

This follows from 3.2 and 3.3.

3.5. *The following equivalence holds*:

$$\mathrm{Forc}_{H_1\vee H_2}(\pi, t) \equiv (\varrho)_\Pi\Big((U_\varrho \subseteq U_\pi) \to$$
$$\to (E\sigma)_\Pi\big\{(U_\sigma \subseteq U_\varrho) \wedge [\mathrm{Forc}_{H_1}(\sigma, t|\mathrm{Fr}(H_1)) \vee \mathrm{Forc}_{H_2}(\sigma, t|\mathrm{Fr}(H_2))]\big\}\Big).$$

This follows from 3.1 and 3.3.

3.6. *If* $U_\varrho \subseteq U_\pi$ *and* $\mathrm{Forc}_H(\pi, t)$, *then* $\mathrm{Forc}_H(\varrho, t)$.

To see this we notice that a subset of a set of the first category is of the first category.

We note some more properties of the forcing relation, although they will not be directly used in our constructions.

3.7. *If* H *is logically valid, then* $\mathrm{Forc}_H(\pi, t)$ *for arbitrary* π *in* Π *and* t *in* $T^{\mathrm{Fr}(H)}$; *in particular, if* H_2 *follows from* H_1 *on the basis of logic alone, then for arbitrary* π *in* Π *and* $t \in T^{\mathrm{Fr}(H_1)\cup \mathrm{Fr}'H_2)}$ *the formula* $\mathrm{Forc}_{H_1}(\pi, t|\mathrm{Fr}(H_1))$ *implies* $\mathrm{Forc}_{H_2}(\pi, t|\mathrm{Fr}(H_2))$.

Proof. If H is logically valid, then $\mathscr{F}_{H,t} = \mathscr{X}$; if $H_1 \to H_2$ is logically valid, then $\mathscr{F}_{H_1, t|\mathrm{Fr}(H_1)} \subseteq \mathscr{F}_{H_2, t|\mathrm{Fr}(H_2)}$.

It can be shown that theorems converse to 3.7 are, in general, false.

The set of formulae H which are forced by any π for any t in $T^{\mathrm{Fr}(H)}$ is closed under the usual rules of proof and forms thus an interesting extension of the set of logically valid formulae. The properties of this set have not yet been fully investigated.

4. A special valuation

Let us assume that to each point p of $\mathscr{X}$ and each t in T corresponds a set $S_t(p)$. Put

$$N(p) = \{S_t(p)\colon\ t \in T\}$$

and define for $t \in T^{\mathrm{Fr}(H)}$

$$\text{(i)} \qquad \mathscr{F}_{H,t} = \{p\colon\ \vdash_{N(p)} H[S_t(p)]\}$$

where $S_t(p)$ denotes the sequence $\{\langle n, S_{t(n)}(p)\rangle\colon\ n \in \mathrm{Fr}(H)\}$.

4.1. $\mathscr{F}$ *as defined in* (i) *is a valuation.*

The verification is immediate.

We now assume that this valuation satisfies the assumptions (6), (7) of Section 2, i.e., that $\mathscr{F}$ is adequate and that Baire's theorem is valid in $\mathscr{X}$.

4.2. *If $\mathscr{F}$ is defined by* (i), *p is generic with respect to $\mathscr{F}$ and Π^* is the set of π such that $p \in U_\pi$, then*

$$\vdash_{N(p)} H[S_t(p)] \equiv (E\pi)_{\Pi^*} \operatorname{Forc}_H(\pi, t).$$

PROOF. The left-hand side is equivalent to $p \in \mathscr{F}_{H,t}$, whence, p being generic, there is a π in Π^* such that $\operatorname{Forc}_H(\pi, t)$.

If there is a π in Π^* such that $\operatorname{Forc}_H(\pi, t)$ but the left-hand side of 4.2 is false, then we infer similarly that $\operatorname{Forc}_{\neg H}(\varrho, t)$ for a ϱ in Π^*. Take σ in Π^* such that $U_\sigma \subseteq U_\pi \cap U_\varrho$. Hence

$$U_\sigma - \mathscr{F}_{H,t} \in I \quad \text{and} \quad U_\sigma - \mathscr{F}_{\neg H,t} \in I.$$

Since $\mathscr{F}_{H,t} \cap \mathscr{F}_{\neg H,t} = 0$, we obtain $U_\sigma \in I$, which is a contradiction.

5. Application of forcing to constructions of models

We now compare the results obtained in the previous sections with those of Chapter VIII. In view of the close similarity between condition VIII.1.1 and theorem 4.2 we try to impose further conditions on the valuation $\mathscr{F}$ and the space $\mathscr{X}$, which will make theorem 4.2 identical with condition VIII.1.1. In this way we shall obtain a model of ZF.

First we select a denumerable model M of ZF and a topological space $\mathscr{X}$. With each point p of $\mathscr{X}$ we correlate a transfinite sequence $a(p)$:

$$(A){:}\ p \to a(p)$$

such that the following conditions are satisfied:

CONDITION I. *The sequence $a(p)$ is transitive of a type $\alpha_0 < \pi(M)$.*

CONDITION II. *The space $\mathscr{X}$ is semi-regular* [1]) *and satisfies the theorem of Baire.*

CONDITION III. *There are a set Π in M and a mapping $\pi \to U_\pi$ of Π onto a regular basis of $\mathscr{X}$ such that the relation*

$$\pi \prec \varrho \equiv U_\varrho \subseteq U_\pi$$

is parametrically definable in M [1]).

[1]) Neither the semi-regularity of $\mathscr{X}$ nor the definability of $\prec$ are necessary here. We shall need the former assumption in X.3.1 and the latter in 5.2 and also in Chapter X.

Since we want the $S_t(p)$ of the present chapter to become the $C_\xi(a)$ of Chapter VIII, we select as T the set $\pi(M)$ and put

$$S_\xi(p) = C_\xi^B(a(p)) \quad \text{for} \quad \xi < \pi(M)$$

where B is a function satisfying conditions (B.0)–(B.4) of III.2. (We shall omit the upper index B wherever possible.) Let

$$\mathscr{E}_{\alpha\beta} = \{p \in \mathscr{X}:\ C_\alpha(a(p)) \in C_\beta(a(p))\},$$

$$\mathscr{I}_{\alpha\beta} = \{p \in \mathscr{X}:\ C_\alpha(a(p)) = C_\beta(a(p))\} \quad \text{for} \quad \alpha, \beta < \pi(M).$$

CONDITION IV. *There are functions $G^{(1)}$, $G^{(2)}$, $N^{(1)}$, $N^{(2)}$ such that for arbitrary α, $\beta \in \pi(M)$, $n \in \omega$ and $i = 1, 2$ the set $G^{(i)}_{\alpha\beta}$ is open, $N^{(i)}_{n,\alpha,\beta}$ is nowhere dense and*

$$\mathscr{E}_{\alpha\beta} \dot{-} G^{(1)}_{\alpha\beta} \subseteq \bigcup_n N^{(1)}_{n,\alpha,\beta},$$

$$\mathscr{I}_{\alpha\beta} \dot{-} G^{(2)}_{\alpha\beta} \subseteq \bigcup_n N^{(2)}_{n,\alpha,\beta}.$$

This condition will be used in establishing the adequacy of the valuation

(1) $$\mathscr{F}_{H,\xi} = \{p \in \mathscr{X}:\ \vdash_{C_{\pi(M)}(a(p))} H[C_\xi(a(p))]\}$$

where $\xi \in \pi(M)^{\mathrm{Fr}(H)}$.

CONDITION V. *The forcing relations*

$$U_\pi - \mathscr{E}_{\alpha\beta} \in I, \qquad U_\pi - \mathscr{I}_{\alpha\beta} \in I$$

are parametrically definable in M.

The valuation (1) depends only on the function B, the mapping (A) and the height $\pi(M)$ of M and should properly be denoted by $\mathscr{F}^{\pi(M)}_{B,A}$. In the next theorem we shall show that this valuation is adequate and hence that there exist points generic with respect to this valuation. The set of these generic points will be denoted by $\mathrm{Gen}(\mathscr{X})$ although the notation $\mathrm{Gen}^{\pi(M)}_{B,A}(\mathscr{X})$ would be more accurate; like the valuation (1) the set $\mathrm{Gen}(\mathscr{X})$ depends only on the height of M, the function B and the mapping (A) [1]).

[1]) In more advanced theories one considers valuations different from (1) which depend not only on the height of M but also on its width. Points generic with respect to this valuation depend not only on A, B and $\pi(M)$ but on the whole of M. Cf. [7] and [18].

In the future we shall consider only the valuation (1); accordingly we shall simplify our terminology and refer to the elements of Gen($\mathscr{X}$) simply as to the generic points of $\mathscr{X}$.

5.1. *Let B be a function which satisfies* (B.0)–(B.4); *further let Conditions* I–V *be satisfied. Then valuation* (1) *is adequate* (*i.e., satisfies conditions* (6), (7) *defined in Section* 2).

PROOF. If H is the atomic formula $x_0 \in x_1$ and $\xi = \{\langle 0, \alpha\rangle, \langle 1, \beta\rangle\}$, then $\mathscr{F}_{H,\xi} = \mathscr{E}_{\alpha\beta}$, and thus we can put $G_{H,\xi} = G^{(1)}_{\alpha\beta}$, $N_{n,H,\xi} = N^{(1)}_{n,\alpha,\beta}$. We proceed similarly if H is the formula $x_0 = x_1$. If H is the formula $x_i \in x_j$ where $i \neq j$, then

$$\mathscr{F}_{H,\{\langle i,\alpha\rangle,\langle j,\beta\rangle\}} = \mathscr{F}_{x_0 \in x_1,\{\langle 0,\alpha\rangle,\langle 1,\beta\rangle\}},$$

and thus this case is reduced to the previous one. The proof is similar in the case where H is the formula $x_i = x_j$, $i \neq j$. Finally, if H is the formula $x_i \in x_i$, then $\mathscr{F}_{H,\xi} = 0$, and thus we can take $G_{H,\xi} = N_{H,n,\xi} = 0$. Similarly, if H is the formula $x_i = x_i$, then we take $G_{H,\xi} = \mathscr{X}$, $N_{n,H,\xi} = 0$. Thus we have proved that for atomic formulae H there exist functions G_H, N_H such that $G_{H,\xi}$ is an open set, $N_{H,n,\xi}$ is a nowhere dense set and

$$\mathscr{F}_{H,\xi} \dot{-} G_{H,\xi} \subseteq \bigcup_n N_{H,n,\xi}.$$

Let us assume that these facts are established for the formulae H and H'.

Take $G_{\neg H,\xi} = \mathrm{Int}(\mathscr{X} - G_{H,\xi})$ and $N_{\neg H,0,\xi} = (\mathscr{X} - G_{H,\xi}) - \mathrm{Int}(\mathscr{X} - G_{H,\xi})$, $N_{\neg H,n+1,\xi} = N_{H,n,\xi}$. Then $G_{\neg H,\xi}$ is open, $N_{\neg H,n,\xi}$ is nowhere dense and

$$\begin{aligned}\mathscr{F}_{\neg H,\xi} \dot{-} G_{\neg H,\xi} &= \mathscr{F}_{H,\xi} \dot{-} (\mathscr{X} \dot{-} \mathrm{Int}(\mathscr{X} - G_{H,\xi}))\\ &= \mathscr{F}_{H,\xi} \dot{-} \mathscr{X} \dot{-} G_{H,\xi} \dot{-} \mathrm{Int}(\mathscr{X} - G_{H,\xi}) \dot{-} G_{H,\xi}\\ &= (\mathscr{F}_{H,\xi} \dot{-} G_{H,\xi}) \dot{-} N_{\neg H,0,\xi} \subseteq N_{\neg H,0,\xi} \cup \bigcup_n N_{H,n,\xi}\\ &= \bigcup_n N_{\neg H,n,\xi}.\end{aligned}$$

Thus the theorem is true for the formula $\neg H$.

We now consider the conjunction $H \wedge H'$, which we write briefly as K. Let $\eta \in \pi(M)^{\mathrm{Fr}(K)}$, $\xi = \eta|\mathrm{Fr}(H)$, $\xi' = \eta|\mathrm{Fr}(H')$. Then

$$\mathscr{F}_{K,\eta} = \mathscr{F}_{H,\xi} \cap \mathscr{F}_{H',\xi'}.$$

We define $G_{K,\eta} = G_{H,\xi} \cap G_{H',\xi'}$ and $N_{K,n,\eta} = N_{H,n,\xi} \cup N_{H',n,\xi'}$ and easily verify that $G_{K,\eta}$ is open, $N_{K,n,\eta}$ is nowhere dense and

$$\mathscr{F}_{K,\eta} \dot{-} G_{K,\eta} \subseteq \bigcup_n N_{K,n,\eta}\,.$$

Finally, let Q be the formula $(x_j)H$. If $j \notin \operatorname{Fr}(H)$, then

$$\mathscr{F}_{Q,\xi} = \mathscr{F}_{H,\xi},$$

and it is sufficient to take $G_{Q,\xi} = G_{H,\xi}$, $N_{Q,n,\xi} = N_{H,n,\xi}$. If $j \in \operatorname{Fr}(H)$, then

$$\mathscr{F}_{Q,\xi} = \bigcap_{\alpha \in \pi(M)} \mathscr{F}_{H,\xi\frown\alpha}$$

where as usual $\xi\frown\alpha = \{\langle j, \alpha\rangle\} \cup \xi$. We let $G_{Q,\xi} = \operatorname{Int}\big(\bigcap_\alpha (\overline{G}_{H,\xi\frown\alpha})\big)$; thus $G_{Q,\xi}$ is an open set. It remains to define the sets $N_{Q,n,\xi}$. Let α_n be a fixed sequence of all elements of $\pi(M)$ and let $n \rightleftarrows (n', n'')$ be a one-to-one correspondence between positive integers and pairs of non-negative integers. We let for $n > 0$

$$N_{Q,2n,\xi} = N_{H,n',\xi\frown\alpha_{n''}},$$

$$N_{Q,2n-1,\xi} = \overline{G}_{H,\xi\frown\alpha_n} - G_{H,\xi\frown\alpha_n},$$

and

$$N_{Q,0,\xi} = \bigcap_\alpha \overline{G}_{H,\xi\frown\alpha} - \operatorname{Int}\big(\bigcap_\alpha \overline{G}_{H,\xi\frown\alpha}\big)\,.$$

Thus $N_{Q,0,\xi}$ is nowhere dense because the intersection $\bigcap_\alpha \overline{G}_{H,\xi\frown\alpha}$ is closed. Sets $N_{Q,2n-1,\xi}$ are nowhere dense because if X is an open set, then the difference $\overline{X} - X$ is nowhere dense. Finally $N_{Q,2n,\xi}$ is nowhere dense by the inductive assumption.

We easily find that

$$\begin{aligned}
\mathscr{F}_{Q,\xi} \dot{-} G_{Q,\xi} &= \bigcap_\alpha \mathscr{F}_{H,\xi\frown\alpha} \dot{-} \operatorname{Int}\big(\bigcap_\alpha \overline{G}_{H,\xi\frown\alpha}\big)\\
&= \bigcap_\alpha \mathscr{F}_{H,\xi\frown\alpha} \dot{-} \bigcap_\alpha \overline{G}_{H,\xi\frown\alpha} \dot{-} N_{Q,0,\xi}\\
&\subseteq \bigcup_\alpha (\mathscr{F}_{H,\xi\frown\alpha} \dot{-} \overline{G}_{H,\xi\frown\alpha}) \cup N_{Q,0,\xi}\\
&= \bigcup_\alpha [(\mathscr{F}_{H,\xi\frown\alpha} \dot{-} G_{H,\xi\frown\alpha}) \dot{-} (\overline{G}_{H,\xi\frown\alpha} - G_{H,\xi\frown\alpha})] \cup N_{Q,0,\xi}
\end{aligned}$$

$$= \bigcup_\alpha [\bigcup_n N_{H, n, \xi \frown \alpha} \cup \bigcup_{n>0} N_{Q, 2n-1, \xi}] \cup N_{Q, 0, \xi}$$

$$= \bigcup_{n>0} N_{Q, 2n, \xi} \cup \bigcup_{n>0} N_{Q, 2n-1, \xi} \cup N_{Q, 0, \xi} = \bigcup_n N_{Q, n, \xi} \,.$$

The proof of 5.1 is thus complete.

5.2. *Under the same assumptions as in 5.1 if p is a generic point of $\mathscr{X}$ with respect to the valuation $\mathscr{F}$, then $C^B_{\pi(M)}(a(p))$ is reducible to M and thus is a model of* ZF.

PROOF. We have to verify condition VIII.1.1. Let Π^* be the set $\{\pi \colon p \in U_\pi\}$.

We prove that for every formula H the relation Forc_H is definable in M in such a way that one and the same sequence $\mathfrak{a}$ of parameters is used in the definitions of Forc_H for each H.

We select for $\mathfrak{a}$ the sequence consisting of Π, of all the parameters used in the definition (in M) of the relation $\prec$ (cf. Condition III) and of all the parameters used in the definition (in M) of the forcing relations from Condition V.

It follows from Condition V that if H is an atomic formula, then the relation Forc_H is parametrically definable in M and the unique parameters used in the definition are terms of $\mathfrak{a}$.

If H and H' have this property, then so do the formulae $\neg H, H \wedge H'$ and $(x_j)H$ in view of theorems 3.1–3.3. These theorems show how to define the forcing relation for a composite formula from the forcing relations for simpler formulae; it is obvious that these definitions do not require any parameters different from the ones which are terms of $\mathfrak{a}$.

The parametric definability of the relations Forc_H (with a fixed sequence $\mathfrak{a}$ of parameters) can be expressed by stating that for each formula H satisfying the conditions $0 \notin \mathrm{Fr}(H)$ and $\mathrm{Dom}(\mathfrak{a}) \cap \mathrm{Fr}(H) = 0$ there is a formula Φ_H with $\mathrm{Fr}(\Phi_H) = \{0\} \cup \mathrm{Dom}(\mathfrak{a}) \cup \mathrm{Fr}(H)$ such that for an arbitrary sequence ξ in $\pi(M)^{\mathrm{Fr}(H)}$ and arbitrary π in Π

(∗) $\mathrm{Forc}_H(\pi, \xi) \equiv \vdash_M \Phi_H[\{\langle 0, \pi \rangle\} \cup \xi \cup \mathfrak{a}]$.

If we now replace the expression $\mathrm{Forc}_H(\pi, t)$ in 4.2 by the right-hand side of (∗) and adjust the notation so that t is replaced by ξ and S_t by C_ξ, then we infer from 4.2 that $N(p)$ is reducible to M. Theorem 5.2 is thus proved.

In the above proof we established an important fact which later will frequently be used and which we note separately for further reference.

5.3. *If the assumptions of* 5.1 *are satisfied and* H *is an arbitrary formula, then the relation* Forc_H *is parametrically definable in* M.

In the next two chapters we shall carry out a construction for which Conditions I–V are satisfied. Apart from M there will be three essential parameters left free in this construction: the space $\mathscr{X}$, the mapping (A): $p \to a(p)$ and the function B which determines the sets $C_\xi^B(a(p))$. Thus we shall have a relatively great freedom in fixing the parameters so as to obtain models with prescribed properties.

CHAPTER X

POLYNOMIALS

In the preceding chapter we reduced the problem of construction of models to the satisfiability of Conditions I–V. The first three of these conditions are easy to verify in each particular case because they are formulated by means of very simple notions. This can not be said of Conditions IV and V, which deal with sets

$$\begin{aligned} \mathscr{E}^B_{\alpha\beta} &= \{p\colon\ C^B_\alpha(a(p)) \in C^B_\beta(a(p))\}, \\ \mathscr{I}^B_{\alpha\beta} &= \{p\colon\ C^B_\alpha(a(p)) = C^B_\beta(a(p))\}, \end{aligned} \tag{1}$$

where the sets $C^B_\alpha(a(p))$ are defined by a complicated transfinite induction whose form depend on the function B and which, moreover, depends on the initial sequence $a(p)$.

We shall reduce Conditions IV and V to simpler ones by expressing sets (1) as values of certain functions for the arguments α, β and $\mathscr{E}^B_{\xi\eta}$, $\mathscr{I}^B_{\xi\eta}$ where ξ, η precede α, β in a suitable partial well-ordering. In this way the validity of IV, V will be reduced to the validity of these conditions for pairs α, β, which are minimal elements for the partial ordering in question. The functions which will be used to express sets (1) will be called *polynomials*.

Throughout the whole chapter we assume that M is a denumerable model of ZF, $\Pi \in M$, $\mathscr{X}$ is a space and Conditions I–III are satisfied.

1. Polynomials

Let Φ be the family of functions whose values are subsets of $\mathscr{X}$ and whose domains are contained in $\pi(M)^2$. Thus

$$\Phi = \bigcup_{X \subseteq \pi(M)^2} P(\mathscr{X})^X.$$

Elements of Φ will be denoted by letters $e, f, \ldots$

The polynomials which we are going to define are functions of several variables some of which range over Φ and some over $\pi(M)$; the values of a polynomial are subsets of $\mathscr{X}$. The definition of the polynomials proceeds by induction.

1. The function of three variables, e ranging over Φ and ξ, η ranging over $\pi(M)$, whose value is $e(\xi, \eta)$ is a polynomial. The domain of this function is the set of triples $\langle e, \xi, \eta\rangle$ such that $e \in \Phi$ and $\langle \xi, \eta\rangle$ is in the domain of e.

2. If $\sigma\colon \pi(M)^n \to \Pi$ is a function parametrically definable in M, then the function $f(\xi) = U_{\sigma(\xi)}$ is a polynomial. The domain of this polynomial is $\pi(M)^n$.

3. If f is a polynomial of n variables ranging over Φ and m variables ranging over $\pi(M)$, then each function obtained from f by an identification of any two variables which range over Φ or over $\pi(M)$ or by a permutation of any two variables which range over Φ or over $\pi(M)$ is also a polynomial; also a function obtained by adding any variable is a polynomial.

Note that the domain of a polynomial obtained by an identification of variables from a polynomial f may be very different from the domain of f and may even become a void set. Thus for instance if f has two variables ranging over Φ and three variables ranging over $\pi(M)$ and if g is obtained by the identification of the first two variables, then the domain of g consists of quadruples $\langle e, \xi, \eta, \zeta\rangle$ such that $\langle e, e, \xi, \eta, \zeta\rangle$ is in the domain of f.

The addition of a variable which ranges over Φ leads from a function f of, say, n variables which range over Φ and m variables which range over $\pi(M)$ to a function of $n+1$ variables ranging over Φ and m variables which range over $\pi(M)$ such that $g(e, h, \xi) = f(e, \xi)$; similarly for the variables which range over $\pi(M)$.

4. If f is a polynomial, then so is the complement of f. Of course the domain of $\mathscr{X}-f$ is the same as that of f.

5. If for $i = 1, 2$ the functions f_i are polynomials with n_i varables ranging over Φ and m_i variables ranging over $\pi(M)$, then the function of n_1+n_2 variables ranging over Φ and of m_1+m_2 variables ranging

over $\pi(M)$ given by the formula

$$g(e_1, e_2, \xi_1, \xi_2) = f_1(e_1, \xi_1) \cap f_2(e_2, \xi_2)$$

is a polynomial.

The domain of g consists of sequences $\langle e_1, e_2, \xi_1, \xi_2\rangle$ such that $\langle e_i, \xi_i\rangle$ is in the domain of f_i for $i = 1, 2$.

6. If Δ is a function of k variables parametrically definable in M whose arguments vary over $\pi(M)$ and values over subsets of $\pi(M)$ and f is a polynomial with n variables ranging over Φ and $k+1$ variables which range over $\pi(M)$, then the function g given by the formula

$$g(e, \xi) = \bigcap_{\zeta \in \Delta(\xi)} f(e, \xi, \zeta)$$

is a polynomial.

The domain of g consists of sequences $\langle e, \xi\rangle$ such that for every ordinal ζ in $\Delta(\xi)$ the sequence $\langle e, \xi, \zeta\rangle$ is in the domain of f.

It is clear that if φ and ψ are polynomials, then there is a polynomial which in the intersection of the domains of φ and ψ has the value $\varphi(e, \xi) \cup \psi(e, \xi)$, and similarly for other Boolean operations. We shall use for this polynomials the notation $\varphi \cup \psi$ or, more generally, $\varphi \bigcirc \psi$ where $\bigcirc$ is any Boolean operation. In particular, we shall use $\varphi * \psi$ for the polynomial $\mathscr{X} - [(\varphi - \psi) \cup (\psi - \varphi)]$ and $\bigcup_{\zeta \in \Delta(\xi)} \varphi(e, \xi, \zeta)$ for the polynomial $\mathscr{X} - \bigcap_{\zeta \in \Delta(\xi)} [\mathscr{X} - \varphi(e, \xi, \zeta)]$.

If we take in 6 for Δ the function $\xi \to \{\varphi(\xi)\}$ where φ is a mapping of $\pi(M)^n$ into $\pi(M)$ and which is parametrically definable in M, then we find that if f is a polynomial, then so is the function g defined as

$$g(e, \xi) = f(e, \xi, \varphi(\xi)).$$

The domain of g consists of sequences $\langle e, \xi\rangle$ such that $\langle e, \xi, \varphi(\xi)\rangle$ is in the domain of f.

The following theorem is concerned with what might be called the continuity of polynomials:

1.1. *Let* $e = (e_1, \ldots, e_n)$, $f = (f_1, \ldots, f_n)$ *be two sequences of functions in* Φ *such that the domain of each* e_i *and of each* f_i *is one and the same set* $X \subseteq \pi(M)^2$. *Then for every polynomial* φ *and every sequence* ξ *such that both* $\langle e, \xi\rangle$ *and* $\langle f, \xi\rangle$ *belong to the domain of* φ *the following inclusion holds*:

$$\varphi(e, \xi) \dot{-} \varphi(f, \xi) \subseteq \bigcup_{j \leqslant n} \bigcup_{\langle\alpha, \beta\rangle \in X} [e_j(\alpha, \beta) \dot{-} f_j(\alpha, \beta)].$$

The proof proceeds by induction. For polynomials 1 and 2 the theorem is obvious. If ψ results from φ by an identification of variables and the theorem is true for φ, then it is true for ψ since the values of ψ are just the values of φ for suitable arguments. In the same way we see that the theorem remains valid if ψ is obtained from φ by a permutation of arguments or by the addition of a new variable. If ψ results from φ_1, φ_2 by one of the operations 4, 5, 6, then the theorem is valid for ψ if it was valid for φ_1 and φ_2, as we immediately see from the inclusions

$$(\mathscr{X} - A) \dot{-} (\mathscr{X} - B) = A \dot{-} B,$$

$$(A \cap A_1) \dot{-} (B \cap B_1) \subseteq (A \dot{-} B) \cup (A_1 \dot{-} B_1),$$

$$\Big(\bigcap_t A_t \dot{-} \bigcap_t B_t\Big) \subseteq \bigcup_t A_t \dot{-} B_t.$$

We shall now assume that $e_j(\xi, \eta)$ are open sets and we shall try to find an open set G such that $\varphi(e, \xi) \dot{-} G$ is a union of $\aleph_0$ nowhere dense sets.

1.2. *Let* $e = (e_1, \ldots, e_n)$ *where* $e_j \in \Phi$ *and* $\langle e, \xi\rangle$ *is in the domain of a polynomial* φ. *Assume that* $e_j(\alpha, \beta)$ *whenever defined is an open set. Then there exist an open set* $G = G(\varphi, e, \xi)$ *and a sequence of nowhere dense sets* $N_n = N(\varphi, n, e, \xi)$ *such that*

(1) $$\varphi(e, \xi) \dot{-} G \subseteq \bigcup_n N_n.$$

Remark. The sets G and N_n will be determined explicitly in the following proof. Thus a more correct formulation of the result is that there exist two functions G and N such that (1) holds and $G(\varphi, e, \xi)$ is open and $N(\varphi, n, e, \xi)$ is nowhere dense whenever the values $e_j(\alpha, \beta)$ are open sets.

PROOF. If φ is the polynomial 1, we take $G = e(\xi, \eta)$ and $N_n = 0$. In case 2 we take $G = U_{\sigma(\xi)}$, $N_n = 0$. If ψ results from φ by a permutation or identification of variables or by the addition of a new variable, then $G(\psi, e, \xi)$ and $N(\psi, n, e, \xi)$ arise from $G(\varphi, e, \xi)$ and $N(\varphi, n, e, \xi)$ by the same operations. If $\psi = \varphi_1 \cap \varphi_2$, then we take

$$G(\psi, e_1, e_2, \xi_1, \xi_2) = G(\varphi_1, e_1, \xi_1) \cap G(\varphi_2, e_2, \xi_2),$$

$$N(\psi, n, e_1, e_2, \xi_1, \xi_2) = N(\varphi_1, n, e_1, \xi_1) \cup N(\varphi_2, n, e_2, \xi_2).$$

If $\psi = \mathscr{X} - \varphi$, then we take

$$G(\psi, e, \xi) = \operatorname{Int}(\mathscr{X} - G(\varphi, e, \xi)),$$

$$N(\psi, 0, e, \xi) = [\mathscr{X} - G(\varphi, e, \xi)] - \operatorname{Int}(\mathscr{X} - G(\varphi, e, \xi)),$$

$$N(\psi, n+1, e, \xi) = N(\varphi, n, e, \xi).$$

The verification that formula (1) holds is practically the same as in theorem IX.5.1.

Finally let ψ be defined as $\bigcap_{\zeta \in \Delta(\xi)} \varphi(e, \xi, \zeta)$. In this case we choose an enumeration of $\Delta(\xi)$ (determined by a fixed enumeration of the model M) and represent the elements of $\Delta(\xi)$ as $\zeta_0, \zeta_1, \ldots$ Let $n \rightleftarrows (n', n'')$ be a one-to-one mapping of $\omega - \{0\}$ onto ω^2. Then we put

$$G(\psi, e, \xi) = \operatorname{Int}\Big(\bigcap_{\zeta \in \Delta(\xi)} \bar{G}(\varphi, e, \xi, \zeta)\Big),$$

$$N(\psi, 2n, e, \xi) = N(\varphi, n', e, \xi, \zeta_{n''}) \quad \text{if} \quad n > 0,$$

$$N(\psi, 2n-1, e, \xi) = \bar{G}(\varphi, e, \xi, \zeta_n) - G(\varphi, e, \xi, \zeta_n) \quad \text{if} \quad n > 0,$$

$$N(\psi, 0, e, \xi) = \bigcap_{\zeta \in \Delta(\xi)} \bar{G}(\varphi, e, \xi, \zeta) - G(\psi, e, \xi).$$

We verify exactly as in IX.5.1 that with this choice of G and N formula (1) is valid. Thus theorem 1.2 is proved.

2. Reduction of Condition IV

Let $\preccurlyeq$ be an irreflexive relation with the field $\pi(M)^2$. If $e \in \Phi$ and $\alpha, \beta < \pi(M)$, then we denote by $e|(\alpha, \beta)$ the function e restricted to arguments $\preccurlyeq (\alpha, \beta)$. We shall show that Conditions IV and V can be reduced to the following:

CONDITION VI. $\ll$ *is a parametrically definable well-founded partial ordering of* $\pi(M)^2$.

CONDITION VII. *There is an integer* P, *a partition*

$$\pi(M)^2 = Y_1 \cup \ldots \cup Y_P$$

into sets parametrically definable in M *and* $2P$ *polynomials* φ_j, ψ_j *such that whenever* $\langle\alpha, \beta\rangle \in Y_j$ *then* $\langle \mathscr{E}|(\alpha, \beta), \mathscr{I}|(\alpha, \beta), \alpha, \beta\rangle$ *is in the domains of* φ_j *and of* ψ_j *and*

$$\mathscr{E}_{\alpha\beta} = \varphi_j\big(\mathscr{E}|(\alpha, \beta), \mathscr{I}|(\alpha, \beta), \alpha, \beta\big), \tag{1}$$

$$\mathscr{I}_{\alpha\beta} = \psi_j\big(\mathscr{E}|(\alpha, \beta), \mathscr{I}|(\alpha, \beta), \alpha, \beta\big). \tag{2}$$

2.1. *If Conditions* VI–VII *are satisfied, then so is Condition* IV.

PROOF. We construct functions $G^{(1)}$, $G^{(2)}$, $N^{(1)}$, $N^{(2)}$ satisfying Condition IV by transfinite induction on the well-founded partial ordering $\ll$.

We assume that $G^{(i)}_{\xi\eta}$ and $N^{(i)}_{n,\xi,\eta}$ are defined for $n \in \omega$ and for the arguments $\langle\xi, \eta\rangle \ll \langle\alpha, \beta\rangle$. We denote these partial functions by $G^{(i)}|(\alpha, \beta)$ and $N^{(i)}_n|(\alpha, \beta)$. They are void if $\langle\alpha, \beta\rangle$ is a minimal point.

For given α, β we first determine the integer j such that $\langle\alpha, \beta\rangle \in Y_j$ and thus have formulae (1) and (2). From the continuity theorem 1.1 and the inductive assumption we obtain

$$\mathscr{E}_{\alpha\beta} \dot{-} \varphi_j\big(G^{(1)}|(\alpha, \beta), G^{(2)}|(\alpha, \beta), \alpha, \beta\big) \subseteq \bigcup_{i=1,2} \bigcup_{\langle\xi,\eta\rangle \ll \langle\alpha,\beta\rangle} \bigcup_n N^{(i)}(n, \xi, \eta).$$

For $\langle\alpha, \beta\rangle$ minimal the right-hand side is void and φ_j does not depend on the first two arguments.

Next we use theorem 1.2 and determine an open set

$$G = G\big(\varphi_j, G^{(1)}|(\alpha, \beta), G^{(2)}|(\alpha, \beta), \alpha, \beta\big)$$

and a sequence of nowhere dense sets

$$N_n = N_n\big(\varphi_j, G^{(1)}|(\alpha, \beta), G^{(2)}|(\alpha, \beta), \alpha, \beta\big)$$

such that

$$\varphi_j\big(G^{(1)}|(\alpha, \beta), G^{(2)}|(\alpha, \beta), \alpha, \beta\big) \dot{-} G \subseteq \bigcup_n N_n,$$

whence we obtain

$$\mathscr{E}_{\alpha\beta} \dot{-} G \subseteq \bigcup_{i=1,2} \bigcup_{\langle\xi,\eta\rangle \ll \langle\alpha,\beta\rangle} \bigcup_n \big(N^{(i)}(n, \xi, \eta) \cup N_n\big).$$

Finally, we arrange the nowhere dense sets $N^{(i)}(n, \xi, \eta) \cup N_n$ into an ordinary ω-sequence N'_n using a fixed enumeration of elements of M (and hence of pairs $\langle \xi, \eta \rangle \ll \langle \alpha, \beta \rangle$). We see that it is sufficient to take $G^{(1)}_{\alpha\beta} = G$ and $N^{(1)}_{n,\alpha,\beta} = N'_n$.

Replacing $\mathscr{E}$ by $\mathscr{I}$ and φ_j by ψ_j we arrive in a similar way at the proper choice of $G^{(2)}_{\alpha\beta}$ and of $N^{(2)}_{n,\alpha,\beta}$.

Theorem 2.1 is thus proved.

3. Reduction of Condition V

In this section we shall show that Condition V is satisfied provided that so are Conditions VI–VII. The general idea of this reduction is to express the truth-values of the relations $U_\pi - \mathscr{E}_{\alpha\beta} \in I$, $U_\pi - \mathscr{I}_{\alpha\beta} \in I$ as parametrically definable functions of the truth values of $U_{\pi'} - \mathscr{E}_{\xi\eta} \in I$, $U_{\pi'} - \mathscr{I}_{\xi\eta} \in I$ for $\langle \xi, \eta \rangle \ll \langle \alpha, \beta \rangle$. The theorem on the definability in M of functions defined by transfinite induction then gives immediately the required result.

We shall denote by Φ^* the set of functions whose values are 0 or 1 and which have three arguments the first of which ranges over Π and the remaining two over $\pi(M)$. In general, the domain of a function in Φ^* is a subset of $\Pi \times \pi(M)^2$. Note that the characteristic functions $\mathscr{E}^*$, $\mathscr{I}^*$ of the relations $U_\pi - \mathscr{E}_{\alpha\beta} \in I$ and $U_\pi - \mathscr{I}_{\alpha\beta} \in I$ are elements of Φ^*.

With each polynomial φ we associate a relation R_φ. Before giving an exact definition we remark that we want to define it so that conditions $U_\pi - \varphi(\mathscr{E}|(\alpha, \beta), \mathscr{I}|(\alpha, \beta), \alpha, \beta) \in I$ and $R_\varphi(\pi, \mathscr{E}^*|(\alpha, \beta), \mathscr{I}^*|(\alpha, \beta), \alpha, \beta)$ be equivalent.

If φ is a polynomial whose first n variables range over Φ and last m variables range over $\pi(M)$, then the associated relation R_φ will be a subset of $\Pi \times \Phi^{*n} \times \pi(M)^m$, i.e. it will be a relation whose first argument ranges over Π, the next n arguments over Φ^* and the last m arguments over $\pi(M)$. The definition proceeds by induction:

1. If $\varphi(e, \xi, \eta) = e(\xi, \eta)$, then

$$R_\varphi(\pi, e^*, \xi, \eta) \equiv [\langle \pi, \xi, \eta \rangle \in \mathrm{Dom}(e^*)] \wedge \big(e^*(\pi, \xi, \eta) = 1\big).$$

2. If $\varphi(\xi) = U_{\sigma(\xi)}$ where σ is a definable mapping of $\pi(M)^n$ into Π, then

$$R_\varphi(\pi, \xi) \equiv \pi \succ \sigma(\xi).$$

3. If φ is obtained by an identification or a permutation of variables from ψ or by adding a dummy variable, then R_φ is obtained from R_ψ by the same permutation or identification of variables or by adding a new variable.

4. If $\varphi(e, \xi) = \mathscr{X} - \psi(e, \xi)$, then

$$R_\varphi(\pi, e^*, \xi) \equiv (\varrho)[\varrho \succ \pi \rightarrow \neg R_\psi(\varrho, e^*, \xi)].$$

5. If $\varphi(e_1, e_2, \xi_1, \xi_2) = \psi_1(e_1, \xi_1) \cap \psi_2(e_2, \xi_2)$, then

$$R_\varphi(\pi, e_1^*, e_2^*, \xi_1, \xi_2) \equiv R_{\psi_1}(\pi, e_1^*, \xi_1) \wedge R_{\psi_2}(\pi, e_2^*, \xi_2).$$

6. If $\varphi(e, \xi) = \bigcap_{\zeta \in \Delta(\xi)} \psi(e, \xi, \zeta)$, then

$$R_\varphi(\pi, e^*, \xi) \equiv (\zeta)_{\Delta(\xi)} R_\psi(\pi, e^*, \xi, \zeta).$$

3.1. *For every polynomial φ the associated relation R_φ restricted to arguments in M is parametrically definable in M.*

The proof proceeds by induction. The relations defined in 1 and 2 above become parametrically definable in M after we restrict their arguments to M. The parameters are Π and $\prec$ and elements which act as parameters in the definition of σ. If the theorem is true for relations R_ψ, R_{ψ_1}, R_{ψ_2}, then it remains true for the relations defined in 3–6 because we gave there explicit formulae for R_φ in terms of R_ψ, R_{ψ_1}, R_{ψ_2}, relation $\prec$ and parametrically definable sets Π and Δ.

For every e in Φ, arbitrary π in Π and $\langle\xi, \eta\rangle$ in the domain of e put $e^*(\pi, \xi, \eta) = 1$ or 0 according as $U_\pi - e(\xi, \eta)$ is or is not of the first category. If $e = (e_1, \ldots, e_n)$, then we put $e^* = (e_1^*, \ldots, e_n^*)$. Obviously $e \in \Phi$ implies $e^* \in \Phi^*$.

3.2. *Let φ be a polynomial with n variables ranging over Φ and m variables ranging over $\pi(M)$. Let $e = (e_1, \ldots, e_n) \in \Phi^n$ be a sequence of functions with a common domain X, $\xi \in \pi(M)^m$ and let $\langle e, \xi\rangle$ be in the domain of φ. Finally let there exist functions g_j, h_j such that for every $\langle\xi, \eta\rangle$ in the domain of e_j the set $g_j(\xi, \eta)$ is open, $h_j(n, \xi, \eta)$ is nowhere* *dense and* $e_j(\xi, \eta) \dot{-} g_j(\xi, \eta) \subseteq \bigcup_n h_j(n, \xi, \eta)$. *If Conditions* II *and* III *are satisfied, then*

$$R_\varphi(\pi, e^*, \xi) \equiv U_\pi - \varphi(e, \xi) \in I. \tag{1}$$

The proof proceeds by induction. If φ is the polynomial whose value is $e(\xi, \eta)$, then the left-hand side of (1) is equivalent to $e^*(\pi, \xi, \eta) = 1$, i.e., to $U_\pi - e(\xi, \eta) \in I$, whence the theorem is evident. If φ is the polynomial whose value is $U_{\sigma(\xi)}$, then the left-hand side of (1) is $\pi \succ \sigma(\xi)$, which, by the definition of $\prec$, is equivalent to $U_\pi - \varphi(\xi) = 0$. Hence the left-hand side of (1) implies the right-hand side. If the left-hand side of (1) is false, then $U_\pi - U_{\sigma(\xi)} \neq 0$. Since $U_{\sigma(\xi)} = V$ is regular, i.e., $= \text{Int}\,(\overline{U_{\sigma(\xi)}}) = \text{Int}(\overline{V})$ it follows that $U_\pi - U_{\sigma(\xi)}$ contains a non-void open set and hence is not of the first category. For if $U - V \neq 0$, then $U - \text{Int}\,(\overline{V}) \neq 0$, whence $U - \overline{V} \neq 0$ because otherwise $U \subseteq \overline{V}$ and $U \subseteq \text{Int}(\overline{V})$. Thus the right-hand side of (1) is false.

Now let (1) be valid for the polynomials φ_1 and φ_2. If ψ results from φ by an identification of variables, then performing the same identification in (1), we obtain the required result for the polynomial ψ. We proceed similarly in cases where ψ results from φ by a permutation of variables or by an addition of a dummy variable. If ψ is the polynomial $\varphi_1 \cap \varphi_2$, then the left-hand side of (1) is $R_{\varphi_1} \wedge R_{\varphi_2}$ and the right-hand side is equivalent to

$$[U_\pi - \varphi_1(e_1, \xi_1)] \cup [U_\pi - \varphi_2(e_2, \xi_2)] \in I.$$

Hence both sides are equivalent because I is an ideal. In the case where

$$\psi(e, \xi) = \bigcap_{\zeta \in \Delta(\xi)} \varphi(e, \xi, \zeta)$$

the left-hand side of (1) is equivalent to

$$(\zeta)_{\Delta(\xi)}[U_\pi - \varphi(e, \xi, \zeta) \in I]. \tag{2}$$

If we had the σ-additivity of I, we could directly infer from (2) that the right-hand side of (1) is true. Since, however, the σ-additivity of I cannot be established without the axiom of choice, we must proceed in a more complicated way.

First we use the "continuity theorem" 1.1 and obtain

$$\varphi(e, \xi, \zeta) \dot{-} \varphi(g, \xi, \zeta) \subseteq \bigcup_{j \leqslant n} \bigcup_{\langle \alpha, \beta \rangle \in X} \bigcup_{p} h_j(p, \alpha, \beta);$$

(g denotes here the sequence of functions $(g_1, \ldots, g_n)$).

Next we use theorem 1.2 and find an open set G_ζ and a sequence $N_{n,\zeta}$ of nowhere dense sets such that

$$\varphi(g, \xi, \zeta) \dot{-} G_\zeta \subseteq \bigcup_{p} N_{p,\zeta}.$$

Sets G_ζ and $N_{n,\zeta}$ are determined by ξ and ζ. We obtain thus

$$(3) \qquad \varphi(e, \xi, \zeta) \dot{-} G_\zeta \subseteq \bigcup_{j \leqslant n} \bigcup_{\langle \alpha, \beta \rangle \in X} \bigcup_{p} \big(h_j(p, \alpha, \beta) \cup N_{p,\zeta}\big).$$

Thus (2) is equivalent to

$$(\zeta)_{\Delta(\xi)} [U_\pi - G_\zeta \in I]$$

and hence to

$$(\zeta)_{\Delta(\xi)} [U_\pi - \overline{G}_\zeta \in I]$$

because the difference $\overline{G}_\zeta - G_\zeta$ is nowhere dense. Since $U_\pi - \overline{G}_\zeta$ is open, we infer that the previous condition is equivalent to $U_\pi - \overline{G}_\zeta = 0$ and hence to $U_\pi \subseteq \bigcap_{\zeta \in \Delta(\xi)} \overline{G}_\zeta$. Thus (2) entails

$$U_\pi - \psi(e, \xi) \subseteq \bigcap_{\zeta} \overline{G}_\zeta \dot{-} \bigcap_{\zeta} \varphi(e, \xi, \zeta) \subseteq \bigcup_{\zeta} (\overline{G}_\zeta \dot{-} \varphi(e, \xi, \zeta))$$
$$\subseteq \bigcup_{\zeta} (\overline{G}_\zeta - G_\zeta) \cup \bigcup_{\zeta} (G_\zeta \dot{-} \varphi(e, \xi, \zeta)) \; ^{1)}.$$

In view of (3) the right-hand side is of the first category and we see that the left-hand side of (1) implies the right-hand side. If we now assume that $U_\pi - \psi(e, \xi) \in I$, then

$$\bigcup_{\zeta} [U_\pi - \varphi(e, \xi, \zeta)] \in I,$$

and hence we obtain (2) because I is an ideal. Thus (1) is true for the polynomial ψ.

[1]) In all union and intersection symbols the variable ζ ranges over $\Delta(\xi)$.

Let us finally assume that ψ is the complement of φ. We have to show (1) for the polynomial ψ, i.e.,

$$(\varrho)[\varrho \succ \pi \to \neg R_\varphi(\varrho, e^*, \xi)] \equiv U_\pi - \psi(e, \xi) \in I,$$

which is equivalent to

$$(4) \qquad (E\varrho)_{\succ\pi}[U_\varrho - \varphi(e, \xi) \in I] \equiv U_\pi \cap \varphi(e, \xi) \notin I.$$

If the right-hand side of this equivalence is false, then $U_\varrho \cap \varphi(e, \xi) \in I$ for every $\varrho \succ \pi$ and hence the left-hand side must be false in view of the fact that $U_\varrho \notin I$. Now we assume the right-hand side of (4). Repeating the proof which led us to formula (3), we obtain an open set G such that

$$\varphi(e, \xi) \dot{-} G \in I.$$

Hence the right-hand side of (4) is equivalent to $U_\pi \cap G \notin I$, whence $G \neq 0$. Take ϱ such that $U_\varrho \subseteq G$. Then $U_\varrho - G = 0$, whence $U_\varrho - -\varphi(e, \xi) \in I$. Thus the left-hand side of (4) is true and the theorem is proved.

3.3. *If Conditions* I–III, VI, VII *are satisfied, then so is Condition* V, *i.e., the relations* $U_\pi - \mathscr{E}_{\alpha\beta} \in I$, $U_\pi - \mathscr{I}_{\alpha\beta} \in I$ *are parametrically definable in* M.

PROOF. We denote, as on p. 147, the characteristic functions of the relations $U_\pi - \mathscr{E}_{\alpha\beta} \in I$ and $U_\pi - \mathscr{I}_{\alpha\beta} \in I$ by $\mathscr{E}^*$ and $\mathscr{I}^*$.

For a given pair $\langle \alpha, \beta \rangle$ of elements of $\pi(M)$ we denote by $\iota(\alpha, \beta)$ the integer j for which $\langle \alpha, \beta \rangle \in Y_j$. Thus ι is a function parametrically definable in M.

We define two functions, f_1 and f_2, with domain $\Pi \times M \times M \times \pi(M) \times \times \pi(M)$: Let $f_1(\pi, x, y, \alpha, \beta)$ be 1 or 0 according as $R_{\varphi_{\iota(\alpha,\beta)}}(\pi, x, y, \alpha, \beta)$ is true or false; similarly let $f_2(\pi, x, y, \alpha, \beta)$ be 1 or 0 according as $R_{\psi_{\iota(\alpha,\beta)}}(\pi, x, y, \alpha, \beta)$ is true or false. Functions f_1 and f_2 are parametrically definable in view of theorem 3.1.

Now we use theorem IV.4.4 and obtain two functions, e_1 and e_2, parametrically definable in M with domain $\Pi \times \pi(M) \times \pi(M)$ such that

$$e_i|(\alpha, \beta) \in M,$$

$$e_i(\pi, \alpha, \beta) = f_i(\pi, e_1|(\alpha, \beta), e_2|(\alpha, \beta), \alpha, \beta)$$

for $i = 1, 2$ and for arbitrary α, β in $\pi(M)$ and arbitrary π in Π [1]). In these formulae the symbol $e|(\alpha, \beta)$ denotes the function e restricted to arguments (ϱ, ξ, η) satisfying $\langle \xi, \eta \rangle \ll \langle \alpha, \beta \rangle$.

We now prove by induction that $e_1(\pi, \alpha, \beta) = \mathscr{E}^*_{\pi\alpha\beta}$ and $e_2(\pi, \alpha, \beta) = \mathscr{I}^*_{\pi\alpha\beta}$. Let us assume these equations for $\langle \xi, \eta \rangle \ll \langle \alpha, \beta \rangle$. We then obtain $\mathscr{E}^*|(\alpha, \beta) = e_1|(\alpha, \beta)$ and $\mathscr{I}^*|(\alpha, \beta) = e_2|(\alpha, \beta)$. From the definitions of e_1 it follows that $e_1(\pi, \alpha, \beta) = 1$ if and only if

$$R^{\Pi}_{\varphi_\iota(\alpha, \beta)}\big(\pi, \mathscr{E}^*|(\alpha, \beta), \mathscr{I}^*|(\alpha, \beta), \alpha, \beta\big);$$

in view of 3.2 we infer that this condition is equivalent to

$$U_\pi - \varphi_{\iota(\alpha, \beta)}\big(\mathscr{E}|(\alpha, \beta), \mathscr{I}|(\alpha, \beta), \alpha, \beta\big) \in I$$

and hence to $U_\pi - \mathscr{E}_{\alpha\beta} \in I$. Thus this relation is parametrically definable in M and we can prove similarly that the same is true for the relation $U_\pi - \mathscr{I}_{\alpha\beta} \in I$. Theorem 3.3 is thus proved.

[1]) Strictly speaking we rely here on the "strengthened" version of 4.4 mentioned on bottom of p. 64.

CHAPTER XI

EXPLICIT CONSTRUCTION OF POLYNOMIALS FOR FUNCTIONS $B^{\min}$, B^0, B^Z

In the present chapter we shall further simplify Conditions VI, VII, introduced in the previous chapter. While in Chapter X we discussed these conditions for an arbitrary function B, we shall now limit ourselves to the cases where B is either $B^{\min}$ or B^0 or B^Z. We shall show that Conditions VI, VII can be fulfilled provided that the mapping (A): $p \to a(p)$ which determines the sets $C^B_\alpha(a(p))$ and along with them the sets $\mathscr{E}^B_{\alpha\beta}$, $\mathscr{I}^B_{\alpha\beta}$ satisfies certain conditions similar to VII. In this way the problem of constructing models is reduced to a discussion of some simple properties of the mapping (A).

We retain the notation introduced in Chapter X. Thus $\mathscr{X}$ is a topological space, (A) a mapping $p \to a(p)$ of $\mathscr{X}$ into the class of transitive sequences of length $\alpha_0 < \pi(M)$, M is a denumerable model of ZF. Sets $\mathscr{E}^B_{\alpha\beta}$, $\mathscr{I}^B_{\alpha\beta}$ are defined as on p. 141:

$$(1)\qquad \begin{aligned} \mathscr{E}^B_{\alpha\beta} &= \{p \in \mathscr{X}:\ C^B_\alpha(a(p)) \in C^B_\beta(a(p))\}, \\ \mathscr{I}^B_{\alpha\beta} &= \{p \in \mathscr{X}:\ C^B_\alpha(a(p)) = C^B_\beta(a(p))\}. \end{aligned}$$

1. The partial ordering $\leqslant_0$

Before formulating an exact definition of $\leqslant_0$ we explain the reasons which lead us to the choice of this particular ordering. We consider pairs, or "points" as we shall call them, $\langle\alpha, \beta\rangle$ in $\pi(M)\times\pi(M)$ and want to express sets (1) as polynomials depending on α, β and on the sequences of sets $\mathscr{E}^B_{\xi\eta}$, $\mathscr{I}^B_{\xi\eta}$ where the points $\langle\xi, \eta\rangle$ are "earlier" than $\langle\alpha, \beta\rangle$.

If $I(r, \alpha) = I(r, \beta) = 10$ where r is the integer determined by the function B, then $C^B_\alpha(a(p))$ and $C^B_\beta(a(p))$ are terms of $a(p)$. Thus, sets

(1) are determined by the sequence $a(p)$ and should be considered as given once the sequence $a(p)$ is fixed. Hence such points $\langle\alpha, \beta\rangle$ will be placed before points for which $I(r, \alpha) \neq 10$ or $I(r, \beta) \neq 10$. If $\alpha = \beta$, then the first of the sets (1) is equal to 0 and the second to $\mathscr{X}$; hence points $\langle\alpha, \alpha\rangle$ will be placed before all the other points.

Let us now consider the case where $\alpha \neq \beta$ and either $I(r, \alpha) \neq 10$ or $I(r, \beta) \neq 10$ or both. We shall call such points "ordinary". It is obvious that $\mathscr{I}^B_{\alpha\beta} = \mathscr{I}^B_{\beta\alpha}$, and we shall see (cf. 3.1, case 1) that there is an identity which permits us to express $\mathscr{E}^B_{\alpha\beta}$ with $\alpha > \beta$ by means of sets $\mathscr{E}^B_{\xi\beta}$ and $\mathscr{I}^B_{\xi\alpha}$ with $\xi < \beta$. For this reason we shall consider each point $\langle\xi, \alpha\rangle$ with $\xi < \alpha$ as earlier than any ordinary point $\langle\alpha, \beta\rangle$ with $\alpha > \beta$. If $I(r, \beta) \neq 10$, then $C^B_\beta(a(p))$ can be obtained from sets $C^B_\xi(a(p))$ with $\xi < \beta$ by means of set theoretical operations. This allows us to represent sets (1) where $\alpha < \beta$ as polynomials whose arguments are α, β and sequences of sets $\mathscr{E}^B_{\xi\eta}$, $\mathscr{I}^B_{\xi\eta}$ depending on indices ξ, η such that $\max(\xi, \eta) < \beta$.

Finally, if $\alpha < \beta$ and $I(r, \beta) = 10$, then sets (1) are expressible as polynomials whose arguments are α, β and the sequences of sets $\mathscr{E}^B_{\xi\eta}$, $\mathscr{I}^B_{\xi\eta}$ depending on points $\langle\xi, \eta\rangle$ for which either $\max(\xi, \eta) < \beta$ or $I(r, \xi) = I(r, \eta) = 10$. For $C^B_\beta(a(p))$ is one of the terms of $a(p)$ and hence all the elements of $C^B_\beta(a(p))$ are also terms of $a(p)$ with smaller indices; they are therefore representable as $C^B_\eta(a(p))$ where $I(r, \eta) = 10$ and $\eta < \beta$. Thus (see 3.1, case 2)

$$p \in \mathscr{E}^B_{\alpha\beta} \equiv (E\eta)_{(I(r,\eta)=10)\wedge(\eta<\beta)}\Big[\big(C^B_\alpha(a(p)) = C^B_\eta(a(p))\big) \wedge \wedge \big(C^B_\eta(a(p)) \in C^B_\beta(a(p))\big)\Big] \equiv p \in \bigcup_{(I(r,\eta)=10)\wedge(\eta<\beta)} (\mathscr{I}^B_{\alpha\eta} \cap \mathscr{E}^B_{\eta\beta}).$$

Similarly we obtain the required representation of $\mathscr{I}^B_{\alpha\beta}$ by expressing the fact that elements of $C^B_\alpha(a(p))$ are elements of $C^B_\beta(a(p))$ and conversely (see 3.2, case 2).

For these reasons we shall agree that whenever $\langle\xi, \eta\rangle$ and $\langle\alpha, \beta\rangle$ are ordinary points and $\max(\xi, \eta) < \max(\alpha, \beta)$, then $\langle\xi, \eta\rangle$ precedes $\langle\alpha, \beta\rangle$.

We now formulate precise definitions. Let B be one of the functions $B^{\min}$, B^0, B^Z and let r be equal, accordingly, to 10, 11 or 12.

DEFINITION 1.

$$D_1 = \{\langle\alpha, \alpha\rangle: \alpha < \pi(M)\},$$
$$D_2 = \{\langle\alpha, \beta\rangle \in \pi(M)^2: \alpha \neq \beta \wedge I(r, \alpha) = I(r, \beta) = 10\},$$
$$D_3 = \pi(M)^2 - (D_1 \cup D_2).$$

Pairs in D_3 are called *ordinary*, those in D_2—*special*.

DEFINITION 2. For $\langle\xi, \eta\rangle$, $\langle\alpha, \beta\rangle \in \pi(M)^2$ we write

$$\langle\xi, \eta\rangle \leqslant_0 \langle\alpha, \beta\rangle$$

if one of the following cases occur:

(i) $\langle\xi, \eta\rangle \in D_1, \langle\alpha, \beta\rangle \in D_2 \cup D_3$,

(ii) $\langle\xi, \eta\rangle \in D_2, \langle\alpha, \beta\rangle \in D_3$,

(iii) $\langle\xi, \eta\rangle, \langle\alpha, \beta\rangle \in D_3$ and $\xi < \eta = \alpha > \beta$,

(iv) $\langle\xi, \eta\rangle, \langle\alpha, \beta\rangle \in D_3$ and $\max(\xi, \eta) < \max(\alpha, \beta)$.

We note the following properties of $\leqslant_0$:

1.1. $\leqslant_0$ *is a partial ordering of* $\pi(M)^2$, *i.e., it is irreflexive and transitive.*

1.2. $\leqslant_0$ *is well-founded.*

The proofs of these properties are obvious.

1.3. *If* $I(r, \beta) \neq 10$ *and* $\alpha < \beta$, $\xi < \beta$ *then*

$$\langle\sigma, \tau\rangle \leqslant_0 \langle\alpha, \beta\rangle \equiv \langle\sigma, \tau\rangle \leqslant_0 \langle\xi, \beta\rangle$$

for arbitrary σ *and* τ.

PROOF. If $\langle\sigma, \tau\rangle \in D_1 \cup D_2$, then both sides of this equivalence are obviously true. Now we assume that $\langle\sigma, \tau\rangle \in D_3$ and consider various cases. If $\max(\sigma, \tau) < \beta$, then both sides of the equivalence are true; if $\max(\sigma, \tau) > \beta$, they are both false. Finally, if $\max(\sigma, \tau) = \beta$, then both sides of the equivalence are false because in view of (iii) and (iv) the left-hand side of the equivalence implies that $\alpha > \beta$ and the right-hand side that $\xi > \beta$.

2. Auxiliary polynomials

We define

$$\mathscr{E}^B|(\alpha, \beta) = \{\langle\langle\xi, \eta\rangle, \mathscr{E}^B_{\xi\eta}\rangle: \langle\xi, \eta\rangle \leqslant_0 \langle\alpha, \beta\rangle\},$$

and similarly for $\mathscr{I}^B|(\alpha, \beta)$.

Consider sets

$$S_1(\xi, \eta, \zeta) = \{p \in \mathscr{X}: C_\xi(a(p)) = \{C_\eta(a(p)), C_\zeta(a(p))\}\},$$

$$S_2(\xi, \eta, \zeta) = \{p \in \mathscr{X}: C_\xi(a(p)) = \langle C_\eta(a(p)), C_\zeta(a(p))\rangle\},$$

$$S_3(\xi, \eta, \zeta) = \{p \in \mathscr{X}: C_\xi(a(p)) = C_\eta(a(p)) \cup C_\zeta(a(p))\},$$

$$S_4(\xi, \eta, \zeta) = \{p \in \mathscr{X}: C_\xi(a(p)) = C_\eta(a(p)) - C_\zeta(a(p))\},$$

$$S_5(\xi, \eta, \zeta) = \{p \in \mathscr{X}: C_\xi(a(p)) = C_\eta(a(p)) \circ C_\zeta(a(p))\}.$$

2.1. *There exist polynomials $\vartheta_1, \ldots, \vartheta_5$ with two variables ranging over Φ and three variables ranging over $\pi(M)$ such that whenever $\langle\alpha, \beta\rangle \in D_3$, $\alpha < \beta$, $\xi, \eta, \zeta < \beta$, then*

$$\langle \mathscr{E}^B|(\alpha, \beta), \mathscr{I}^B|(\alpha, \beta), \xi, \eta, \zeta\rangle \tag{1}$$

belongs to the domain of ϑ_i and

$$\vartheta_i(\mathscr{E}^B|(\alpha, \beta), \mathscr{I}^B|(\alpha, \beta), \xi, \eta, \zeta) = S_i(\xi, \eta, \zeta). \tag{2}$$

PROOF. We discuss in full the case $i = 1$ and indicate the construction for the remaining cases.

Case $i = 1$. We define

$$\vartheta_1(e, f, \xi, \eta, \zeta)$$
$$= e(\eta, \xi) \cap e(\zeta, \xi) \cap \bigcap_{\gamma < \xi} \{[\mathscr{X} - e(\gamma, \xi)] \cup f(\gamma, \eta) \cup f(\gamma, \zeta)\}.$$

If α, β, ξ, η, ζ satisfy the assumptions of the theorem, then $\langle\eta, \xi\rangle \ll_0 \langle\alpha, \beta\rangle$, and thus $\langle\eta, \xi\rangle$ belongs to the domain of $\mathscr{E}^B|(\alpha, \beta)$. Similarly $\langle\zeta, \xi\rangle$ belongs to this domain and so does $\langle\gamma, \xi\rangle$ for any $\gamma < \xi$. Also $\langle\gamma, \eta\rangle$ and $\langle\gamma, \zeta\rangle$ belong to the domain of $\mathscr{I}^B|(\alpha, \beta)$. It follows that quintuple (1) belongs to the domain of ϑ_1.

Denote by X the set on the left-hand side of (2) for $i = 1$. From the definition of ϑ_1 we infer that if $p \in X$, then $p \in \mathscr{E}^B_{\zeta\xi}$ and $p \in \mathscr{E}^B_{\eta\xi}$ and thus that $C^B_\eta(a(p)) \in C^B_\xi(a(p))$ and $C^B_\zeta(a(p)) \in C^B_\xi(a(p))$. Hence

$$p \in X \to C^B_\xi(a(p)) \supseteq \{C^B_\eta(a(p)), C^B_\zeta(a(p))\}.$$

Furthermore, for each $\gamma < \xi$ we have either $p \notin \mathscr{E}^B_{\gamma\xi}$ or $p \in \mathscr{I}^B_{\gamma\eta}$ or $p \in \mathscr{I}^B_{\gamma\zeta}$. Hence if $C^B_\gamma(a(p)) \in C^B_\xi(a(p))$, then either $C^B_\gamma(a(p)) = C^B_\eta(a(p))$ or $C^B_\gamma(a(p)) = C^B_\zeta(a(p))$. Since every element of $C^B_\xi(a(p))$ has the form $C^B_\gamma(a(p))$ with $\gamma < \xi$, we obtain

$$C^B_\xi(a(p)) \subseteq \{C^B_\eta(a(p)), C^B_\zeta(a(p))\}.$$

Thus

$$p \in X \to C_\xi^B(a(p)) = \{C_\eta^B(a(p)), C_\zeta^B(a(p))\} \to p \in S_1(\xi, \eta, \zeta).$$

The proof of the converse implication is similar

Case $i = 2$. In this case we take as ϑ_2 the polynomial

$$\bigcup_{\varrho<\xi} \bigcup_{\tau<\xi} [\vartheta_1(e, f, \varrho, \eta, \eta) \cap \vartheta_1(e, f, \tau, \eta, \zeta) \cap \vartheta_1(e, f, \xi, \varrho, \tau)].$$

Case $i = 3$. In this case ϑ_3 is

$$\bigcap_{\gamma<\max(\xi,\eta,\zeta)} [e(\gamma, \xi) * (e(\gamma, \eta) \cup e(\gamma, \zeta))].$$

Case $i = 4$. In this case the required polynomial is

$$\bigcap_{\gamma<\max(\xi,\eta,\zeta)} [e(\gamma, \xi) * (e(\gamma, \eta) - e(\gamma, \zeta))].$$

Case $i = 5$. In this case $\vartheta_5 = \vartheta_5' \cap \vartheta_5''$ where

$$p \in \vartheta_5'(\mathscr{E}^B|(\alpha, \beta), \mathscr{I}^B|(\alpha, \beta), \xi, \eta, \zeta)$$
$$\equiv [C_\xi^B(a(p)) \subseteq C_\eta^B(a(p)) \circ C_\zeta^B(a(p))]$$

and similarly for the polynomial ϑ_5'' with the sign of inclusion reversed. The polynomial ϑ_5' is

$$\bigcap_{\gamma<\xi} \{[\mathscr{X} - e(\gamma, \xi)] \cup \bigcup_{\varkappa, \lambda, \varrho, \sigma, \tau < \max(\eta, \zeta)} [\vartheta_2(e, f, \gamma, \varrho, \sigma) \cap$$
$$\cap \vartheta_2(e, f, \tau, \varrho, \varkappa) \cap \vartheta_2(e, f, \lambda, \varkappa, \sigma) \cap e(\tau, \eta) \cap e(\lambda, \zeta)]\},$$

and the polynomial ϑ_5'' is

$$\bigcap_{\varphi<\eta} \bigcap_{\psi<\zeta} \bigcap_{\varrho<\varphi} \bigcap_{\sigma<\psi} \bigcap_{\tau<\sigma} \{[\mathscr{X} - (\vartheta_2(e, f, \varphi, \varrho, \tau) \cap \vartheta_2(e, f, \psi, \tau, \sigma) \cap$$
$$\cap e(\varphi, \eta) \cap e(\psi, \zeta))] \cup \bigcup_{\gamma<\xi} (\vartheta_2(e, f, \gamma, \varrho, \sigma) \cap e(\gamma, \xi))\}.$$

3. Expressing $\mathscr{E}_{\alpha\beta}^B$ and $\mathscr{I}_{\alpha\beta}^B$ as polynomials of $\mathscr{E}^B|(\alpha, \beta)$ and $\mathscr{I}^B|(\alpha, \beta)$

We first consider the case $B = B^{\min}$, $r = 10$. Let $D_3 = A_1 \cup \ldots \cup A_{12}$ be the following partition into sets definable in M:

$$\langle\alpha, \beta\rangle \in A_1 \equiv \alpha > \beta,$$
$$\langle\alpha, \beta\rangle \in A_2 \equiv (\alpha < \beta) \wedge (I(r, \alpha) \neq 10) \wedge (I(r, \beta) = 10),$$
$$\langle\alpha, \beta\rangle \in A_{3+j} \equiv (\alpha < \beta) \wedge (I(r, \beta) = j), \quad j = 0, 1, \ldots, 9.$$

In what follows we shall omit the index $B^{\min}$ in the expressions $\mathscr{E}_{\alpha\beta}$, $\mathscr{I}_{\alpha\beta}$ and also in $\mathscr{E}|(\alpha, \beta)$, $\mathscr{I}|(\alpha, \beta)$.

3.1. *For* $i = 1, 2, \ldots, 12$ *there are polynomials* φ_i *with the following properties: Whenever* $\langle\alpha, \beta\rangle \in A_i$, *then the quadruple*

$$\langle \mathscr{E}|(\alpha, \beta), \mathscr{I}|(\alpha, \beta), \alpha, \beta\rangle \tag{1}$$

belongs to the domain of φ_i *and*

$$\varphi_i\big(\mathscr{E}|(\alpha, \beta), \mathscr{I}|(\alpha, \beta), \alpha, \beta\big) = \mathscr{E}_{\alpha\beta}.$$

The proof proceeds by considering several cases. Since their number is rather large, only some of them will be discussed in full.

In the Appendix to this chapter we give a full list of all the polynomials φ_i.

Case 1. $\langle\alpha, \beta\rangle \in A_1$. Since all elements of $C_\beta(a(p))$ have the form $C_\xi(a(p))$ with $\xi < \beta$, we obtain the equivalence

$$\begin{aligned} &C_\alpha(a(p)) \in C_\beta(a(p)) \\ &\qquad \equiv (E\xi)_\beta\{[C_\alpha(a(p)) = C_\xi(a(p))] \wedge [C_\xi(a(p)) \in C_\beta(a(p))]\} \end{aligned}$$

and hence

$$p \in \mathscr{E}_{\alpha\beta} \equiv (E\xi)_\beta(p \in \mathscr{I}_{\alpha\xi} \cap \mathscr{E}_{\xi\beta}) \equiv p \in \bigcup_{\xi<\beta} (\mathscr{I}_{\xi\alpha} \cap \mathscr{E}_{\xi\beta}).$$

Thus the required polynomial is given by the equation

$$\varphi_1(e, f, \alpha, \beta) = \bigcup_{\xi<\beta} [f(\xi, \alpha) \cap e(\xi, \beta)].$$

In order to check that quadruple (1) belongs to the domain of φ_1 it is sufficient to remark that according to Definition 2, (iii), (iv), p. 155, the pairs $\langle\xi, \alpha\rangle$ and $\langle\xi, \beta\rangle$, where $\xi < \beta$, are in relation $\leqslant_0$ to $\langle\alpha, \beta\rangle$. Thus the quintuple

$$\langle \mathscr{E}|(\alpha, \beta), \mathscr{I}|(\alpha, \beta), \alpha, \beta, \xi\rangle$$

belongs to the domain of the polynomial $f(\xi, \alpha) \cap e(\xi, \beta)$ and therefore (1) belongs to the domain of φ_1.

Case 2. $\langle\alpha, \beta\rangle \in A_2$. The construction is similar to that applied in case 1 but some changes are necessary. Observe first that in case 2 we have $I(r, \beta) = 10$ and $\alpha < \beta$; hence $C_\beta(a(p))$ is a term of $a(p)$

and so are all the members of $C_\beta(a(p))$. The condition $p \in \mathscr{E}_{\alpha\beta}$ is equivalent to the statement

$$(E\xi)_{(\xi\in\beta)\wedge(I(r,\xi)=10)}\{[C_\alpha(a(p)) = C_\xi(a(p))]\wedge[C_\xi(a(p)) \in C_\beta(a(p))]\}.$$

It follows that

$$\mathscr{E}_{\alpha\beta} = \bigcup_{(\xi<\beta)\wedge(I(r,\xi)=10)} (\mathscr{I}_{\xi\alpha} \cap \mathscr{E}_{\xi\beta}),$$

and the required polynomial φ_2 is

$$\bigcup_{(\xi<\beta)\wedge(I(r,\xi)=10)} [e(\xi, \beta) \cap f(\xi, \alpha)].$$

This is indeed a polynomial because the function I is definable in M. In order to see that quadruple (1) belongs to the domain of φ_2 we note that if $\xi < \beta$ and $I(r, \xi) = 10$, then $\langle \xi, \alpha\rangle \leqslant_0 \langle \alpha, \beta\rangle$ because $\max(\xi, \alpha) < \beta = \max(\alpha, \beta)$. On the other hand, $\langle \xi, \beta\rangle \leqslant_0 \langle \alpha, \beta\rangle$ because $\langle \xi, \beta\rangle \in D_2$ and $\langle \alpha, \beta\rangle \in D_3$.

Case 3. $\langle \alpha, \beta\rangle \in A_3$. In this case $\alpha < \beta$ and $I(r, \beta) = 0$. Hence $C_\beta(a(p))$ has as its elements all sets $C_\xi(a(p))$ with $\xi < \beta$, and thus $C_\alpha(a(p)) \in C_\beta(a(p))$ for every p. Hence $\mathscr{E}_{\alpha\beta} = \mathscr{X}$ and we can take for φ_3 an everywhere defined polynomial with constant value $\mathscr{X}$.

Cases 4–12. In these cases

$$C_\beta(a(p)) = A_{I(r,\beta)}\big(C_{K(r,\beta)}(a(p)), C_{L(r,\beta)}(a(p))\big) \cap C_{M(r,\beta)}(a(p))$$

and thus the condition $p \in \mathscr{E}_{\alpha\beta}$ is equivalent to the conjunction of

$$C_\alpha(a(p)) \in C_{M(r,\beta)}(a(p)), \quad \text{i.e.,} \quad p \in \mathscr{E}_{\alpha,M(r,\beta)}$$

and of

(2) $$C_\alpha(a(p)) \in A_{I(r,\beta)}\big(C_{K(r,\beta)}(a(p)), C_{L(r,\beta)}(a(p))\big).$$

We now have various sub-cases according to the value of $I(r, \beta)$. We shall illustrate the procedure on some examples:

Let $I(r, \beta) = 2$; thus $A_{I(r,\beta)}$ is the operation of forming pairs so that (2) becomes $p \in \mathscr{I}_{\alpha, K(r,\beta)} \cup \mathscr{I}_{\alpha, L(r,\beta)}$. The required polynomial φ_5 is thus

$$e(\alpha, M(r, \beta)) \cap [f(\alpha, K(r, \beta)) \cup f(\alpha, L(r, \beta))]$$

or, in a more accurate form,

$$\bigcup_{\xi=M(r,\beta)} \bigcup_{\eta=K(r,\beta)} \bigcup_{\zeta=L(r,\beta)} \{e(\alpha,\xi)\cap[f(\alpha,\eta)\cup f(\alpha,\zeta)]\}.$$

Note that this is a polynomial since the functions K, L, M are definable in M. The verification that the quadruple (1) belongs to the domain of φ_5 is left to the reader.

Let $I(r,\beta)=7$. The value of $A_{I(r,\beta)}(a,b)$ is thus given by $\{x\circ y: (x\in a)\wedge(y\in b)\}$. Hence (2) becomes

$$(E\sigma)(E\tau)\Big[\big(C_\sigma(a(p))\in C_{K(r,\beta)}(a(p))\big)\wedge\big(C_\tau(a(p))\in C_{L(r,\beta)}(a(p))\big)\wedge \wedge\big(C_\alpha(a(p))=C_\sigma(a(p))\circ C_\tau(a(p))\big)\Big].$$

Since all elements of $C_{K(r,\beta)}(a(p))$ have the form $C_\sigma(a(p))$ with $\sigma<K(r,\beta)$, we can limit the variability of σ to $K(r,\beta)$ and similarly that of τ to $L(r,\beta)$. Hence (2) is equivalent to

$$(E\sigma)_{K(r,\beta)}(E\tau)_{L(r,\beta)}\big[p\in\mathscr{E}_{\sigma,K(r,\beta)}\cap\mathscr{E}_{\tau,L(r,\beta)}\cap \cap\vartheta_5(\mathscr{E}|(\alpha,\beta),\mathscr{I}|(\alpha,\beta),\alpha,\sigma,\tau)\big]$$

where ϑ_5 is the polynomial defined in 2.1. Hence the required polynomial φ_{10} is

$$e(\alpha,M(r,\beta))\cap\bigcup_{\sigma<K(r,\beta)}\bigcup_{\tau<L(r,\beta)}\big[e(\sigma,K(r,\beta))\cap e(\tau,L(r,\beta))\cap \cap\vartheta_5(e,f,\alpha,\sigma,\tau)\big].$$

The construction of the remaining polynomials is similar to the two examples considered above. The reader should have no difficulty in writing them down if necessary. For the sake of completeness we list all those polynomials in the Appendix (p. 168).

We now derive a similar result for sets $\mathscr{I}_{\alpha\beta}$:

3.2. *For* $i=1,2,\ldots,12$ *there are polynomials* ψ_i *with the following properties*: *whenever* $\langle\alpha,\beta\rangle\in A_i$, *then*

(3) $$\langle\mathscr{E}|(\alpha,\beta),\mathscr{I}|(\alpha,\beta),\alpha,\beta\rangle$$

belongs to the domain of ψ_i *and*

(4) $$\psi_i(\mathscr{E}|(\alpha,\beta),\mathscr{I}|(\alpha,\beta),\alpha,\beta)=\mathscr{I}_{\alpha\beta}.$$

PROOF. If $i = 1$, then we take $\psi_1(e, f, \alpha, \beta) = f(\beta, \alpha)$. Since $\langle\alpha, \beta\rangle \in A_1$ implies $\langle\beta, \alpha\rangle \leqslant_0 \langle\alpha, \beta\rangle$, we infer that (3) belongs to the domain of ψ_1 and

$$p \in \psi_1(\mathscr{E}|(\alpha, \beta), \mathscr{I}|(\alpha, \beta), \alpha, \beta) \equiv p \in \mathscr{I}_{\beta\alpha} \equiv p \in \mathscr{I}_{\alpha\beta}.$$

If $i = 2$, then we take

$$\psi_2(e, f, \alpha, \beta) = \bigcap_{(\xi<\beta)\wedge(I(r,\xi)=10)} [e(\xi, \beta) * e(\xi, \alpha)].$$

Note that $\langle\alpha, \beta\rangle \in A_2$ implies $\langle\xi, \alpha\rangle \leqslant_0 \langle\alpha, \beta\rangle$ whenever $\xi < \beta$.

Also $\langle\xi, \beta\rangle \leqslant_0 \langle\alpha, \beta\rangle$ whenever $I(r, \xi) = 10$ because $\langle\xi, \beta\rangle \in D_2$. Hence (3) belongs to the domain of ψ_2 and the verification of formula (4) is immediate.

For $i > 2$ we define ψ_i as follows:

$$\psi_i(e, f, \alpha, \beta) = \bigcap_{\xi<\beta} [e(\xi, \alpha) * \varphi_i(e, f, \xi, \beta)].$$

We first verify that quadruple (3) belongs to the domain of ψ_i. Thus let $\langle\alpha, \beta\rangle \in A_i$; hence $I(r, \beta) \neq 10$ and $\langle\xi, \beta\rangle \in A_i$ for each $\xi < \beta$. By theorem 3.1 the quadruple

(5) $$\langle\mathscr{E}|(\xi, \beta), \mathscr{I}|(\xi, \beta), \xi, \beta\rangle$$

belongs to the domain of φ_i for each $\xi < \beta$. We can replace here $\mathscr{E}|(\xi, \beta)$ by $\mathscr{E}|(\alpha, \beta)$ and $\mathscr{I}|(\xi, \beta)$ by $\mathscr{I}|(\alpha, \beta)$ because these functions are identical in view of 1.3. Since $\langle\xi, \alpha\rangle \leqslant_0 \langle\alpha, \beta\rangle$, we see that $\langle\xi, \alpha\rangle$ belongs to the domain of $\mathscr{E}|(\alpha, \beta)$ and therefore the quintuple

$$\langle\mathscr{E}|(\alpha, \beta), \mathscr{I}|(\alpha, \beta), \xi, \alpha, \beta\rangle$$

belongs to the domain of the polynomial $e(\xi, \alpha) * \varphi_i(e, f, \xi, \beta)$. This proves that (3) belongs to the domain of the polynomial ψ_i.

We can now verify formula (4). It follows from the definition of the polynomial ψ_i that an arbitrary point p is an element of the left-hand side of (4) if and only if

$$(\xi)_\beta[p \in \mathscr{E}_{\xi,\alpha} \equiv p \in \varphi_i(\mathscr{E}|(\alpha, \beta), \mathscr{I}|(\alpha, \beta), \xi, \beta)].$$

We can again replace $\mathscr{E}|(\alpha, \beta)$ by $\mathscr{E}|(\xi, \beta)$ and $\mathscr{I}|(\alpha, \beta)$ by $\mathscr{I}|(\xi, \beta)$. Since the quadruple (5) belongs to the domain of φ_i we infer that this condition is equivalent to

$$(\xi)_\beta[p \in \mathscr{E}_{\xi,\alpha} \equiv p \in \mathscr{E}_{\xi,\beta}],$$

i.e., to

$$(\xi)_\beta\Big[\big(C_\xi(a(p))\in C_\alpha(a(p))\big)\equiv\big(C_\xi(a(p))\in C_\beta(a(p))\big)\Big].$$

Since each element of $C_\alpha(a(p))$ and each element of $C_\beta(a(p))$ have the form $C_\xi(a(p))$ with $\xi<\beta$, we infer that the last condition is equivalent to $C_\alpha(a(p))=C_\beta(a(p))$.

Theorem 3.2 is thus proved.

4. Generalization to the cases $B=B^Z_\lrcorner$ and $B=B^0$

In this section we indicate briefly the changes which must be made in theorem 3.1 in the cases where $B=B^Z$ or $B=B^0$.

Let us first deal with the case $B=B^Z$. Accordingly we take $r=12$; indices B^Z in expressions $\mathscr{E}$ and $\mathscr{I}$ will again be omitted.

This time we define the following partition of D_3:

$$D_3=A^Z_1\cup\ldots\cup A^Z_{14},$$

where $A^Z_j=A_j$ for $j\leqslant 12$ and

$$\langle\alpha,\beta\rangle\in A^Z_i\equiv(\alpha<\beta)\wedge\big(I(r,\beta)=i\big)\quad\text{for}\quad i=13,14.$$

Theorem 3.1 is valid with the following changes: i is assumed to range over the values 1, 2, ..., 14 and A_i is replaced by A^Z_i. We shall refer to the modified theorem as theorem 3.1^Z.

The proof of theorem 3.1^Z is the following. We let the definitions of φ_i unchanged for $i\leqslant 12$ and add two new polynomials φ_{13} and φ_{14}.

The definition of polynomial φ_{13} is

$$\varphi_{13}(e,f,\alpha,\beta)=\bigcup_{\xi\in\Gamma(\beta)}f(\alpha,\xi),\tag{1}$$

where $\Gamma(\beta)=\{\xi<\beta\colon I(r,\xi)=11\}$. Since I is definable in M, we see that φ_{13} is a polynomial. The verification that

$$\langle\mathscr{E}|(\alpha,\beta),\mathscr{I}|(\alpha,\beta),\alpha,\beta\rangle\tag{$*$}$$

belongs to the domain of φ_{13} is easy. From (1) we obtain

$$\begin{aligned}p\in\varphi_{13}&\big(\mathscr{E}|(\alpha,\beta),\mathscr{I}|(\alpha,\beta),\alpha,\beta\big)\\&\equiv(E\xi)_{(\xi<\beta)\wedge(I(r,\xi)=11)}\big(C_\alpha(a(p))=C_\xi(a(p))\big)\\&\equiv C_\alpha(a(p))\in\big\{C_\xi(a(p))\colon(\xi<\beta)\wedge\big(I(r,\xi)=11\big)\big\}\\&\equiv\big(C_\alpha(a(p))\in C_\beta(a(p))\big)\equiv p\in\mathscr{E}_{\alpha\beta}.\end{aligned}$$

In order to define the polynomial φ_{14} we take

$$\Xi(\beta) = \{\varrho < \pi(M)\colon \mathrm{pl}(r, \varrho) < K(r, \beta)\}$$

and

$$\varphi_{14}(e, f, \alpha, \beta) = e\big(\alpha, M(r, \beta)\big) \cap \bigcup_{\varrho \in \Xi(\beta)} \vartheta_2\big(e, f, \alpha, \mathrm{pl}^*(r, \varrho), \varrho\big).$$

φ_{14} is a polynomial because the mapping $\beta \to \Xi(\beta)$ is definable in M. If $\varrho \in \Xi(\beta)$, then $\mathrm{pl}^*(r, \varrho) < \mathrm{pl}(r, \varrho) < \beta$ (cf. III.1.5) and also $\varrho < \beta$ since pl is an increasing function.

Hence if $\langle \alpha, \beta \rangle \in A^Z_{14}$, then the quintuple

$$\langle \mathscr{E}|(\alpha, \beta), \mathscr{I}|(\alpha, \beta), \alpha, \mathrm{pl}^*(r, \varrho), \varrho \rangle$$

belongs to the domain of ϑ_2. Since $\langle \alpha, M(r, \beta)\rangle \lessdot_0 \langle \alpha, \beta \rangle$, we infer that $(*)$ belongs to the domain of φ_{14}.

Finally, the condition

$$p \in \varphi_{14}\big(\mathscr{E}|(\alpha, \beta), \mathscr{I}|(\alpha, \beta), \alpha, \beta\big) \tag{2}$$

is equivalent to the conjunction of $p \in \mathscr{E}_{\alpha, M(r, \beta)}$ and of

$$(E\varrho)_{\mathrm{pl}(r, \varrho) < K(r, \beta)} \Big(C_\alpha\big(a(p)\big) = \langle C_{\mathrm{pl}^*(r, \varrho)}\big(a(p)\big), C_\varrho\big(a(p)\big)\rangle\Big)$$

and thus (2) is equivalent to

$$C_\alpha\big(a(p)\big) \in \big\{\langle C_{\mathrm{pl}^*(r, \varrho)}\big(a(p)\big), C_\varrho\big(a(p)\big)\rangle\colon \mathrm{pl}(r, \varrho) < K(r, \beta)\big\} \cap \\ \cap C_{M(r, \beta)}\big(a(p)\big);$$

in view of $C_{\mathrm{pl}^*(r, \varrho)}\big(a(p)\big) = \varrho$ this is equivalent to

$$C_\alpha\big(a(p)\big) \in C_\beta\big(a(p)\big),$$

which is the same as $p \in \mathscr{E}_{\alpha\beta}$.

This proves theorem 3.1^Z.

For $B = B^0$ we have an analogous theorem, which we shall refer to as 3.1^0. This time we take $r = 11$ and $A_j = A^Z_j$ for $j = 1, 2, \ldots, 13$. These sets form a partition of D_3. Defining polynomials φ_j for $j = 1, 2, \ldots, 13$ as in theorem 3.1^Z we obtain the statement of theorem 3.1^0.

Theorem 3.2 can also be proved for the functions B^0 and B^Z and the proof remains practically the same. We shall refer to the modified theorems as to theorems 3.2^0 and 3.2^Z.

5. Final reduction of Conditions IV and V

In this section we will obtain the final reduction of Conditions IV and V. We shall formulate conditions on the sequence $a(p)$ alone which will ensure that Conditions IV and V are satisfied. Thus after fixing suitably the sequence $a(p)$ we shall be sure that the union of the sequence $C_\xi^B(a(p))$, $\xi < \pi(M)$ (where $B = B^{\min}$ or $B = B^Z$ or $B = B^0$) is a model of ZF.

First we introduce the notation. Let $a(p)$ be a transitive sequence of type $\alpha_0 < \pi(M)$. For $\xi, \eta < \alpha_0$ we put

$$e_{\xi\eta} = \{p: a_\xi(p) \in a_\eta(p)\},$$
$$i_{\xi\eta} = \{p: a_\xi(p) = a_\eta(p)\}.$$

These sets play for the sequence $a(p)$ a similar role to that played by $\mathscr{E}^B_{\xi\eta}$ and $\mathscr{I}^B_{\xi\eta}$ for the whole sequence of constructible sets $C^B_\alpha(a(p))$ with $\alpha < \pi(M)$.

In the sequel we shall be concerned exclusively with the cases where $B = B^{\min}$ or $B = B^0$ or $B = B^Z$ and we shall use the notation $\mathscr{E}^{\min}_{\alpha\beta}$, $\mathscr{E}^0_{\alpha\beta}$ and $\mathscr{E}^Z_{\alpha\beta}$ and the corresponding notation for the sets $\mathscr{I}_{\alpha\beta}$.

When dealing with the case $B = B^{\min}$ we take $r = 10$; for $B = B^0$ and $B = B^Z$ we take $r = 11$ and $r = 12$.

CONDITION VIII. *There exist an integer Q, a partition $\alpha_0 \times \alpha_0 = X_1 \cup \ldots \cup X_Q$ into sets which are parametrically definable in M and polynomials p_j, q_j ($j = 1, 2, \ldots, Q$) each with two ordinal and no functional variables such that whenever $\langle\alpha, \beta\rangle \in X_j$, then $\langle\alpha, \beta\rangle$ is in the domain of p_j and in the domain of q_j and*

$$e_{\alpha\beta} = p_j(\alpha, \beta),$$
$$i_{\alpha\beta} = q_j(\alpha, \beta).$$

5.1. *If Conditions* I–III (see p. 135) *and* VIII *are satisfied and if B is one of the functions $B^{\min}$, B^0, B^Z, then Conditions* VI, VII, *and hence also Conditions* IV, V, *are satisfied.*

PROOF. We first give informal explanations. In theorems 3.1, 3.2 we expressed $\mathscr{E}_{\alpha\beta}$, $\mathscr{I}_{\alpha\beta}$ by means of polynomials, but those results were limited to the case where $\langle\alpha, \beta\rangle$ was in one of the sets A_i whose union was D_3 (see p. 155, 158 and p. 160). In order to prove 5.1 we have to obtain a similar representation also in cases where $\langle\alpha,\beta\rangle\in D_1\cup D_2$. This is easy where $\langle\alpha,\beta\rangle\in D_1$ because then $\alpha=\beta$. We must now discuss pairs $\langle\alpha,\beta\rangle$ in D_2.

We proceed as follows. We know that each term $a_\xi(p)$ of $a(p)$ appears in the sequence $C_\eta(a(p))$ at the place with the index $\eta=\mathrm{pl}'(r,\xi)$ with $\xi<\alpha_0$ (cf. p. 40). The set of all these ordinals η we denote by Δ_0. Other ordinals η for which $I(r,\eta)=10$ are uninteresting because for them $C_\eta(a(p))=0$; we denote the set of those uninteresting ordinals by Δ_1.

The set D_2 can be decomposed into 4 parts: $\Delta_0\times\Delta_0$, $\Delta_1\times\Delta_1$, $\Delta_0\times\times\Delta_1$, $\Delta_1\times\Delta_0$. The first square is in a one-to-one correspondence with $\alpha_0\times\alpha_0$, and thus the partition assumed in VIII can be carried over to $\Delta_0\times\Delta_0$; for $\langle\alpha,\beta\rangle$ in $\Delta_0\times\Delta_0$ we obtain in this way the desired expressions for $\mathscr{E}_{\alpha\beta}$ and $\mathscr{I}_{\alpha\beta}$. For $\langle\alpha,\beta\rangle$ in $\Delta_1\times\Delta_1$ the representability is obvious because then $\mathscr{E}_{\alpha\beta}=0$ and $\mathscr{I}_{\alpha\beta}=\mathscr{X}$. Finally, pairs in $\Delta_0\times\Delta_1$ can be identified with pairs in $\Delta_0\times\{0\}$ because $C_\beta(a(p))=0=C_0(a(p))$ for $\beta\in\Delta_1$. Similarly, pairs in $\Delta_1\times\Delta_0$ can be identified with pairs in $\{0\}\times\Delta_0$. In this way we obtain the result in all cases.

We now present the details of the proof.

We start by remarking that the function $g\colon\ \beta\to\mathrm{pl}'(r,\beta)=\mathrm{pl}_{10}(r,\beta)$ maps α_0 into the set

(1) $$\Delta=\{\xi<\pi(M)\colon\ I(r,\xi)=10\}$$

and is one-to-one. We denote the image of α_0 by Δ_0 and put $\Delta_1=\Delta-\Delta_0$. Since $\alpha_0<\pi(M)$ the set Δ_1 is $\neq 0$. The relation $\leqslant_0$ which we introduced in Definition 2, p. 155, is definable in M since the function I is definable. Hence Condition VI is satisfied.

In order to satisfy Condition VII we have to define a partition

(2) $$Y_0\cup\ldots\cup Y_P$$

of $\pi(M)^2$ and polynomials φ_j, ψ_j $(j=0,1,\ldots,P)$ with the properties formulated on p. 146. We carry out the proof only for the case $B=B^{\min}$ and indicate later changes which are necessary to cover the cases $B=B^0$ and $B=B^Z$.

In the case $B=B^{\min}$ there will be $14+3Q$ sets Y_j. We take as Y_0 the "diagonal" $D_1=\{\langle\alpha,\alpha\rangle\colon\ \alpha<\pi(M)\}$. The next 12 sets $Y_1,\ldots,Y_{12}$ are defined as $A_1,\ldots,A_{12}$. Further we define sets Y_{12+k} for $k=1,\ldots,Q$

$$\langle\alpha,\beta\rangle\in Y_{12+k}\equiv\langle\alpha,\beta\rangle\in D_2\wedge\langle g^{-1}(\alpha),g^{-1}(\beta)\rangle\in X_k$$

and sets Y_{13+Q}, Y_{13+Q+k} and $Y_{13+2Q+k}$, $k = 1, \ldots, Q$:

$$\langle\alpha, \beta\rangle \in Y_{13+Q} \equiv (\alpha \in \Delta_1) \wedge (\beta \in \Delta_1),$$
$$\langle\alpha, \beta\rangle \in Y_{13+Q+k} \equiv (\alpha \in \Delta_1) \wedge (\beta \in \Delta_0) \wedge (\langle 0, g^{-1}(\beta)\rangle \in X_k),$$
$$\langle\alpha, \beta\rangle \in Y_{13+2Q+k} \equiv (\alpha \in \Delta_0) \wedge (\beta \in \Delta_1) \wedge (\langle g^{-1}(\alpha), 0\rangle \in X_k).$$

Next we have to define polynomials φ_j, ψ_j. First we deal with polynomials φ_j. For $j = 0$ we take $\varphi_0 = 0$. The formula

$$(3) \qquad \langle\alpha, \beta\rangle \in Y_j \to [p \in \mathscr{E}_{\alpha\beta} \triangleq p \in \varphi_j(\mathscr{E}|(\alpha, \beta), \mathscr{I}|(\alpha, \beta), \alpha, \beta)]$$

is satisfied since $\langle\alpha, \beta\rangle \in Y_0$ implies $\alpha = \beta$, and hence $\mathscr{E}_{\alpha\beta} = 0$. For $j = 1, 2, \ldots, 12$ we take as φ_j the polynomials defined in 3.1. Formula (3) then follows from theorem 3.1. For $j = 12+k$ we take as φ_j the polynomial for which

$$(4) \qquad \varphi_j(x, y, \alpha, \beta) = p_k(g^{-1}(\alpha), g^{-1}(\beta)).$$

If $\langle\alpha, \beta\rangle \in Y_j$, then $\langle g^{-1}(\alpha), g^{-1}(\beta)\rangle \in X_k$, whence the right-hand side of (4) is

$$e_{g^{-1}(\alpha), g^{-1}(\beta)} = \{x\colon a_{g^{-1}(\alpha)}(x) \in a_{g^{-1}(\beta)}(x)\}.$$

Since $a_{g^{-1}(\alpha)}(x) = C_\alpha(a(x))$ and $a_{g^{-1}(\beta)}(x) = C_\beta(a(x))$, we infer that the right-hand side is $\mathscr{E}_{\alpha\beta}$. Since the polynomial φ_j does not depend on the first two arguments, we obtain (3).

We must still consider the cases $j = 13+Q+k$, $k = 0, 1, \ldots, 2Q$.

For $j = 13+Q$ we take $\varphi_j = 0$. Since $\langle\alpha, \beta\rangle \in Y_j$ implies $\beta \in \Delta_1$, i.e., $I(r, \beta) = 10$ and $\overline{\mathrm{pl}}'(r, \beta) \geqslant \alpha_0$, we have $C_\beta(a(x)) = 0$ and hence $\mathscr{E}_{\alpha\beta} = 0$. Thus (3) is satisfied in this case. Also for $j = 13+2Q+k$ ($k > 0$) it is sufficient to take $\varphi_j = 0$.

For $j = 13+Q+k$ where $k = 1, 2, \ldots, Q$ we define

$$\varphi_j(x, y, \alpha, \beta) = p_k(0, g^{-1}(\beta)).$$

If $\langle\alpha, \beta\rangle \in Y_j$, then $I(r, \alpha) = 10$ and $\overline{\mathrm{pl}}'(r, \alpha) \geqslant \alpha_0$, whence $C_\alpha(a(x)) = 0$ (cf. p. 40). Since $a(x)$ is a transitive sequence, we also have $C_0(a(x)) = 0$ and hence

$$\mathscr{E}_{\alpha\beta} = \{x\colon C_0(a(x)) \in C_\beta(a(x))\} = e_{0, g^{-1}(\beta)} = p_k(0, g^{-1}(\beta)).$$

Condition (3) is thus satisfied.

We shall now construct polynomials ψ_j. For $j = 0$ we take $\psi_j = \mathscr{X}$. The formula

(5) $\langle \alpha, \beta \rangle \in Y_j \to [p \in \mathscr{I}_{\alpha\beta} \equiv p \in \psi_j(\mathscr{E}|(\alpha, \beta), \mathscr{I}|(\alpha, \beta), \alpha, \beta)]$

is satisfied because $\langle \alpha, \beta \rangle \in Y_0$ implies $\alpha = \beta$ and $\mathscr{I}_{\alpha\alpha} = \mathscr{X}$.

For $j = 1, 2, \ldots, 12$ the polynomials ψ_j have been constructed in 3.2.

For $j = 12+k$, $k = 1, 2, \ldots, Q$, we take

$$\psi_j(x, y, \alpha, \beta) = q_k(g^{-1}(\alpha), g^{-1}(\beta)).$$

Since $\langle \alpha, \beta \rangle \in Y_j$ implies $\mathscr{I}_{\alpha\beta} = i_{g^{-1}(\alpha), g^{-1}(\beta)}$, we obtain formula (5).

Finally, we define

$$\psi_{13+Q}(x, y, \alpha, \beta) = \mathscr{X},$$
$$\psi_{13+Q+k}(x, y, \alpha, \beta) = q_k(0, g^{-1}(\beta)), \quad k = 1, 2, \ldots, Q,$$
$$\psi_{13+2Q+k}(x, y, \alpha, \beta) = q_k(g^{-1}(\alpha), 0), \quad k = 1, 2, \ldots, Q.$$

We leave the verification of (5) for these polynomials to the reader.

Theorem 5.1 is thus proved for the case $B = B^{\min}$.

The proof for $B = B^0$ and $B = B^Z$ requires only insignificant changes: we replace sets A_i by A_j^0 or by A_k^Z ($j = 1, 2, \ldots, 13$, $k = 1, 2, \ldots, 14$) and use theorems 3.1^0, 3.2^0 or 3.1^Z, 3.2^Z instead of 3.1 and 3.2. The details of the proof can be left to the reader.

We can now summarize the result obtained in the previous theorems:

5.2. *Let M be a denumerable model of* ZF, $\mathscr{X}$ *a space and* $p \to a(p)$ *a mapping of* $\mathscr{X}$ *into the family of sequences of a fixed length* $\alpha_0 < \pi(M)$. *Let the following conditions be satisfied*:

I. *$a(p)$ is transitive*;

II. *$\mathscr{X}$ is a semi-regular space and the theorem of Baire is valid in* $\mathscr{X}$;

III. *There exist a set $\Pi \in M$ and a mapping $\pi \to U_\pi$ of Π onto a regular basis of $\mathscr{X}$ such that the relation $U_\pi \subseteq U_\varrho^!$ is parametrically definable in M.*

VIII. *There exist a partition $\alpha_0 \times \alpha_0 = X_1 \cup \ldots \cup X_Q$ into sets parametrically definable in M and $2Q$ polynomials p_j, q_j such that each of them has exactly two ordinal and no functional variables and has the property that whenever $\langle \alpha, \beta \rangle \in X_j$, then $\langle \alpha, \beta \rangle$ belongs to the domain of p_j and of q_j and*

$$\{x\colon a_\alpha(x) \in a_\beta(x)\} = p_j(\alpha, \beta),$$
$$\{x\colon a_\alpha(x) = a_\beta(x)\} = q_j(\alpha, \beta).$$

Under these conditions the space $\mathscr{X}$ *contains a residual set* $\mathrm{Gen}(\mathscr{X})$ *such that for every* p *in* $\mathrm{Gen}(\mathscr{X})$ *each of sets* $C^{B^{\min}}_{\pi(M)}(a(p))$, $C^{B^{o}}_{\pi(M)}(a(p))$, $C^{BZ}_{\pi(M)}(a(p))$ *is a model of* ZF.

6. Appendix: list of the polynomials $\varphi_j, j \leqslant 12$

The polynomials $\varphi_1, \varphi_2, \varphi_3, \varphi_5, \varphi_{10}$ were given in Section 3.

$$\varphi_4(e,f,\alpha,\beta) = e(\alpha, M(r,\beta)) \cap$$
$$\cap \bigcup_{\sigma<K(r,\beta)} \bigcup_{\tau<K(r,\beta)} \bigcup_{\varrho<\alpha} \bigcup_{\mu<\alpha} \bigcup_{\nu<\alpha} [e(\sigma,\tau) \cap e(\sigma, K(r,\beta)) \cap$$
$$\cap e(\tau, K(r,\beta)) \cap \vartheta_2(e,f,\varrho,0,\sigma) \cap \vartheta_1(e,f,\nu,0,0) \cap$$
$$\cap \vartheta_2(e,f,\mu,\nu,\tau) \cap \vartheta_1(e,f,\alpha,\varrho,\mu)].$$

Note: we use the fact that $C_0(a(p)) = 0$; thus

$$p \in \vartheta_2(\mathscr{E}|(\alpha,\beta), \mathscr{I}|(\alpha,\beta), \varrho, 0, \sigma) \equiv C_\varrho(a(p)) = \langle 0, C_\sigma(a(p))\rangle$$

and

$$p \in \vartheta_1(\mathscr{E}|(\alpha,\beta), \mathscr{I}|(\alpha,\beta), \nu, 0, 0) \equiv C_\nu(a(p)) = 1.$$

$$\varphi_6(e,f,\alpha,\beta) = e(\alpha, M(r,\beta)) \cap \bigcup_{\sigma<K(r,\beta)} [e(\alpha,\sigma) \cap e(\sigma, K(r,\beta))].$$

$$\varphi_7(e,f,\alpha,\beta) = e(\alpha, M(r,\beta)) \cap$$
$$\cap \bigcup_{\sigma<K(r,\beta)} \bigcup_{\tau<L(r,\beta)} \bigcup_{\varrho<\alpha} [e(\sigma, K(r,\beta)) \cap e(\tau, L(r,\beta)) \cap$$
$$\cap \vartheta_2(e,f,\varrho,\sigma,\vartheta) \cap \vartheta_1(e,f,\alpha,\varrho,\varrho)].$$

$$\varphi_8(e,f,\alpha,\beta) = e(\alpha, M(r,\beta)) \cap \bigcup_{\sigma<K(r,\beta)} \bigcup_{\tau<L(r,\beta)} [e(\sigma, K(r,\beta)) \cap$$
$$\cap e(\tau, L(r,\beta)) \cap \vartheta_3(e,f,\alpha,\sigma,\tau)].$$

$\varphi_9(e,f,\alpha,\beta)$ as φ_8 but with ϑ_3 replaced by ϑ_4.

$$\varphi_{11}(e,f,\alpha,\beta) = e(\alpha, M(r,\beta)) \cap \vartheta_4(e,f,\alpha,K(r,\beta),L(r,\beta)).$$

$$\varphi_{12}(e,f,\alpha,\beta) = e(\alpha, M(r,\beta)) \cap \vartheta_5(e,f,\alpha,K(r,\beta),L(r,\beta)).$$

CHAPTER XII

EXAMPLES OF MODELS AND OF INDEPENDENCE PROOFS

In this chapter we use the results obtained in Chapter XI, and in particular in theorem XI.5.2, to construct models of ZF and to establish the simplest proofs of independence. We start with examples of topological spaces and of mappings (A): $p \to a(p)$ which we shall later use in proofs of independence.

1. Examples of topological spaces

As before, let M be a denumerable model of ZF and consider a transitive sequence Q in M. The length of Q will be denoted by λ_0. For an $\alpha < \pi(M)$ we consider a sequence r of type α such that $r \in M$ and $r_\xi \subseteq \mathrm{Rg}(Q)$ for each $\xi < \alpha$.

The spaces $\mathscr{X}$ which we shall consider will be the product spaces $\mathop{\mathrm{P}}_{i<\alpha} \mathscr{X}_i$, where $\mathscr{X}_i \subseteq P(r_i)$, with the Tichonoff topology. In some cases one can use with advantage a stronger topology in the product space; we mention those topologies in theorems 1.4, 1.5 below, although we shall not have occasion to carry out independence proofs with their help.

We recall (see IX.1) that in the Tichonoff topology the neighbourhoods are determined by functions π with the following properties:

(1) $\mathrm{Dom}(\pi)$ is a finite subset of α;

(2) for each i in $\mathrm{Dom}(\pi)$ the value $\pi(i)$ is an ordered pair $\langle X_i, Y_i\rangle$ of finite disjoint subsets of r_i.

The neighbourhood U_π determined by π consists of points p in $\mathscr{X}$ whose coordinates p_i satisfy the conditions

$$(X_i \subseteq p_i) \wedge (Y_i \cap p_i = 0) \qquad \text{for } i \text{ in } \mathrm{Dom}(\pi).$$

In the case where $\alpha = 1$ the neighbourhoods in $\mathscr{X}$ are determined simply by ordered pairs of finite subsets of r_0.

In order to have short notation we shall write $\Pi_1(r_0)$ for the set of pairs $\langle X, Y\rangle$, where X, Y are disjoint finite subsets of r_0, and $\Pi_2^\alpha(r)$ for the set of functions π with properties (1) and (2).

The ordering of neighbourhoods U_π by inclusion corresponds to the following relations between the elements of $\Pi_1(r_0)$ resp. $\Pi_2^\alpha(r)$:

$$\langle\langle X, Y\rangle, \langle X_1, Y_1\rangle\rangle \in R_1(r_0) \equiv (X \supseteq X_1) \wedge (Y \supseteq Y_1),$$

$$\langle \pi, \varrho\rangle \in R_2^\alpha(r) \equiv [\mathrm{Dom}(\pi) \subseteq \mathrm{Dom}(\varrho)] \wedge (i)_{\mathrm{Dom}(\pi)}[\langle \pi(i), \varrho(i)\rangle \in R_1(r_i)].$$

The notation $\Pi_1(r_0)$, $\Pi_2^\alpha(r)$, $R_1(r_0)$, $R_2^\alpha(r)$ will be used later also in the cases where r_0 and r are not necessarily elements of M.

1.1. (a) *The spaces* $P(r_0)$ *and* $\underset{i<\alpha}{\mathbf{P}}\,(P(r_i))$ *are semi-regular; the same is true for the product spaces* $\underset{i<\alpha}{\mathbf{P}}\,\mathscr{X}_i$ *with* $\mathscr{X}_i \subseteq P(r_i)$. (b) *In all these spaces Baire's theorem is valid provided* $\mathscr{X}_i$ *is closed in* $P(r_i)$.

PROOF. (a) Spaces under consideration possess bases consisting of closed and open sets; (b) follows from the sufficient condition formulated on p. 129.

1.2. *The sets* $\Pi_1(r_0)$, $R_1(r_0)$, $\Pi_2^\alpha(r)$ *and* $R_2^\alpha(r)$ *belong to* M *whenever* r_0, r, α *are elements of* M.

PROOF. The set $P_\omega(r_0)$ of finite subsets of r_0 belongs to M, and hence so does the set S of pairs $\langle X, Y\rangle$ where X, Y are finite subsets of r_0. Since

$$t \in \Pi_1(r_0) \equiv (EX, Y)[(t = \langle X, Y\rangle) \wedge (t \in S) \wedge (X \cap Y = 0)],$$

we see that $\Pi_1(r_0)$ can be defined in the form $\{t \in S\colon \vdash_M H[t]\}$ where H is a formula. This proves that $\Pi_1(r_0)$ belongs to M.

For the remaining sets the proof is similar.

1.3. $U_\pi \subseteq U_\varrho \equiv \langle \pi, \varrho\rangle \in R_1(r_0)$ *in the case of the space* $P(r_0)$; *similarly* $U_\pi \subseteq U_\varrho \equiv \langle \pi, \varrho\rangle \in R_2^\alpha(r)$ *in the case of the product space.*

We now give some examples of generalized topology:

Let r_0 be an infinite subset of $\mathrm{Rg}(Q)$ and J an ideal of subsets of r_0 such that $J \in M$ and all finite subsets of r_0 belong to J. We define

$\Pi_{3,J}(r_0)$ as the set of ordered pairs $\pi = \langle X, Y\rangle$ of disjoint elements of J. The neighbourhoods U_π are defined as before. The ordering relation is in this case identical with $R_1(r_0)$ because 1.3 holds for the elements of $\Pi_{3,J}(r_0)$. We again have the following obvious theorems:

1.4. *The space* $\mathscr{X} = P(r_0)$ *with topology determined by neighbourhoods* U_π, *where* $\pi \in \Pi_{3,J}(r_0)$, *satisfies the Baire theorem. The neighbourhoods* U_π *form a regular basis of* $\mathscr{X}$.

1.5. *The set* $\Pi_{3,J}(r_0)$ *belongs to* M *whenever* r_0 *and* J *belong to* M.

We can generalize the construction to the case of the product space $\mathscr{X} = \mathop{\mathrm{P}}_{i<\alpha} \mathscr{X}_i$ where $\mathscr{X}_i = P(r_i)$ and the sequence r of length α consists of subsets of $\mathrm{Rg}(Q)$.

Let K be an ideal of subsets of α which contains all finite sets and let J be a sequence of type α such that for each $i < \alpha$ the set J_i is an ideal of subsets of r_i and J_i contains all finite subsets of r_i. We assume that K and J belong to M. We denote by $\Pi_{4,J,K}(r)$ the set of functions π satisfying conditions analoguous to (1) and (2):

(1′) $\mathrm{Dom}(\pi) \in K$;

(2′) if $i \in \mathrm{Dom}(\pi)$, then $\pi(i)$ is an ordered pair of disjoint sets $\langle X_i, Y_i\rangle$ such that X_i and Y_i belong to J_i.

Theorems 1.4 and 1.5 remain true (with obvious changes) and their proofs are easy.

The examples which were discussed above are very general. As a special case we can take r_0 to be the Cartesian product of two sets $a \times b$; the set $P(r_0)$ then consists of all binary relations with domain contained in a and range contained in b. Furthermore we can choose a closed subset of $P(r_0)$ as the space $\mathscr{X}$ and obtain new examples. E.g., if $a = b$ we can take as $\mathscr{X}$ the family of reflexive relations, of transitive relations, etc. More important is the case of the space of functions which we shall consider now.

Let a, b be terms of Q and let us assume that Q contains as terms all pairs $\{x, y\}$ and all ordered pairs $\langle x, y\rangle$ with $x, y \in a \cup b$. We can then take as $\mathscr{X}$ the space a^b of all mappings of b into a with the usual Tichonoff topology. Thus $\Pi = \Pi_5(a, b)$ is in this case the set of all functions π with finite domain $\mathrm{Dom}(\pi) \subseteq b$ such that $\pi(i) \in a$ for all

i in $\mathrm{Dom}(\pi)$. The set U_π consists of functions p in a^b which are extensions of π; the formulae $U_\pi \subseteq U_\varrho$ and $\pi \supseteq \varrho$ are equivalent. It is easy to formulate and to prove analogues of theorems 1.4 and 1.5.

We can also introduce the product space $\mathbf{P}_{i<\alpha} \mathscr{X}_i$ where $\mathscr{X}_i$ is the set of all mappings of a set b_i into a_i. Finally, we can modify these examples by introducing a stronger topology, in which the neighbourhoods are determined by functions whose domains belong to a given ideal. The details of these constructions are left to the reader.

2. Examples of mappings $p \to a(p)$

As before, we consider a transitive sequence Q of length λ_0 such that $Q \in M$ and a sequence r of length $\alpha < \pi(M)$ of sets $r_i \subseteq \mathrm{Rg}(Q)$. We let $\mathscr{X} = \mathbf{P}_{i<\alpha} \mathscr{X}_i$ where $\mathscr{X}_i \subseteq P(r_i)$.

We shall define two categories of sequences $a(p)$.

Sequences of the first category. We put $\lambda_1 = \lambda_0 + \alpha$ and choose ordinals $\lambda_2, \lambda_3, \ldots, \lambda_k$ satisfying the inequalities

$$\lambda_1 < \lambda_2 < \ldots < \lambda_k < \pi(M).$$

Let $R_1, \ldots, R_{k-1}$ be binary relations such that $R_i \in M$ and

$$\langle \xi, \eta \rangle \in R_i \to (\xi < \lambda_i) \wedge (\lambda_i \leqslant \eta < \lambda_{i+1})$$

for $i = 1, 2, \ldots, k-1$.

We define $a(p)$ as follows:

$$a_\xi(p) = Q_\xi \quad \text{for} \quad \xi < \lambda_0,$$

$$a_{\lambda_0+i}(p) = p_i \quad \text{for} \quad i < \alpha,$$

$$a_\eta(p) = \{a_\xi(p) \colon \langle \xi, \eta \rangle \in R_j\}$$
$$\text{for} \quad \lambda_j \leqslant \eta < \lambda_{j+1},\ j = 1, 2, \ldots, k-1.$$

The length α_0 of $a(p)$ is λ_k. We do not exclude the case where $k = 1$; in this case $a(p)$ is simply the sequence Q followed by the sequence p_i of the coordinates of p and the length of $a(p)$ is $\lambda_0 + \alpha = \lambda_1$.

Example. Let $\mathscr{X} = [P(\omega)]^\omega$ and let $a(p)$ be the sequence

$$0, 1, 2, \ldots, p_0, p_1, p_2, \ldots, \{p_0, p_1\}, \{p_2, p_3\}, \ldots, \{\{p_0, p_1\}, \{p_2, p_3\}, \ldots\}.$$

Here $\lambda_0 = \omega$, $\alpha = \omega$, $\lambda_1 = \omega \cdot 2$, $\lambda_2 = \omega \cdot 3$, $\lambda_3 = \omega \cdot 3+1$. We have two relations, R_1, R_2, defined thus: R_1 is the set of pairs $\langle \omega+2i, \omega \cdot 2+i \rangle$, $\langle \omega+2i+1, \omega \cdot 2+i \rangle$ $(i = 0, 1, 2, \ldots)$ and R_2 is the set of pairs $\langle \omega \cdot 2+j, \omega \cdot 3 \rangle$ $(j = 0, 1, 2, \ldots)$.

Sequences of the second category. The initial terms of those sequences are terms of Q; they are followed by terms of the form $(p_i \cap m) \cup (n - p_i)$ where m and n are subsets of $\mathrm{Rg}(Q)$ depending on i. The precise definition is as follows: Let f, X, Y be functions which are elements of M and have the domain α; let $f(i)$ be an ordinal $< \alpha$ and $X(i)$, $Y(i)$ subsets of λ_0 (for arbitrary $i < \alpha$). With Q as before we put

$$a_\xi(p) = Q_\xi \quad \text{for} \quad \xi < \lambda_0,$$

$$a_{\lambda_0+i}(p) = [p_{f(i)} \cap \{Q_\xi(p)\colon \xi \in X(i)\}] \cup$$
$$\cup [\{Q_\eta(p)\colon \eta \in Y(i)\} - p_{f(i)}] \quad \text{for} \quad i < \alpha.$$

The length of $a(p)$ is $\lambda_0 + \alpha$.

Example. Let $\mathscr{X} = [P(\omega)]^\omega$, $\lambda_0 = \omega$, $Q =$ the sequence of all integers. Let $X \in M$ be a sequence of subsets ω and $Y(k) = \omega - X(k)$ for $k = 0, 1, 2, \ldots$ The sequence of the second category determined by X, Y and a sequence $f \in M$ has the terms

$$0, 1, 2, \ldots, p_{f(0)} * X(0),\ p_{f(1)} * X(1), \ldots, p_{f(k)} * X(k), \ldots,$$

where $x * y$ denotes the complement of the symmetric difference of x and y.

3. Proof of Condition VIII for sequences of the first and the second category

The reader who survived the lengthy calculations given in Chapter XI will certainly not welcome this section, in which we give the not less cumbersome verification of Condition VIII for the two types of sequences described in Section 2. The verification is complicated, but it is well to notice that this is due only to the great number of special cases which we have to consider. Each particular case is very easy.

Let us consider as an example a very simple sequence of the first category

$$a(x)\colon\ 0, 1, 2, \ldots, x_0, x_1, \{x_0, x_1\}$$

of length $\omega+3$, where $x = (x_0, x_1)$ is an element of the space $[P(\omega)]^2$.

We have thus to consider the sets

$$e_{\xi\eta} = \{x\colon\ a_\xi(x) \in a_\eta(x)\},$$

$$i_{\xi\eta} = \{x\colon\ a_\xi(x) = a_\eta(x)\}$$

and to look for a suitable partition of the set $(\omega+3)\times(\omega+3)$. For each member X of the partition we have to define two polynomials, p and q, each with two ordinal variables and such that whenever $\langle\xi, \eta\rangle$ belongs to X, then

$$e_{\xi\eta} = p(\xi, \eta), \qquad i_{\xi\eta} = q(\xi, \eta).$$

If $\xi < \omega$ and $\eta < \omega$, then $a_\xi(x) = \xi$ and $a_\eta(x) = \eta$. The values of $e_{\xi\eta}$ and of $i_{\xi\eta}$ are thus either 0 or $\mathscr{X}$, and which of these cases occurs depends on whether $\xi < \eta$ or $\xi = \eta$ or $\xi > \eta$. Thus we take as the first three sets of our partition the sets

$$X_0 = \{\langle\xi, \eta\rangle\colon\ \xi < \eta < \omega\}, \qquad X_1 = \{\langle\xi, \eta\rangle\colon\ \xi = \eta < \omega\},$$

$$X_2 = \{\langle\xi, \eta\rangle\colon\ \eta < \xi < \omega\}.$$

The polynomials p and q have constant values: $p_0 = \mathscr{X}$, $q_0 = 0$, $p_1 = 0$, $q_1 = \mathscr{X}$, $p_2 = 0$, $q_2 = 0$. We verify that this is a proper choice for the case where $\langle\xi, \eta\rangle \in X_0$. We have in this case $\xi \in \eta$ and hence $a_\xi(x) \in a_\eta(x)$ independently of x, and thus $x \in e_{\xi\eta}$ for arbitrary x. Similarly $a_\xi(x) = a_\eta(x)$ for no x, and thus $i_{\xi\eta} = 0$.

There still remain various pairs to be considered. The most interesting are the pairs $\langle n, \omega+i\rangle$ where $n < \omega$ and $i = 0, 1$. Let the set of these pairs be denoted by X_3. A point $x = (x_0, x_1)$ belongs to $e_{n,\omega+i}$ if and only if $n \in x_i$, which is equivalent to the statement that x belongs to the neighbourhood U_π consisting of points whose ith coordinate contains the finite set $\{n\}$. Hence if $\pi_{i,n}$ is the function whose domain is the one-element set $\{i\}$ and whose unique value is the pair $\langle\{n\}, 0\rangle$, then the conditions $x \in e_{n,\omega+i}$ and $x \in U_{\pi_{i,n}}$ are equivalent. Thus we see that in this case it is sufficient to take as p the polynomial $p_3(\xi, \eta) = U_{\pi_{\eta-\omega,\xi}}$[1]. This is a polynomial because the function which correlates

[1]) If $\eta \leqslant \omega$, then we assume that $\eta - \omega = 0$.

with each pair $\langle\alpha, \beta\rangle$ the function $\pi_{\alpha\beta} = \{\langle\alpha, \langle\{\beta\}, 0\rangle\rangle\}$ is definable in M.

The polynomial q for this case can be taken as

$$q_3(\xi, \eta) = \bigcap_{m<\xi} p_3(m, \eta) \cap \bigcap_{\xi\leqslant m<\omega} [\mathscr{X} - p_3(m, \eta)].$$

For the pairs $\langle\omega+i, \omega+2\rangle$ where $i = 0, 1$ we can evidently take as p the polynomial which is identically $\mathscr{X}$ and as q the polynomial which is identically 0.

Although many various types of pairs are still to be considered, we shall stop here the discussion of our example. The cases which we have dealt with should be sufficient to explain how we shall discuss the general case, to which we now proceed.

Let $a(x)$ [1]) be a sequence of the first category as described in Section 2. We introduce the following partition of $\alpha_0 \times \alpha_0$:

$$\langle\xi, \eta\rangle \in E_0 \equiv (\xi = \eta),$$
$$\langle\xi, \eta\rangle \in E_{0\alpha} \equiv (\xi < \eta < \lambda_0) \wedge (Q_\xi \in Q_\eta),$$
$$\langle\xi, \eta\rangle \in E_{0\beta} \equiv (\xi < \eta < \lambda_0) \wedge (Q_\xi = Q_\eta),$$
$$\langle\xi, \eta\rangle \in E_{0\gamma} \equiv (\xi < \eta < \lambda_0) \wedge (Q_\xi \notin Q_\eta) \wedge (Q_\xi \neq Q_\eta),$$
$$\langle\xi, \eta\rangle \in E_{z1} \equiv (\xi < \lambda_0 \leqslant \eta < \lambda_1) \wedge (Q_\xi \notin r_{\eta-\lambda_0}),$$
$$\langle\xi, \eta\rangle \in E_{01} \equiv (\xi < \lambda_0 \leqslant \eta < \lambda_1) \wedge (Q_\xi \in r_{\eta-\lambda_0}),$$
$$\langle\xi, \eta\rangle \in E_{jh} \equiv (\lambda_{j-1} \leqslant \xi < \lambda_j) \wedge (\lambda_{h-1} \leqslant \eta < \lambda_h) \wedge (\xi < \eta)$$
$$j, h = 0, 1, 2, \ldots, k, \ j \leqslant h \quad \text{and} \quad (j, h) \neq (0, 0), (j, h) \neq (0, 1),$$
$$\langle\xi, \eta\rangle \in E^{jh} \equiv \langle\eta, \xi\rangle \in E_{jh} \quad \text{for arbitrary indices } j, h.$$

For each of these sets we define two polynomials, p and q, with appropriate indices. We give the definitions of these polynomials and verify that for arbitrary x in $\mathscr{X}$ and arbitrary $\langle\xi, \eta\rangle$ in any of the sets E the polynomials p, q with the same indices as E satisfy the equivalences

$$\begin{aligned} &[x \in p(\xi, \eta)] \equiv [a_\xi(x) \in a_\eta(x)], \\ &[x \in q(\xi, \eta)] \equiv [a_\xi(x) = a_\eta(x)]. \end{aligned} \tag{1}$$

[1]) In this section we use the letter x for points of the space $\mathscr{X} = \mathrm{P}\mathscr{X}_i$ in order to avoid confusion with notation for polynomials. The coordinates of x will be denoted by adding a suffix to the letter x.

1. $\langle\xi, \eta\rangle \in E_0$; $p_0(\xi, \eta) = 0$, $q_0(\xi, \eta) = \mathscr{X}$,

2. $\langle\xi, \eta\rangle \in E_{0\alpha}$; $p_{0\alpha}(\xi, \eta) = \mathscr{X}$, $q_{0\alpha}(\xi, \eta) = 0$,

3. $\langle\xi, \eta\rangle \in E_{0\beta}$; $p_{0\beta}(\xi, \eta) = 0$, $q_{0\beta}(\xi, \eta) = \mathscr{X}$,

4. $\langle\xi, \eta\rangle \in E_{0\gamma}$; $p_{0\gamma}(\xi, \eta) = 0$, $q_{0\gamma}(\xi, \eta) = 0$.

The verification of formulae (1) in these cases is immediate.

5. $\langle\xi, \eta\rangle \in E_{z1}$; $p_{z1}(\xi, \eta) = 0$.

Verification. Since $a_\xi(x) = Q_\xi \notin r_{\eta-\lambda_0}$ and $a_\eta(x) = x_{\eta-\lambda_0} \subseteq r_{\eta-\lambda_0}$, the right-hand side of the first formula (1) is false.

The polynomial $q_{z1}(\xi, \eta)$ will be defined later.

6. $\langle\xi, \eta\rangle \in E_{01}$.

We put $\sigma(\xi, \eta) = \{\langle\eta-\lambda_0, \langle\{Q_\xi\}, 0\rangle\rangle\}$ if $\eta \geqslant \lambda_0$ and $\sigma(\xi, \eta) = 0$ if $\eta < \lambda_0$. Thus if $\eta \geqslant \lambda_0$, then $\sigma(\xi, \eta)$ is a function with the one-element domain $\{\eta-\lambda_0\}$ whose value is the pair $\langle\{Q_\xi\}, 0\rangle$. Hence if $\eta \geqslant \lambda_0$, then $U_{\sigma(\xi, \eta)}$ consists of points $x \in \mathscr{X}$ such that $\{Q_\xi\} \subseteq x_{\eta-\lambda_0}$. This inclusion is equivalent to $Q_\xi \in x_{\eta-\lambda_0}$, i.e. to $a_\xi(x) \in a_\eta(x)$.

We now define polynomials q_{z1} and q_{01}. First of all we need a polynomial $w(\xi, \eta)$ with the property: if $\xi < \lambda_0 \leqslant \eta < \lambda_1$, then $w(\xi, \eta)$ is $\mathscr{X}$ or 0 according as Q_ξ is or is not a subset of $r_{\eta-\lambda_0}$. Such a polynomial is for instance

$$w(\xi, \eta) = \mathscr{X} - \bigcup_{\zeta \in \Phi(\xi, \eta)} [U_{\sigma(\zeta)} \cup (\mathscr{X} - U_{\sigma(\zeta)})]$$

where σ is an arbitrary mapping of $\pi(M)$ into Π which is definable in M (e.g., $\sigma(\zeta) = \{\langle 0, \langle\{\zeta\}, 0\rangle\rangle\}$), $\Phi(\xi, \eta) = \{\zeta < \lambda_0 \colon Q_\zeta \in Q_\xi - r_{\eta-\lambda_0}\}$ if $\lambda_0 \leqslant \eta < \lambda_1$ and $\Phi(\xi, \eta) = 0$ otherwise.

We see at once that if $\xi < \lambda_0 \leqslant \eta < \lambda_1$ and $Q_\xi \subseteq r_{\eta-\lambda_0}$, then $\Phi(\xi, \eta) = 0$ and hence $w(\xi, \eta) = \mathscr{X}$; otherwise $\Phi(\xi, \eta) \neq 0$ and hence $w(\xi, \eta) = 0$.

For $\xi < \lambda_0 \leqslant \eta < \lambda_1$ we put

$$\Gamma(\xi, \eta) = \{\zeta < \xi \colon Q_\zeta \in Q_\xi \cap r_{\eta-\lambda_0}\},$$

$$\Delta(\xi, \eta) = \{\zeta < \xi \colon Q_\zeta \in r_{\eta-\lambda_0} - Q_\xi\};$$

for other values of the arguments we define $\Gamma(\xi, \eta)$ and $\Delta(\xi, \eta)$ as 0. The required polynomials are

$$q_{z1} = q_{01} = w(\xi, \eta) \cap \bigcap_{\zeta \in \Gamma(\xi, \eta)} p_{01}(\zeta, \eta) \cap \bigcap_{\zeta \in \Delta(\xi, \eta)} [\mathscr{X} - p_{01}(\zeta, \eta)].$$

V e r i f i c a t i o n. Let $\langle\xi, \eta\rangle \in E_{z1} \cup E_{01}$. Hence $\xi < \lambda_0 \leqslant \eta < \lambda_1$. If $\zeta \in \Gamma(\xi, \eta) \cup \Delta(\xi, \eta)$, then $\langle\zeta, \eta\rangle \in E_{01}$ and hence $x \in p_{01}(\zeta, \eta) \equiv Q_\zeta \in a_\eta(x)$. Thus the condition $x \in q_{z1}(\xi, \eta)$ is equivalent to the conjunction of the formula $x \in w(\xi, \eta)$, of the formulae $Q_\zeta \in a_\eta(x)$ for all Q_ζ in $r_{\eta-\lambda_0}$ satisfying $Q_\zeta \in Q_\xi$ and of the formulae $Q_\zeta \notin a_\eta(x)$ for all Q_ζ in $r_{\eta-\lambda_0}$ satisfying $Q_\zeta \notin Q_\xi$. Since $x \in w(\xi, \eta)$ implies $Q_\xi \subseteq r_{\eta-\lambda_0}$, this conjunction is obviously equivalent to $Q_\xi = a_\eta(x)$.

7. $\langle\xi, \eta\rangle \in E_{11}$. We put

$$A(\eta) = \{\zeta: \langle\zeta, \eta\rangle \in E_{01}\}, \quad B(\eta, \zeta) = A(\eta) \cap \{\tau < \lambda_0: Q_\tau = Q_\zeta\}$$

and

$$p_{11}(\xi, \eta) = \bigcup_{\zeta \in A(\eta)} [p_{01}(\zeta, \eta) \cap q_{01}(\zeta, \xi)],$$

$$q_{11}(\xi, \eta) = q'_{11}(\xi, \eta) \cap q'_{11}(\eta, \xi)$$

where

$$q'_{11}(\xi, \eta) = \bigcap_{\zeta \in A(\xi)} \bigcup_{\tau \in B(\eta, \zeta)} \{[\mathscr{X} - p_{01}(\zeta, \xi)] \cup p_{01}(\tau, \eta)\}.$$

V e r i f i c a t i o n. The condition $x \in p_{11}(\xi, \eta)$ is equivalent to the existence of a Q_ζ in $r_{\eta-\lambda_0}$ such that $Q_\zeta \in x_{\eta-\lambda_0}$ and $Q_\zeta = x_{\xi-\lambda_0}$. This is equivalent to $x_{\xi-\lambda_0} \in x_{\eta-\lambda_0}$, i.e., to $a_\xi(x) \in a_\eta(x)$.

The condition $x \in q'_{11}(\xi, \eta)$ is equivalent to the following statement: for every $\zeta < \lambda_0$ such that $Q_\zeta \in r_{\xi-\lambda_0} \cap x_{\xi-\lambda_0}$ there is a $\tau < \lambda_0$ such that $Q_\zeta = Q_\tau$ and $Q_\tau \in x_{\eta-\lambda_0}$. Hence

$$(x \in q'_{11}(\xi, \eta)) \equiv (x_{\xi-\lambda_0} \subseteq x_{\eta-\lambda_0}) \equiv (a_\xi(x) \subseteq a_\eta(x))$$

and therefore the conditions $x \in q_{11}(\xi, \eta)$ and $a_\xi(x) = a_\eta(x)$ are equivalent.

8. $\langle\xi, \eta\rangle \in E_{jh}$ where $h, j = 0, 1, \ldots, k, j \leqslant h$ and $h \geqslant 2$.

We shall count a pair (r, s) with $r \leqslant s$ as lower than (j, h) if either $s < h$ or $s = h$ and $r < j$. Let us assume that polynomials p_{rs} and q_{rs} with (r, s) lower than (j, h) have already been constructed.

We put

$$R_h(\eta) = \{\xi: \langle\xi, \eta\rangle \in R_{h-1}\} \quad \text{and} \quad p_{jh}(\xi, \eta) = \bigcup_{\zeta \in R_h(\eta)} q_{j,h-1}(\zeta, \xi).$$

(In the case where $h = j$ we replace here $q_{j,h-1}$ by $q_{j-1,j}$.)

Verification. $x \in p_{jh}(\xi, \eta)$ is equivalent to the existence of a ζ such that $\langle \zeta, \eta \rangle \in R_{h-1}$ and $a_\zeta(p) = a_\xi(p)$, i.e., to

$$a_\xi(p) \in \{a_\zeta(p): \langle \zeta, \eta \rangle \in R_{h-1}\} = a_\eta(p).$$

If $j \geqslant 2$, we put

$$q_{jh}(\xi, \eta) = \bigcap_{\zeta \in R_h(\eta)} \bigcup_{\tau \in R_j(\xi)} q_{j-1, h-1}(\zeta, \tau) \cap \bigcap_{\tau \in R_j(\xi)} \bigcup_{\zeta \in R_h(\eta)} q_{j-1, h-1}(\zeta, \tau).$$

Verification. We represent $q_{jh}(\xi, \eta)$ as $A \cap B$. Then $x \in A$ if and only if for every ζ such that $a_\zeta(x) \in a_\eta(x)$ there is a τ such that $a_\tau(x) \in a_\xi(x)$ and $a_\zeta(x) = a_\tau(x)$. This is equivalent to $a_\eta(x) \subseteq a_\xi(x)$. We show similarly that $x \in B$ if and only if the converse inclusion holds. Hence the conditions $x \in q_{jh}(\xi, \eta)$ and $a_\xi(x) = a_\eta(x)$ are equivalent.

In the cases where $j = 0$ or $j = 1$ the definition of q_{jh} must be modified because sets $R_j(\eta)$ are not defined. We put

$$q_{1h}(\xi, \eta) = q'_{1h}(\xi, \eta) \cap q''_{1h}(\xi, \eta),$$

where

$$q'_{1h}(\xi, \eta) = \bigcap_{\zeta \in A(\xi)} \bigcup_{\tau \in R_h(\eta)} \{[\mathscr{X} - p_{01}(\zeta, \xi)] \cup q_{0, h-1}(\zeta, \tau)\},$$

$$q''_{1h}(\xi, \eta) = \bigcap_{\tau \in R_h(\eta)} \bigcup_{\zeta \in A(\xi)} q_{0, h-1}(\zeta, \tau).$$

Verification. The condition $x \in q'_{1h}(\xi, \eta)$ is equivalent to the following statement: for every $\zeta < \lambda_0$ if $Q_\zeta \in x_{\xi - \lambda_0}$, then there is a τ such that $a_\tau(x) = Q_\zeta$ and $\langle \tau, \eta \rangle \in R_{h-1}$. Since $\langle \tau, \eta \rangle \in R_{h-1}$ is equivalent to $a_\tau(x) \in a_\eta(x)$, we infer that the condition $x \in q'_{1h}(\xi, \eta)$ is equivalent to $x_{\xi - \lambda_0} \subseteq a_\eta(x)$, i.e., to $a_\xi(x) \subseteq a_\eta(x)$.

We show similarly that $[x \in q''_{1h}(\xi, \eta)] \equiv [a_\eta(x) \subseteq a_\xi(x)]$.

Finally, if $j = 0$, then we put $C(\xi) = \{\zeta < \lambda_0: Q_\zeta \in Q_\xi\}$ and

$$q_{0h}(\xi, \eta) = q'_{0h}(\xi, \eta) \cap q''_{0h}(\xi, \eta)$$

where

$$q'_{0h}(\xi, \eta) = \bigcap_{\zeta \in C(\xi)} \bigcup_{\tau \in R_h(\eta)} q_{0, h-1}(\zeta, \tau),$$

$$q''_{0h}(\xi, \eta) = \bigcap_{\tau \in R_h(\eta)} \bigcup_{\zeta \in C(\xi)} q_{0, h-1}(\zeta, \tau).$$

We easily verify the equivalences $[x \in q'_{0h}(\xi, \eta)] \equiv [a_\xi(x) \subseteq a_\eta(x)]$ and $[x \in q''_{0h}(\xi, \eta)] \equiv [a_\xi(x) \supseteq a_\eta(x)]$.

Owing to the above definitions the polynomials p_{jh} and q_{jh} are determined by induction. It remains to define polynomials p, q with upper indices.

9. $\langle\xi,\eta\rangle \in E^{jh}$. In this case we put $q^{jh}(\xi,\eta) = q_{jh}(\eta,\xi)$; the verification of the second of the formulae (1) is obvious. In order to define the polynomial p^{jh} we put

$$B_{mnjh}(\xi,\eta) = \{\zeta\colon \langle\zeta,\eta\rangle \in E_{mh} \wedge \langle\zeta,\xi\rangle \in E_{nj}\},$$

$$p^{jh}(\xi,\eta) = \bigcup_{m,n} \bigcup_{\zeta \in B_{mnjh}(\xi,\eta)} p_{mh}(\zeta,\eta) \cap q_{nj}(\zeta,\xi).$$

V e r i f i c a t i o n. $x \in p^{jh}(\xi,\eta)$ is equivalent to the existence of integers m, n and of an ordinal ζ such that $\langle\zeta,\eta\rangle \in E_{mh}$, $\langle\zeta,\xi\rangle \in E_{nj}$ and $x \in p_{mh}(\zeta,\eta) \cap q_{nj}(\zeta,\xi)$. Hence $a_\zeta(x) \in a_\eta(x)$ and $a_\zeta(x) = a_\xi(x)$, and therefore $a_\xi(x) \in a_\eta(x)$. Conversely, if $a_\xi(x) \in a_\eta(x)$, then $a_\xi(x)$ can be represented as $a_\zeta(x)$ with $\zeta < \eta$ and the implications indicated above can be reversed. Thus we have proved that:

3.1. *Sequences of the first category satisfy Condition* VIII.

Proof of Condition VIII for sequences of the second category.

We define the partition of $\alpha_0 \times \alpha_0$ into the following sets:

$$F_0 = E_0, \quad F_{0\alpha} = E_{0\alpha}, \quad F_{0\beta} = E_{0\beta}, \quad F_{0\gamma} = E_{0\gamma}, \quad F_{z1} = E_{z1},$$

$$\langle\xi,\eta\rangle \in F_{01} \equiv \xi < \lambda_0 \leqslant \eta < \lambda_0 + \alpha,$$

$$\langle\xi,\eta\rangle \in F_{11} \equiv \lambda_0 \leqslant \xi < \eta < \lambda_0 + \alpha,$$

$$\langle\xi,\eta\rangle \in F^{jh} \equiv \langle\eta,\xi\rangle \in F_{jh}.$$

Polynomials $p_0, q_0, p_{0\alpha}, \ldots, q_{0\gamma}$ are the same as before.

Let us denote by X, Y, f the functions which determine the sequence of the second category $a(x)$ (cf. p. 173). We put

$$F_{jh}(\xi) = \{\zeta\colon \langle\zeta,\xi\rangle \in F_{jh}\}$$

and similarly for the upper indices. It is then easy to check that the polynomial

$$\bar{p}(\xi,\eta) = \bigcup_{\zeta \in X(\eta-\lambda_0) \cap F_0(\xi)} q_0(\zeta,\xi) \cup \bigcup_{\zeta \in X(\eta-\lambda_0) \cap F_{0\beta}(\xi)} q_{0\beta}(\zeta,\xi) \cup$$

$$\cup \bigcup_{\zeta \in X(\eta-\lambda_0) \cap F^{0\beta}(\xi)} q^{0\beta}(\zeta,\xi)$$

has the following property: whenever $\xi < \lambda_0 \leqslant \eta < \lambda_0 + \alpha$, then

(2) $$x \in \bar{p}(\xi, \eta) \equiv a_\xi(x) \in \{Q_\zeta\colon \zeta \in X(\eta - \lambda_0)\}.$$

Replacing everywhere X by Y we obtain a polynomial $\bar{\bar{p}}(\xi, \eta)$ satisfying for the same ξ, η the equivalence

$$x \in \bar{\bar{p}}(\xi, \eta) \equiv a_\xi(x) \in \{Q_\zeta\colon \zeta \in Y(\eta - \lambda_0)\}.$$

It is now sufficient to take

$$p_{01}(\xi, \eta) = q_{01}(\xi, \eta) = 0 \quad \text{if} \quad \eta \geqslant \lambda_0;$$

otherwise

$$p_{01}(\xi, \eta) = [U_{\sigma(\xi, \lambda_0 + f(\eta - \lambda_0))} \cap \bar{p}(\xi, \eta)] \cup [\bar{\bar{p}}(\xi, \eta) - U_{\sigma(\xi, \lambda_0 + f(\eta - \lambda_0))}],$$

$$q_{01}(\xi, \eta) = \bigcap_{\zeta \in F_{0\alpha}(\xi)} p_{01}(\zeta, \eta) \cap \bigcap_{\zeta \in \lambda_0 - F_{0\alpha}(\xi)} (\mathscr{X} - p_{01}(\zeta, \eta)).$$

V e r i f i c a t i o n. Assume that $\langle \xi, \eta \rangle \in F_{01}$. Condition $x \in p_{01}(\xi, \eta)$ is equivalent to a disjunction of two conditions:

(i) $$[x \in U_{\sigma(\xi, \lambda_0 + f(\eta - \lambda_0))}] \wedge (x \in \bar{p}(\xi, \eta)),$$

(ii) $$(x \in \bar{\bar{p}}(\xi, \eta)) \wedge [x \notin U_{\sigma(\xi, \lambda_0 + f(\eta - \lambda_0))}].$$

From the definition of σ and from (2) we infer that (i) is equivalent to

$$a_\xi(x) \in x_{f(\eta - \lambda_0)} \cap \{Q_\zeta\colon \zeta \in X(\eta - \lambda_0)\}.$$

In a similar way (ii) is equivalent to

$$a_\xi(x) \in \{Q_\zeta\colon \zeta \in Y(\eta - \lambda_0)\} - x_{f(\eta - \lambda_0)},$$

and thus the first of the formulae (1) is true.

Condition $x \in q_{01}(\xi, \eta)$ means that whenever $\zeta < \lambda_0$ and $Q_\zeta \in Q_\xi$, then $x \in p_{01}(\zeta, \eta)$ and whenever $Q_\zeta \notin Q_\xi$, then $x \notin p_{01}(\zeta, \eta)$. Since $x \in p_{01}(\zeta, \eta) \equiv Q_\zeta \in x_{\eta - \lambda_0} = a_\eta(x)$ we obtain the second equivalence (1).

The polynomials p_{11}, q_{11}, p_{z1}, q_{z1} and the polynomials p, q with upper indices, can be defined in a way similar to that followed in the proof of 3.1. We leave the details of their construction to the reader. After verifying for these polynomials that formulae (1) are true we find that:

3.2. *Sequences of the second category satisfy Condition* VIII.

We have considered in this section sequences of the first and of the second category with all the details because these sequences will be used in subsequent chapters in proofs of independence. One can of course define many more classes of sequences for which Condition VIII is satisfied.

E.g., one can generalize the notion of a sequence of the first category by allowing an infinite number of relations R_i with the obvious requirement that their sequence be an element of M. Furthermore one can combine the operations which serve to define sequences of the second category with those which were used in the definition of sequences of the first category and one can iterate these operations an arbitrary number of times.

4. Examples of models

The theorems proved in Sections 1–3 in conjunction with theorem XI.5.2 allow us to define a great variety of models for ZF. Each of these models is determined by the following data: a denumerable model M of ZF, a space $\mathscr{X}$ which satisfies the conditions set forth in XI.5.2, a set Π in M, a mapping U: $\pi \to U_\pi$ of Π onto a regular basis of $\mathscr{X}$, an ordinal $\alpha_0 < \pi(M)$, a mapping $p \to a(p)$ of $\mathscr{X}$ into the class of sequences of the first or of the second category and of length α_0. A model determined by these data will be denoted by

$$N(M, \mathscr{X}, B, a(p), \Pi),$$

where B is one of the functions $B^{\min}$, B^0, B^Z and p is a generic point of $\mathscr{X}$. Usually we shall introduce simpler symbols for the special models which we shall investigate.

We give some examples of such models.

Simple extensions. We choose a transitive sequence Q of length λ_0 such that $Q \in M$, $r_0 \subseteq \mathrm{Rg}(Q)$ and $\mathscr{X} = P(r_0)$, $\Pi = \Pi_1(r_0)$ (see p. 170). Let $a(p) = Q \cup \{\langle \lambda_0, p\rangle\}$. Thus the length of $a(p)$ is $\alpha_0 = \lambda_0 + 1$ and $a(p)$ is a sequence of the first category. From theorems XI.5.2, 1.1, 1.2 and 3.1 we infer that:

4.1. *If B is one of the functions $B^{\min}$, B^0, B^Z, then for any generic $p \subseteq r_0$ the set*

$$N_1^B(r_0, p) = N(M, P(r_0), B, Q \cup \{\langle\lambda_0, p\rangle\}, \Pi_1(r_0))$$

is a model of ZF.

We call $N_1^B(r_0, p)$ a *simple extension* [1]) (the upper index B will usually be replaced by one of the symbols 0, Z or min). The elements of this model are sets $C_\xi^B(a(p))$ where $\xi < \pi(M)$. Thus we can say that the elements of $N_1^B(r_0, p)$ are sets constructible in $a(p)$ where p is generic. Essentially they are obtained from the terms of Q and from a generic subset p of r_0 by a transfinite iteration of operations $A_i(x, y)$. Since p is not, in general, an element of M, simple extensions contain elements which do not belong to the original model M. The "height" of the simple extension, measured by the least ordinal not in the set, is equal to $\pi(M)$. Thus $N_1^B(r_0, p)$ is "broader" than M but of equal "height" (cf. VI.4).

Other types of simple extensions are obtained by replacing $Q \cup \cup \{\langle\lambda_0, p\rangle\}$ by another sequence of the first or of the second category or by replacing $\Pi_1(r_0)$ by $\Pi_{3,J}(r_0)$, where J is an ideal of subsets of r_0 such that $J \in M$ and all finite subsets of r_0 belong to J. For example J can be the set of sets x which satisfy the formulae

$$x \subseteq r_0, \qquad x \in M, \qquad \vdash_M |x| \leqslant |\omega|.$$

Of course, with the topology of $\mathscr{X}$ changed, the family Gen($\mathscr{X}$) of generic subsets of r_0 is different from the family Gen($\mathscr{X}$) in 4.1.

Multiple extensions. To obtain these extensions we choose a transitive sequence Q as before and a sqeuence r of type $\alpha < \pi(M)$ of subsets of Q. Both Q and r are elements of M. We define $\mathscr{X}$ as the product space $\mathbf{P}_{i<\alpha} \mathscr{X}_i$ where $\mathscr{X}_i = P(r_i)$. As to the topology in $\mathscr{X}$ we have a great variety of choices: we can either provide $\mathscr{X}$ with the Tichonoff topology or a generalized Tichonoff topology determined by an ideal K of subsets of α and a sequence J of ideals J_i consisting of subsets of r_i $(i < \alpha)$. In the former case we choose as Π the set $\Pi_2^\alpha(r)$ and in the latter the set $\Pi_{4,J,K}^\alpha(r)$ (see Section 1). With p in Gen($\mathscr{X}$) and $a(p)$ an arbitrary

[1]) The terminology is not very appropriate since the set $N_1^B(r_0, p)$ does not always contain the whole of M.

sequence of the first or second category we can state the following theorem:

4.2. *If* $\mathscr{X} = \mathop{\mathrm{P}}_{i<\alpha} \mathscr{X}_i$, $\mathscr{X}_i = P(r_i)$ *and* $p \in \mathrm{Gen}(\mathscr{X})$, *then the sets*

$$N^B_\alpha(r, p) = N(M, \mathscr{X}, B, a(p), \Pi^\alpha_2(r)),$$
$$N^B_{\alpha, J, K}(r, p) = N(M, \mathscr{X}, B, a(p), \Pi^\alpha_{4, J, K}(r))$$

are models of ZF; *here* B *is either* $B^{\min}$ *or* B^0 *or* B^Z.

These models will be called *multiple extensions*. The structure of their elements is the same as before, i.e., these elements are $C^B_\xi(a(p))$ with $\xi < \pi(M)$. The essential difference between multiple extensions and simple extensions is that p is not a subset of a fixed r_0 but a sequence p_i of subsets of r_i. Thus in a multiple extension there is not only one single subset p of r_0 taken from outside and added to the model but a whole transfinite sequence of subsets p_i of fixed sets r_i. The "height" of these models is still $\pi(M)$.

Models obtained from generic functions. In this example we take as $\mathscr{X}$ the set a^b of all mappings of b into a. Sets a, b are elements of a transitive sequence Q which belongs to M and which satisfies the condition that each pair $\{x, y\}$ and each ordered pair $\langle x, y\rangle$ whose elements x, y belong to $a \cup b$ is a term of Q. We choose as Π the set $\Pi_5(a, b)$ and as $a(p)$ any sequence of the first or of the second category, e.g., the sequence $Q \cup \{\langle \lambda_G, p\rangle\}$ obtained by adding to Q the last term p. From theorem XI.5.2 and the theorems established in Sections 1 and 3 we infer that

4.3. *If* $p \in \mathrm{Gen}(a^b)$, *then the set*

$$N^B_{a, b}(p) = N(M, a^b, B, a(p), \Pi_5(a, b))$$

is a model of ZF *whenever* B *is one of the functions* $B^{\min}$, B^0, B^Z *and* $a(p)$ *any sequence of the first or of the second category*.

Models $N^B_{a, b}(p)$ can be called *simple functional extensions* because their elements are constructed from a single function $p \in a^b$.

In a similar way we can define multiple functional extensions by choosing for $\mathscr{X}$ the space $\mathop{\mathrm{P}}_{i<\alpha} \mathscr{X}_i$ with $\mathscr{X}_i = a_i^{b_i}$ or more generally with $\mathscr{X}_i$ contained and closed in $a_i^{b_i}$. We again have various possibilities for the choice of topology in $\mathscr{X}$ and the choice of a sequence $a(p)$.

The number of various examples of models which can be constructed in this way is, as we see, unlimited.

5. A theorem on generic points

The properties of models constructed in Sections 1–4 depend mainly on the properties of the generic points p which served to construct them. In general, it is not easy to answer the question whether a given formula H is satisfied in one of the models constructed above. We can prove only the following weak result:

5.1. *Let $\mathscr{X}$ be a space and $A\colon p \to a(p)$ a mapping such that all the assumptions of theorem* XI.5.2 *are satisfied and let $N(p)$ be one of the models $C^B_{\pi(M)}(a(p))$ where, as usual, B is one of the functions $B^{\min}$, B^0, B^Z.*

If H is a formula, $\xi \in \pi(M)^{\mathrm{Fr}(H)}$ and the set

$$\mathscr{F}_{H,\xi} = \{p\colon \vdash_{N(p)} H[C_\xi(a(p))]\}$$

is of the first category, then $\mathrm{Gen}(\mathscr{X}) \cap \mathscr{F}_{H,\xi} = 0$.

PROOF. If $\mathscr{F}_{H,\xi}$ contained a generic point, then it would contain almost all the points of a neighbourhood of p and thus would not be of the first category.

Theorem 5.1 exhibits a large class of formulae such that $\vdash_{N(p)} \neg H[C_\xi(a(p))]$ for any generic p. In spite of its simplicity the theorem has remarkable consequences, as will follow from the examples given below. We first prove the following lemma:

5.2. *Let $\mathscr{X}_\gamma$, $\gamma < \varrho$, be Hausdorff spaces without isolated points* [1]) *and $\mathscr{X} = \mathop{\mathrm{P}}\limits_{\gamma<\varrho} \mathscr{X}_\gamma$ their product with a J-topology where J is an ideal of subsets of ϱ containing all the finite subsets of ϱ.*

Let $\alpha < \beta < \gamma$ and $\mathscr{X}_\alpha = \mathscr{X}_\beta$. Then the set

$$A = A_{\alpha\beta} = \{p \in \mathscr{X}\colon p_\alpha = p_\beta\}$$

is nowhere dense in $\mathscr{X}$. If $\varrho < \omega_1$, then the set

$$\{p\colon (E\alpha, \beta)_\varrho[(\alpha \neq \beta) \wedge (\mathscr{X}_\alpha = \mathscr{X}_\beta) \wedge (p_\alpha = p_\beta)]\}$$

is of the first category.

[1]) In a Hausdorff space each pair p, q of distinct points can be separated by disjoint neighbourhoods: $p \in U$, $q \in V$ and $U \cap V = 0$.

PROOF. Let U be a neighbourhood of a point $p \in A$, U_α and U_β projections of U into $\mathscr{X}_\alpha$, $\mathscr{X}_\beta$. Since $\mathscr{X}_\alpha = \mathscr{X}_\beta$ and there are no isolated points in $\mathscr{X}_\alpha$, we easily see that there are neighbourhoods $U' \subseteq U_\alpha$, $U'' \subseteq U_\beta$ such that $U' \cap U'' = 0$. Let U_0 be the set of points q in U such that $q_\alpha \in U'$ and $q_\beta \in U''$. Then U_0 is a neighbourhood and hence an open subset of U. Moreover, U_0 is disjoint with $A_{\alpha\beta}$. This proves the first part of the lemma. The second part of the lemma follows from the first.

The following is an immediate corollary to lemma 5.2.

5.3. *If* $B = B^Z$, *all terms of the sequence* r *are infinite and* $a(p)$ *is a sequence of the first category, then in the models* $N_\alpha^B(r, p)$ *and* $N_{\alpha, J, K}^B(r, p)$ *obtained by the method of multiple extensions* (cf. 4.2) *there exist one-to-one mappings of* α *into the family of subsets of* $\mathrm{Rg}(Q)$.

PROOF. From V.5.6 it follows that there is a fixed ordinal ν such that $C_\nu^B(a(p)) = a(p)$ for each p. We shall show that if p is generic, then p belongs to the models in question and no two of its coordinates are equal. Once we have shown this, it will be clear that p is the required mapping.

Since $a(p)$ is a sequence of the first category we obtain p from $a(p)$ by forming the composite function $f \circ a(p)$ where

$$f = \{\langle \xi, \lambda_0 + \xi \rangle : \xi < \alpha\}.$$

In view of V.2.1 f belongs to the models considered in the theorem and hence so does p.

We now prove that $p_\varrho \neq p_\sigma$ for $\varrho \neq \sigma$. Notice that $p_\varrho = a_{\lambda_0+\varrho}(p)$ and so we have to show that $a_{\lambda_0+\varrho}(p) \neq a_{\lambda_0+\sigma}(p)$ whenever $\varrho \neq \sigma$ and $\varrho, \sigma < \alpha$.

Let H be the formula

$$(Ex_3)[(\langle x_1, x_3 \rangle \in x_0) \wedge (\langle x_2, x_3 \rangle \in x_0)]$$

and φ the sequence

$$\{\langle 0, \nu \rangle, \langle 1, \mathrm{pl}'(\lambda_0+\varrho) \rangle, \langle 2, \mathrm{pl}'(\lambda_0+\sigma) \rangle\}.$$

From the definition of $\mathscr{F}_{H,\varphi}$ we easily infer that $(p \in \mathscr{F}_{H,\varphi}) \equiv (p_\varrho = p_\sigma)$ for arbitrary p in $\mathscr{X}$. Now we notice that none of the spaces $\mathscr{X}_i = P(r_i)$ has isolated points and hence the assumptions of 5.2 are satisfied. It follows that the set $\mathscr{F}_{H,\varphi}$ is of the first category, which proves that no generic point p belongs to this set. Hence $p_\varrho \neq p_\sigma$ for each generic p, which proves the theorem.

For example we can take as Q the sequence of all integers and as α any ordinal of M and find that there are models which contain as elements sequences of length α whose elements are different sets of integers. We shall see in the next chapter how to obtain an independence proof of the continuum hypothesis from this corollary.

We now consider the case where the elements of $\mathscr{X}$ are mappings. We first prove the following lemma:

5.4. *If $\mathscr{X} = a^b$, b infinite, and the topology in $\mathscr{X}$ is that of Tichonoff and if $x \in a$, then the set $S_x = \{f \in \mathscr{X}\colon x \notin \mathrm{Rg}(f)\}$ is nowhere dense.*

PROOF. Let $f \in S_x$ and let U be the neighbourhood of f determined by a partial function $f|X$ where X is a finite subset of b. Take any $y \in b-X$. The neighbourhood consisting of all extensions of $f|X \cup \{\langle y, x\rangle\}$ is disjoint from S_x.

5.5. *If b is infinite, then the model $N^B_{a,b}(p)$ constructed in* 4.3 *contains a mapping of b onto a.*

PROOF. Since p is a term of $a(p)$, we have $p \in N^B_{a,b}(p)$. We shall show that p is the required mapping.

According to the construction of the sequence $a(p)$ used in 4.3, the place at which p occurs in $a(p)$ is independent of p. Also a is a term of $a(p)$ with a fixed index. Thus there are ordinals $\xi < \pi(M)$, $\eta < \pi(M)$ such that

$$a = C_\eta(a(p)) \quad \text{and} \quad p = C_\xi(a(p)).$$

Let H be the formula

$$(Ez)[(z \in x_1) \wedge (t)(\langle t, z\rangle \notin x_0)].$$

Then to say that a mapping $f = C_\varphi(a(p)) \in N^B_{a,b} = N$ is not a mapping onto a amounts to the same as to say that

$$\vdash_N H[f, a]$$

or, more pedantically,

$$\vdash_N H[\{\langle 0, C_\varphi(a(p))\rangle, \langle 1, C_\eta(a(p))\rangle\}].$$

Take $\varphi = \xi$. We find that the set

$$\mathscr{F}_{H,\{\langle 0,\xi\rangle, \langle 1,\eta\rangle\}} = \{p \in \mathscr{X}\colon \vdash_N H[p, a]\} = \bigcup_{x \in a} S_x$$

is of the first category and therefore no generic p belongs to

$$\mathscr{F}_{H,\{\langle 0,\xi\rangle,\langle 1,\eta\rangle\}}, \quad \text{i.e.,} \quad \vdash_N \neg H[p, a],$$

which proves the theorem.

A similar theorem can obviously be proved not only for the case where the topology in $\mathscr{X}$ is the Tichonoff topology but in the more general case mentioned at the end of Section 1, where the topology is determined by an ideal J of subsets of b. The only assumption we have to add is that the ideal be proper, i.e., that $b \notin J$.

6. Independence of the strong axiom of constructibility

We assume in this section that $\mathscr{X}$ is a space without isolated points and that $\mathscr{X}$, $a(p)$ and U_π satisfy all the assumptions of theorem XI.5.2 and finally that there is a fixed ordinal γ such that $p = C_\gamma^{\mathrm{Z}}(a(p))$ for each p in $\mathscr{X}$. The notion of generic point refers to this space with the basis U_π and to a fixed denumerable model M. We denote by $N^{\mathrm{Z}}(p)$ the model obtained from M and from a generic point p by means of theorem XI.5.2 and for $B = B^{\mathrm{Z}}$. The assumption concerning the ordinal γ is satisfied in this case; see V.5.6 and the proof of theorem 5.3.

6.1. *Let g be a uniformly definable function with one argument ranging over On. Then $p \in \mathrm{Gen}(\mathscr{X})$ implies that $p \neq g(\xi)$ for each ξ in $On \cap M$.*

PROOF. Let ξ be an ordinal in M and H a formula with $\mathrm{Fr}(H) = \{0, 1\}$ which defines g in the sense explained in V.1. If p is generic, then $N^{\mathrm{Z}}(p)$ contains ξ as an element and is a model of ZF and hence $g(\xi)$ belongs to $N^{\mathrm{Z}}(p)$ and can be characterized as its unique element y for which $\vdash_{N^{\mathrm{Z}}(p)} H[y, \xi]$. We can represent ξ in the form (cf. III.5) $C^{\mathrm{Z}}_{\mathrm{pl}^*(\xi)}(a(p))$. Each element y of $N^{\mathrm{Z}}(p)$ can be represented as $C_\eta^{\mathrm{Z}}(a(p))$. We thus obtain the following equivalence, valid for an arbitrary η in $On \cap M$ and an arbitrary generic point p:

$$[C_\eta^{\mathrm{Z}}(a(p)) = g(\xi)] \equiv \vdash_{N^{\mathrm{Z}}(p)} H[C_\eta^{\mathrm{Z}}(a(p)), C^{\mathrm{Z}}_{\mathrm{pl}^*(\xi)}(a(p))].$$

We shall apply this equivalence to the case where $\eta = \gamma$. Denoting by σ the sequence $\{\langle 0, \gamma\rangle, \langle 1, \mathrm{pl}^*(\xi)\rangle\}$ we can represent the right-hand side of the equivalence as $p \in \mathscr{F}_{H,\sigma}$ while the left-hand side becomes

$p = g(\xi)$ according to the meaning of γ explained above. Thus we obtain

$$\mathscr{F}_{H,\sigma} \cap \mathrm{Gen}(\mathscr{X}) = \{g(\xi)\} \cap \mathrm{Gen}(\mathscr{X}).$$

Hence the set $\mathscr{F}_{H,\sigma}$ is of the first category and therefore contains no generic point p, which proves that no generic point is equal to $g(\xi)$.

An example of g is the function $g(\xi) = C_\xi^B(0)$, where B is uniformly definable (cf. V.3.1). If r is an infinite set, then all the assumptions of 6.1 are satisfied by the model $N_1^Z(p)$, which we called a simple extension in 4.1; thus we obtain the following corollary:

6.2. *If B is a uniformly definable function which satisfies conditions* (B.0)–(B.4), *r is infinite and p is a generic point of the space $P(r)$, then the simple extension $N_1^Z(p)$ contains elements which for each ordinal ξ contained in the model are different from $C_\xi^B(0)$.*

This result can be used to obtain a proof of independence of the strong axiom of constructibility, which we discussed in VII.9. As we saw there, the validity of this axiom in a model implies that each element of the model has the form $C_\xi^B(0)$, where ξ is an ordinal which itself belongs to the model. Therefore this axiom is not valid in $N_1^Z(p)$ and we infer that:

6.3. *The strong axiom of constructibility* C^+ *is independent of* ZF.

The weak axiom of constructibility is also independent of ZF. The proof of this meta-mathematical theorem cannot be obtained with the help of the models which we discuss in this book.

CHAPTER XIII

THE CONTINUUM HYPOTHESIS

The aim of this chapter is to construct models in which the continuum hypothesis is not valid. We shall obtain various statements which contradict the continuum hypothesis and which are consistent with ZF and the axiom of choice.

The models in question were already constructed in Chapter XII. We saw in XII.5.3 that given a denumerable model M there exist models N which contain a one-to-one mapping of any given ordinal $\alpha < \pi(M)$ into the family of subsets of ω. Thus N contains at least α subsets of ω. Calling an ordinal $\mu < \pi(M)$ a cardinal of M if M contains no mapping of a smaller ordinal onto μ, we can choose for α, say, the third infinite cardinal of M and find thus that N contains at least as many subsets of N as there are elements in the third infinite cardinal of M. The continuum hypothesis states that there are as many subsets of ω as there are elements in the second infinite cardinal. Hence we see that the continuum hypothesis will be violated in N if we can show that the third infinite cardinal of M coincides with the third infinite cardinal of N. Generalizations of this simple plan of the proof are obvious.

For the reasons explained above we shall devote the main part of this chapter to the problem how cardinals of M are related to cardinals of N. We shall see that sufficiently big cardinals of M are at the same time cardinals of the model N. The proofs depend on certain auxiliary results concerning abstract topological spaces. We shall derive these results in Sections 1–3. As a matter of fact we shall need only very special cases of the theorems to be given in Sections 1–3, but we have thought it useful to give general results rather than very special ones.

1. Auxiliary notions concerning cardinals

Our considerations in this section are based on the axioms ZF and the axiom of choice.

An ordinal α is called a *cardinal* if there is no function f with $\mathrm{Dom}(f) \in \alpha$ and $\mathrm{Rg}(f) = \alpha$. We assume as known the basic operations and properties of cardinals. We denote, the ξth infinite cardinal by ω_ξ.

The *cofinality index* $cf(\alpha)$ of a cardinal α is usually defined as the smallest ordinal ϱ such that α is cofinal with ω_ϱ. It will be more convenient to use a different notion (see Erdös–Rado [8]):

For every ordinal α we denote by α' the smallest ordinal γ such that there is a function f with $\mathrm{Dom}(f) = \gamma$, $\mathrm{Rg}(f) \subseteq \alpha$ and $\bigcup \mathrm{Rg}(f) = \alpha$. For every ordinal α' is a cardinal.

Thus if $\alpha = \omega_{\varrho+1}$, then $\alpha' = \alpha$; if $\alpha = \omega_\varrho$ is cofinal with ω_λ but is not cofinal with ω_μ for $\mu < \lambda$, then $\alpha' = \omega_\lambda$. In the usual terminology we have $\alpha' = \omega_{cf(\alpha)}$ for every cardinal $\alpha = \omega_\varrho$ with a limit index ϱ.

A cardinal α is *regular* or *singular* according as $\alpha' = \alpha$ or $\alpha' < \alpha$.

The cardinal number of a set x is denoted by $|x|$.

The sum and product of two or more cardinals are denoted in the usual way. Moreover, we put

$$\alpha^{\underset{\smile}{\beta}} = \sum |\alpha^\xi|.$$

where the sum is taken over all cardinals $< \beta$.

The *successor of* α is denoted by α^+.

We assume as known the elementary facts concerning cardinals. More special results are noted below:

1.1. *For arbitrary infinite cardinals* α, β *there are cardinals* ν *such that* $\max(\alpha, \beta) \leqslant \nu = \nu^{\underset{\smile}{\alpha}}$.

PROOF. Put $\gamma = \max(\alpha, \beta)$ and $\nu = |\gamma^\alpha|$. Then

$$\nu^{\underset{\smile}{\alpha}} = \sum |\nu^\xi| = \sum |\gamma^{\alpha\xi}| = \sum |\gamma^\alpha| = \alpha|\gamma^\alpha| = |\gamma^\alpha| = \nu .$$

The least cardinal satisfying 1.1 will be denoted by $\nu(\alpha, \beta)$. Since $|\beta^\xi| \leqslant |\nu(\alpha, \beta)^\xi|$ we obtain by taking sums over cardinals

1.2. $\beta^{\underset{\smile}{\alpha}} \leqslant \nu(\alpha, \beta)$.

In general, the exact evaluation of $\nu(\alpha, \beta)$ is not possible without additional hypotheses. We note, however, the following simple result:

1.3. *If β is an infinite cardinal then $\nu(\omega, \beta) = \beta$.*

For $\beta^{\underline{\omega}} = \sum_{n<\omega} \beta^n = \beta$.

In the next theorem we evaluate $\nu(\alpha, \beta)$ under the assumption of the generalized continuum hypothesis:

1.4. *If the generalized continuum hypothesis is true and α, β are infinite cardinals, then $\nu(\alpha, \beta)$ has the following values:*

I. $\alpha \geqslant \beta$;

$$\nu(\alpha, \beta) = \begin{cases} \alpha & \textit{if} \quad \alpha \textit{ is regular}, \\ \alpha^+ & \textit{if} \quad \alpha \textit{ is singular}. \end{cases}$$

II. $\alpha < \beta$, β *regular*;

$$\nu(\alpha, \beta) = \beta.$$

III. $\alpha < \beta$, β *singular*;

$$\nu(\alpha, \beta) = \begin{cases} \beta & \textit{if} \quad \alpha \textit{ has no predecessor and is } \leqslant \beta' \\ & \qquad \textit{or } \alpha = \alpha_1^+ \textit{ and } \alpha_1 < \beta', \\ \beta^+ & \textit{if} \quad \alpha \textit{ has no predecessor and is } > \beta' \\ & \qquad \textit{or } \alpha = \alpha_1^+ \textit{ and } \alpha_1 \geqslant \beta'. \end{cases}$$

PROOF. Assume first that $\alpha \geqslant \beta$. If α has a predecessor α_1, then $\alpha = |2^{\alpha_1}|$ and hence $\alpha^{\underline{\alpha}} = |\alpha^{\alpha_1}| = |2^{\alpha_1}| = \alpha$. If α has no predecessor but is regular, then $\alpha^{\underline{\alpha}} = \alpha$ (see [17], p. 311). Thus in both cases the conditions of 1.1 are satisfied for $\nu = \alpha$ and obviously this value of ν is the least possible one. If α is singular, then $\alpha^{\underline{\alpha}} > \alpha$ (cf. [17], p. 302) but obviously $(\alpha^+)^{\underline{\alpha}} = \alpha^+$ and hence $\nu(\alpha, \beta) = \alpha^+$.

Assume next that $\alpha < \beta$ and β is regular. Then $\beta^{\underline{\alpha}} = \beta$ and therefore $\nu(\alpha, \beta) = \beta$.

Finally, let β be singular and $> \alpha$. Using results stated in [17], p. 330, we find that if α has no predecessor and is $\leqslant \beta'$, then $\beta^{\underline{\alpha}} = \beta$ and hence $\nu(\alpha, \beta) = \beta$. If $\alpha > \beta'$, then $\beta^{\underline{\alpha}} = \beta^+$ and hence $\nu(\alpha, \beta) \geqslant \beta^+$; since $(\beta^+)^{\underline{\alpha}} = \sum_{\xi<\alpha} |2^{\beta_\xi}| = |2^\beta|\alpha = \beta^+$, we obtain $\nu(\alpha, \beta) = \beta^+$.

Finally, if $\alpha = \alpha_1^+$, then $\beta^{\underline{\alpha}} = |\beta^{\alpha_1}| = \beta$ if $\alpha_1 < \beta'$ and $\beta^{\underline{\alpha}} = \beta^+$ if $\alpha_1 \geqslant \beta'$ (cf. [17], p. 329). Hence all the statements of 1.4 are verified.

We shall need the following well-known property of regular cardinals:

1.5. *If* $\alpha = \alpha' \geqslant \omega$ *and* F *is a function with* $\mathrm{Dom}(F) \in \alpha$ *such that* $|F(\xi)| < \alpha$ *for each* ξ *in* $\mathrm{Dom}(F)$, *then*

$$\left|\bigcup \mathrm{Rg}(F)\right| < \alpha.$$

PROOF. Assume that there exists a one-to-one function f which maps α into $\bigcup \mathrm{Rg}(F)$. For each ξ in $\mathrm{Dom}(F)$ the range of $f^{-1}|F(\xi)$ is a subset of α. We shall show that it is not cofinal with α. Otherwise α would be the union of ordinals $f^{-1}(x)$ where $x \in F(\xi)$; this, however, is impossible, because α is regular and the power of $F(\xi)$ is less than α. Let $\alpha_\xi = \sup\{f^{-1}(x)\colon\ x \in F(\xi)\}$. Hence $\alpha_\xi < \alpha$ and $\bigcup_\xi \alpha_\xi = \alpha$ because each $\beta < \alpha$ is the value of f^{-1} for an argument in $\bigcup \mathrm{Rg}(F)$. Thus we obtain a contradiction with the regularity of α.

2. The Souslin coefficient

This section is also based exclusively on the axioms ZF and the axiom of choice. We shall introduce some auxiliary notions.

For any relation $R \subseteq A \times A$ we define

$$R^* = \{\langle x, y\rangle \in A \times A\colon\ \neg(Ez)[(xRz) \wedge (yRz)]\}.$$

Thus for instance if A is a family of sets and R is the relation $x \supseteq y$ limited to A, then R^* is the relation which x bears to y if and only if $x \cap y$ does not contain any element of A, i.e., if $P(x \cap y) \cap A = 0$.

If R is reflexive, then R^* is irreflexive; R^* is always symmetric.

A set $B \subseteq A$ is called *R-disjoint* if xR^*y for any pair of different elements of B.

We denote by $\vartheta(R)$ the smallest ordinal α such that there exists no R-disjoint set $B \subseteq A$ of power $|\alpha|$. This ordinal is called the *Souslin coefficient of R*. Obviously $\vartheta(R)$ is a cardinal.

We shall prove that the Souslin coefficient of a partial order is a regular cardinal (see Erdös–Tarski [9]). To obtain this result we introduce the following definitions:

Let r be a relation which partially orders a set S. Instead of $\langle x, y\rangle \in r$ we write $x \geqslant y$. Thus u and v are *r-disjoint* if there is no y such that $u \geqslant y$ and $v \geqslant y$. If u and v are r-disjoint, then so are u and w for any

$w \leqslant v$. By $\vartheta(r, x)$ we denote the Souslin coefficient of the relation r limited to elements $\leqslant x$:

$$\vartheta(r, x) = \vartheta(r \cap \{y\colon\, y \leqslant x\}^2).$$

It is clear that $x \leqslant y$ implies $\vartheta(r, x) \leqslant \vartheta(r, y)$. Also $\vartheta(r, x) > 0$ for each x in S. We call x *a homogeneous element* if $\vartheta(r, y) = \vartheta(r, x)$ for every $y \leqslant x$.

2.1. *For every x in S there is a homogeneous element y such that $y \leqslant x$.*

PROOF. It is sufficient to choose y so that $\vartheta(r, y)$ be the least cardinal among the cardinals $\vartheta(r, z)$, $z \leqslant x$.

The principal lemma is the following:

2.2. *If $\vartheta(r)$ is a cardinal which is not a successor, then there is a homogeneous element x such that $\vartheta(r, x) = \vartheta(r)$.*

PROOF. We shall derive a contradiction from the assumption that $\vartheta(r, x) < \vartheta(r)$ for each homogeneous element x. We consider the family of subsets T of S with the following two properties:

(1) each x in T is homogeneous;

(2) if x, y are different elements of T, then x, y are r-disjoint.

According to the axiom of choice there is a maximal set $T \subseteq S$ with these two properties. In view of (2)

$$|T| < \vartheta(r)$$

and in view of (1)

$$\vartheta(r, x) < \vartheta(r) \quad \text{for every } x \text{ in } T.$$

It follows by the well-known rules of cardinal arithmetic that

$$\sum_{x \in T} \vartheta(r, x) \leqslant \vartheta(r).$$

We shall show that the sign $\leqslant$ can be replaced by the symbol $=$. Since $\vartheta(r)$ is not a successor, it is sufficient for this purpose to show that if α is a cardinal $< \vartheta(r)$, then $\alpha \leqslant \sum_{x \in T} \vartheta(r, x)$.

Let us therefore assume that $\alpha < \vartheta(r)$. It follows that there is a set $U \subseteq S$ of power α consisting of mutually r-disjoint elements.

It is easy to see that for each u in U there is a t in T which is not r-disjoint with u. Otherwise we could select a homogeneous $u_1 \leqslant u$ which would be r-disjoint with each t in T, and this is impossible by the maximality of T.

For each u in U we select a t_u in T which is not r-disjoint with u; using again the axiom of choice we correlate with each u in U an element $f(u)$ such that $f(u) \leqslant u$ and $f(u) \leqslant t_u$. For different elements u_1, u_2 of U we obviously have $f(u_1) \neq f(u_2)$ since u_1 and u_2 are r-disjoint. Moreover, $f(u_1)$ and $f(u_2)$ are r-disjoint. For a given t in T the set of different $f(u)$'s satisfying the inequality $f(u) \leqslant t$ is $< \vartheta(r, t)$ since these $f(u)$ form a family of r-disjoint elements $\leqslant t$. Hence the cardinal number of all possible $f(u)$'s is $\leqslant \sum_{t \in T} \vartheta(r, t)$, which proves that $\alpha \leqslant \sum_{t \in T} \vartheta(r, t)$. Hence we have shown that

$$\sum_{t \in T} \vartheta(r, t) = \vartheta(r). \tag{3}$$

For any cardinal $\alpha < \vartheta(r)$ there is an x in T such that $\vartheta(r, x) \geqslant \alpha$. Otherwise the left-hand side of formula (3) would be $\leqslant |T| \cdot \alpha = \max(|T|, \alpha) < \vartheta(r)$. It follows that there is a transfinite sequence x_ξ $(\xi < \gamma < \vartheta(r))$ of elements of T such that

$$\vartheta(r, x_\xi) < \vartheta(r, x_{\xi+1}), \tag{4}$$

$$\sup\{\vartheta(r, x_\xi)\colon \xi < \gamma\} = \vartheta(r). \tag{5}$$

From (4) we infer that for each $\xi < \gamma$ there is a set W_ξ of power $\vartheta(r, x_\xi)$ consisting of elements which are mutually r-disjoint and $\leqslant x_{\xi+1}$. Since x_ξ and x_η are r-disjoint for $\xi \neq \eta$, we infer that $W_\xi \cap W_\eta = 0$ for $\xi \neq \eta$. Hence the union $\bigcup W_\xi$ has power

$$\sum_{\xi<\gamma} \vartheta(r, x_\xi) \geqslant \sup\{\vartheta(r, x_\xi)\colon \xi < \gamma\} = \vartheta(r).$$

This is a contradiction because every two elements of $\bigcup\{W_\xi\colon \xi < \gamma\}$ are r-disjoint.

Lemma 2.2 is thus proved.

2.3. *If r is a partial ordering and x is an homogeneous element, then* $\vartheta(r, x) \neq \aleph_0$.

PROOF. Assume otherwise. Then there are at least two r-disjoint elements $x_0, y_0 \leqslant x$ and $\vartheta(r, x_0) = \vartheta(r, y_0) = \aleph_0$. For the element x_0

we similarly find at least two r-disjoint elements $x_1, y_1 \leqslant x_0$. We proceed similarly with x_1 finding r-disjoint elements $x_2, y_2 \leqslant x_1$. The elements $y_1, y_2, \ldots$ are then mutually r-disjoint and $\leqslant x$, which is incompatible with the assumption $\vartheta(r, x) = \aleph_0$.

2.4. *If r is a partial ordering and x an homogeneous element, then $\vartheta(r, x)$ is not singular.*

PROOF. Assume that $\vartheta(r, x) = \alpha > \alpha'$. Hence

$$\alpha = \bigcup \{\alpha_i \colon i < \alpha'\} \qquad \text{where} \qquad \alpha_i < \alpha\,.$$

Since $\alpha' < \alpha$, there is a set $U \subseteq S$ of power α' consisting of mutually r-disjoint elements $\leqslant x$. We can number the elements of U by means of ordinals $i < \alpha'$:

$$U = \{u_i \colon i < \alpha'\} \qquad \text{where} \qquad u_i \neq u_j \text{ for } i \neq j\,.$$

Since x is homogeneous, we have $\vartheta(r, u_i) = \alpha$ for each $i < \alpha'$ and hence for each $i < \alpha'$ there is a set S_i of power α_i consisting of mutually r-disjoint elements $\leqslant u_i$. The union $\bigcup S_i$ consists of mutually r-disjoint elements $\leqslant x$ and has power

$$\sum_{i<\alpha'} \alpha_i \geqslant \sup\{\alpha_i \colon i < \alpha'\} = \alpha\,.$$

This contradicts the definition of α.

From 2.2–2.4 we immediately obtain the following theorem:

2.5 (Erdös–Tarski [9]). *If r is a partial ordering, then $\vartheta(r) \neq \aleph_0$ and $\vartheta(r)$ is a regular cardinal.*

3. The Souslin coefficient of product spaces

This section, like the two previous ones, is based on the axioms of ZF and the axiom of choice.

The notion of the Souslin coefficient is particularly useful in the case where A is the family of open non-void subsets of a topological space $\mathscr{X}$ and R is the relation $x \supseteq y$ limited to A. The cardinal $\vartheta(R)$ is then called the *Souslin coefficient of $\mathscr{X}$*.

We call the *weight of a topological space $\mathscr{X}$* the least cardinal γ such that there is an open basis of $\mathscr{X}$ of power γ. We denote the weight of $\mathscr{X}$ by $\gamma(\mathscr{X})$.

We shall derive a theorem which allows us to evaluate the Souslin coefficient of a Cartesian product of a family of spaces. First results of this kind are due to Marczewski [20]; in our presentation we follow a proof given by Marek [21].

3.1. *If* α, β *are cardinals* $\geqslant \omega$, I *is an arbitrary set*, $\mathscr{X}_i$ *are topological spaces* ($i \in I$), J *is an ideal of subsets of* I *containing all finite subsets of* I *and such that* $X \in J \rightarrow |X| < \alpha$ *and if* $\gamma(\mathscr{X}_i) \leqslant \beta$ *for each* i *in* I, *then*

$$\vartheta\big(\mathop{\mathrm{P}}_{i\in I} \mathscr{X}_i\big) \leqslant \nu(\alpha, \beta)^+$$

provided that the topology in the product space is the J*-topology.*

PROOF. In what follows we abbreviate $\nu(\alpha, \beta)$ to ν. Let us denote by B_i a basis of $\mathscr{X}_i$ of power $\leqslant \beta$. We know that $0 \notin B_i$. We shall derive a contradiction from the assumption that there exists a set of power ν^+ of disjoint non-void open sets. We can assume these sets to be neighbourhoods in the product space. Let R be the set of J-boxes which determine these neighbourhoods. Thus $|R| = \nu^+$ and each g in R is an element of $\mathop{\mathrm{P}}_{i\in \mathrm{Dom}(g)} B_i$ and $\mathrm{Dom}(g) \in J$, whence $|\mathrm{Dom}(g)| < \alpha$. If $g_1, g_2 \in R$ and $g_1 \neq g_2$, then there is an element $i \in \mathrm{Dom}(g_1) \cap \mathrm{Dom}(g_2)$ such that $g_1(i) \cap g_2(i) = 0$.

For each pair $\langle g_1, g_2\rangle$ of distinct elements of R we select an i in $\mathrm{Dom}(g_1) \cap \mathrm{Dom}(g_2)$ for which $g_1(i)$ and $g_2(i)$ are disjoint.

Let C be the set of selected elements. Since there are only ν^+ pairs $\langle g_1, g_2\rangle$ of different elements of R and each pair determines exactly one element in C, it is obvious that $|C| \leqslant \nu^+$.

We consider the ideal J_C induced by J on subsets of C:

$$J_C = \{X \cap C\colon X \in J\}$$

and the product space $\mathop{\mathrm{P}}_{i\in C} \mathscr{X}_i$ with the J_C-topology. For g in R we put $\bar{g} = g|C$. If $g_1 \neq g_2$, then $\bar{g}_1 \neq \bar{g}_2$ because $\bar{g}_1(i) \neq \bar{g}_2(i)$ for the element i determined by g_1, g_2. The J_C-boxes determined in $\mathop{\mathrm{P}}_{i\in C} \mathscr{X}_i$ by $\bar{g}_1$ and $\bar{g}_2$ are disjoint and hence the Souslin coefficient of this product space with the J_C-topology is $\geqslant \nu^+$. We shall now show that this is impossible.

Let $\bar{R} = \{\bar{g}\colon g \in R\}$; we proved above that $|\bar{R}| = \nu^+$.

Case I. $|C| \leqslant \nu$. For a given $X \subseteq C$ of a power $\xi < \alpha$ the set $\mathbf{P}_{i \in X} B_i$ has power $\leqslant |\beta^\xi|$. The set of all subsets of C of power ξ is itself of power $\leqslant |\nu^\xi|$. Hence the set $\bar{R}$ is of power

$$\leqslant \sum_{\xi<\alpha} |(\nu\beta)^\xi| = \sum_{\xi<\alpha} |\nu^\xi| = \nu^{\underline{\alpha}} = \nu.$$

This contradicts the equation $|\bar{R}| = \nu^+$ established above.

Case II. $|C| = \nu^+$. We choose a well-ordering $<$ of C with the order type ν^+. Let $\xi < \alpha$ and $g \in R$. An element i of $\mathrm{Dom}(\bar{g})$ is called its ξth *element* if the set $\{j \in \mathrm{Dom}(\bar{g}) : j < i\}$ has the order type ξ. Since $\mathrm{Dom}(\bar{g})$ is of power $< \alpha$, it is clear that for each i in $\mathrm{Dom}(\bar{g})$ there is exactly one $\xi < \alpha$ such that i is the ξth element of $\mathrm{Dom}(\bar{g})$. If the ξth element of $\mathrm{Dom}(\bar{g})$ exists, it is determined uniquely. We shall denote it by $t_\xi(\bar{g})$ and put

$$T_\xi = \{t_\xi(\bar{g}) : g \in R\}.$$

It is obvious that $T_\xi \subseteq C$. Since each i in C belongs to the domain of at least one $\bar{g}$, we obtain the decomposition

$$C = \bigcup_{\xi<\alpha} T_\xi. \tag{1}$$

We shall show that each T_ξ is of power $\leqslant \nu$. Once this is done, we have the desired contradiction since the union of α sets of power $\leqslant \nu$ is of power $\leqslant \nu$ and hence its power cannot be ν^+.

Let us assume that ξ is the first ordinal for which $|T_\xi| > \nu$, whence T_ξ is of power ν^+. For each t in T_ξ choose a function g_t in R such that $t = t_\xi(\bar{g}_t)$. As t ranges over T_ξ, the sets $\bigcup_{\eta<\xi} T_\eta \cap \mathrm{Dom}(\bar{g}_t)$ range over some subsets of power $< \alpha$ of the union $\bigcup_{\eta<\xi} T_\eta$ whose power is $\leqslant \nu$. Since a set of power $\leqslant \nu$ has at most $\nu^{\underline{\alpha}}$ subsets of a power $< \alpha$, we infer that there is a subset T' of T_ξ whose power is ν^+ such that for each t in T' the intersection $\bigcup_{\eta<\xi} T_\eta \cap \mathrm{Dom}(\bar{g}_t)$ is equal to one and the same constant set X_0. The power of X_0 is $< \alpha$.

The power of the set $\mathbf{P}_{i \in X_0} B_i$ is $\leqslant |\beta^{|X_0|}| \leqslant \beta^{\underline{\alpha}} \leqslant \nu$. Hence there exists a subset T'' of T' of power ν^+ such that for $t \in T''$ the partial function $\bar{g}_t|X_0$ is independent of t. We denote it by φ.

Since $|T''| = \nu^+ = |C|$, the set T'' is cofinal with C.

We now select an arbitrary s_1 in T''. Since the power of $\mathrm{Dom}(\bar{g}_{s_1})$ is $< \alpha \leqslant \nu < \nu^+$, there is an s_2 in T'' which is $> y$ for all $y \in \mathrm{Dom}(\bar{g}_{s_1})$.

The functions $\bar{g}_{s_1}$ and $\bar{g}_{s_2}$ are distinct because the ξth elements of $\mathrm{Dom}(\bar{g}_{s_1})$ and $\mathrm{Dom}(\bar{g}_{s_2})$ are different from each other. Hence there exists an element i of $\mathrm{Dom}(\bar{g}_{s_1}) \cap \mathrm{Dom}(\bar{g}_{s_2})$ for which $\bar{g}_{s_1}(i) \cap \bar{g}_{s_2}(i) = 0$. Obviously $i \in C$. We can assume that i is the first element satisfying these conditions. From $i \in \mathrm{Dom}(\bar{g}_{s_1})$ it follows that $s_2 > i$. In view of (1) there is a smallest $\varrho < \alpha$ such that $i \in T_\varrho$. Since $s_2 > i$ and $s_2 = t_\xi(\bar{g}_{s_2})$, we infer that the order type of the set $\{j \in \mathrm{Dom}(\bar{g}_{s_2}) \colon j < i\}$ is $< \xi$. Hence if i is the ϱ_1th element of $\mathrm{Dom}(\bar{g}_{s_2})$, then $\varrho_1 < \xi$ and consequently $\varrho \leqslant \varrho_1 < \xi$ and $i \in \bigcup_{\zeta < \xi} T_\zeta$. Thus $i \in \bigcup_{\zeta < \xi} T_\zeta \cap \mathrm{Dom}(\bar{g}_{s_2}) = X_0$. Since the partial functions $\bar{g}_{s_1}|X_0$ and $\bar{g}_{s_2}|X_0$ are identical, we obtain $\bar{g}_{s_1}(i) = \bar{g}_{s_2}(i) = \varphi(i)$. It follows that $\bar{g}_{s_1}(i) \cap \bar{g}_{s_2}(i) = \varphi(i)$ and hence $\varphi(i) = 0$. But this is a contradiction since $\varphi(i) \in B_i$ and we have assumed that the void set does not belong to the basis B_i.

Theorem 3.1 is thus proved.

We illustrate the applications of theorem 3.1 on a number of examples, which the reader should compare with the examples given in XII.1.

3.2. *If a is an arbitrary set and $P(a)$ is the space of its subsets (with the Tichonoff topology), then $\vartheta(P(a)) \leqslant \omega^+$.*

PROOF. $P(a)$ is homeomorphic with the product space $\{0, 1\}^a$ of two-element spaces. Hence $\alpha = \omega$, $\beta = \omega$ and $\nu(\alpha, \beta) = \omega^{\omega}_{\smile} = \omega$.

We can formulate the result 3.2 without using the topological language. Let a be a set and $\Pi_1(a)$, $R_1(a)$ the set and the relation defined in XII.1. Since $R_1(a)$ is isomorphic with the relation of inclusion in an open basis of the space $P(a)$, we infer that:

3.3. *For any a every $R_1(a)$-disjoint subset of $\Pi_1(a)$ is at most denumerable.*

As another example we give the following theorem:

3.4. *If a, α are arbitrary sets and $[P(a)]^\alpha$ the Cartesian product of α copies of the space $P(a)$ provided with the Tichonoff topology, then $\vartheta[P(a)]^\alpha \leqslant \omega^+$.*

To prove this theorem we merely notice that the space in question is homeomorphic with the space $\{0, 1\}^{a \times \alpha}$.

To express 3.4 in the language of set theory we use the notation $\Pi_2^\alpha(a)$ and $R_2^\alpha(a)$ introduced in XII.1 and obtain

3.5. *If a, α are arbitrary sets, then every $R_2^\alpha(a)$-disjoint subset of $\Pi_2^\alpha(a)$ is at most denumerable.*

As the last example we consider the space x^y of all functions which map y into x. The space is the usual product space $\mathrm{P}_{i \in y} \mathscr{X}_i$ of y copies of the discrete space $\mathscr{X}_i = x$. The weight of $\mathscr{X}_i$ is $|x|$, whence by 3.1 and 1.3

3.6. $\vartheta(x^y) \leqslant \nu(\omega, |x|)^+ = [\max(\omega, |x|)]^+$.

4. Relative cardinals, relative cofinality and relative Souslin coefficients

From now on we return to meta-mathematics. Thus our considerations will be based on the axiom system M as in all the previous chapters. We want to relativize with respect to an arbitrary (transitive) model of ZF the definitions and results which we dealt with in Sections 1–3.

Let M be a transitive family of sets. The *relative cardinals* (or *cardinals of M*) are ordinals $\gamma < \pi(M)$ such that no f in M is a mapping of an ordinal $< \gamma$ onto γ. The set of cardinals of M is denoted by Card(M).

For $\alpha \in M$ we denote by Cf(M, α) the least ordinal γ of M such that there is in M a function f with $\mathrm{Dom}(f) = \gamma$, $\mathrm{Rg}(f) \subseteq \alpha$ and $\bigcup \mathrm{Rg}(f) = \alpha$ or 0 if such γ does not exist. If M is a model of ZF, then the ordinal Cf(M, α) is a cardinal of M. We call it the *relative cofinality index of α.*

If $r \in M$ and r is a binary relation, then we denote by $\vartheta(M, r)$ the least ordinal $\alpha < \pi(M)$ such that there is no function f in M satisfying the conditions: $\mathrm{Dom}(f) = \alpha$, f is a one-to-one function; $\mathrm{Rg}(f)$ is an r-disjoint set. We put $\vartheta(M, r) = 0$ if r is not a binary relation or no α with the indicated properties exists.

If M is a model of ZF, then $\vartheta(M, r)$ is a cardinal of M. We call it the *relative Souslin coefficient of r.*

4.1. *Functors* Card, Cf, ϑ *are strongly definable.*

PROOF. For almost all M and all f, β, γ in M we have the equivalences

$$\vdash_M \mathbf{Fn}[f] \equiv (f \text{ is a function}),$$

$$\vdash_M \mathbf{dl}[f] = \beta \equiv (\mathrm{Dom}(f) = \beta),$$

$$\vdash_M \mathbf{dp}[f] = \gamma \equiv (\mathrm{Rg}(f) = \gamma).$$

It follows that for almost all M the formula $\alpha \in \mathrm{Card}(M)$ is equivalent to $\vdash_M H[\alpha]$, where H is the formula

(1) $\mathbf{Ord}(x) \wedge (y)\{(y \in x) \to \neg (Ez)[\mathbf{Fn}(z) \wedge (\mathbf{dl}(z) = y) \wedge (\mathbf{dp}(z) = x)]\}$.

In order to prove the theorem for the functor Cf we consider the formula

$$G\colon\ \mathbf{Fn}(x_0) \wedge (\mathbf{dl}(x_0) = x_1) \wedge (\mathbf{dp}(x_0) \subseteq x_2) \wedge (\bigcup \mathbf{dp}(x_0) = x_2)$$

with the obvious meaning of the abbreviations $\subseteq$ and $\bigcup$.

For almost all M and all f, α, β in M

$$\vdash_M G[f, \beta, \alpha]$$

$$\equiv (f \text{ is a function}) \wedge (\mathrm{Dom}(f) = \beta) \wedge (\mathrm{Rg}(f) \subseteq \alpha) \wedge (\bigcup \mathrm{Rg}(f) = \alpha).$$

We let G' be the formula

$$(Ex_0)\, G(x_0, x_1, x_2) \wedge (x_3)(x_0)[(x_3 \in x_1) \to \neg G(x_0, x_3, x_2)].$$

It is then obvious that for almost all M and all α, β in M

(2) $\beta = \mathrm{Cf}(M, \alpha) \equiv [\vdash_M \neg (Ex_1) G'[\alpha] \wedge (\beta = 0)] \vee \vdash_M G'[\beta, \alpha]$.

Finally we prove the theorem for the functor ϑ:

It is obvious that $\vartheta(M, r) \in M$ for every M which contains 0 as an element. Thus it will be sufficient to exhibit a formula θ such that for almost all M and all x, z in M

(3) $$z \in \vartheta(M, x) \equiv \vdash_M \theta[z, x].$$

We construct θ as follows: First we put

$$\mathbf{rel}(x)\colon\ (u)_x (Ev_1, v_2)(u = \langle v_1, v_2 \rangle),$$

$$\mathbf{Dis}(x, y)\colon\ (z_1, z_2)_y \{(z_1 = z_2) \vee \neg (Ez)[(\langle z_1, z \rangle \in x) \wedge (\langle z_2, z \rangle \in x)]\}.$$

For almost all M and all x, y in M we obviously have the equivalences:

(i) $$\vdash_M \mathbf{rel}[x] \equiv (x \text{ is a binary relation});$$

(ii) if x is a binary relation, then

$$\vdash_M \mathbf{Dis}[x, y] \equiv (y \text{ is } x\text{-disjoint}).$$

We can now show that the required formula θ is

$$(Ey)[\mathbf{Dis}(x, y) \wedge |z| \leqslant |y|] \wedge \mathbf{Ord}(z) \wedge \mathbf{rel}(x).$$

For almost all M the formulae (i), (ii) and the equivalence (iii) given below are true:

(iii) $$\vdash_M (|x| \leqslant |y|) \equiv |x| \leqslant_M |y|$$

(cf. VII.3.1). Let M be a family satisfying these conditions and transitive. Let x be an element of M. If x is not a binary relation, then both sides of (3) are false. Thus let x be a binary relation and let us assume that M contains an ordinal α such that for each $\beta < \alpha$ there is an x-disjoint family $y \in M$ for which $|\beta| \leqslant_M |y|$ but no such family exists for α. Then $\vartheta(M, x) = \alpha$ and from the definition of θ we easily see using (i)–(iii) that the conditions $\vdash_M \theta[z, x]$ and $z \in \alpha$ are equivalent.

It remains to show that almost all M contain an ordinal α with the properties indicated above. To see this we notice that for almost all M if x is in M and x is a relation, then the set

$$s = \{y \in M\colon\ y \text{ is an } x\text{-disjoint family}\}$$

belongs to M since it is a parametrically definable subset of $M \cap P(u)$ where u is the field of x (the unique parameter is x). By theorems IV.3.18 and VII.2.4 the union $\bigcup\{\aleph(M, y)\colon\ y \in s\} = \alpha$ belongs to M and is obviously an ordinal. If $\beta < \alpha$, then there is a y in s such that $\beta \in \aleph(M,y)$, i.e., $|\beta| \leqslant_M |y|$. No such family exists for α because $|\alpha| \leqslant_M |y|$ would imply $\alpha < \aleph(M, y)$ and hence $\alpha < \alpha$. Theorem 4.1 is thus proved.

We shall use abbreviated notation for certain relative cardinals. Thus if M is a model of ZF then for every $\alpha < \pi(M)$ there is a smallest ordinal β such that $\vdash_M |\alpha| \leqslant |\beta|$. This ordinal is denoted by $\mathrm{Card}(M, \alpha)$; it is always a cardinal of M. If a is an element of M and there is in M a function which maps a in a one-to-one way onto an ordinal α, then $\mathrm{Card}(M, \alpha)$ is denoted by $\mathrm{Card}(M, a)$.

If $\alpha < \pi(M)$, then there is in M a least ordinal $\beta > \alpha$ such that $\vdash_M \neg(|\beta| \leqslant |\alpha|)$ (see VII.2.4). This ordinal is simply $\aleph(M, \alpha)$. We also use the notation $\aleph(M, a)$ if M contains a one-to-one mapping of a onto an ordinal.

Using the aleph function we introduce a strongly definable functor of the second kind satisfying the inductive equations

$$\omega_0(M) = \omega, \qquad \omega_{\xi+1}(M) = \aleph\big(M, \omega_\xi(M)\big),$$
$$\omega_\lambda(M) = \sup\{\omega_\xi(M)\colon\ \xi < \lambda\} \qquad \text{where} \qquad \lambda \in \mathrm{Lim}(M).$$

The existence of a functor with these properties follows from IV.4.2.

We shall now describe a method which allows us to obtain theorems concerning the relative notions introduced in this section from theorems concerning the "absolute" notions which we derived in Sections 1–4.

Let us suppose that we have in ZF a proof of the formula

$$\mathbf{AC} \wedge P(x, y, \ldots) \to Q(x, y, \ldots). \tag{4}$$

It is then obvious that if M is a model of ZF in which the axiom of choice is valid and if $a, b, \ldots$ are elements of M such that $\vdash_M P[a, b, \ldots]$, then $\vdash_M Q[a, b, \ldots]$. Thus if R and S are relations between elements of M which can be defined by the formulae

$$R(a, b, \ldots) \equiv\ \vdash_M P[a, b, \ldots], \tag{5}$$

$$S(a, b, \ldots) \equiv\ \vdash_M Q[a, b, \ldots], \tag{6}$$

then $R(a, b, \ldots)$ implies $S(a, b, \ldots)$.

As an example we derive the following theorem:

4.2. *Let M be a model of* ZF *in which the axiom of choice is valid and assume that*

$$\vartheta \in \mathrm{Card}(M), \tag{7}$$

$$\mathrm{Cf}(M, \vartheta) = \vartheta, \tag{8}$$

$$(\vartheta > \beta) \wedge (\vartheta \geqslant \omega). \tag{9}$$

Furthermore, let F be an element of M such that

$$F \textit{ is a function with domain } \beta, \tag{10}$$

$$\mathrm{Card}\big(M, F(\xi)\big) < \vartheta \quad \textit{for each } \xi < \beta. \tag{11}$$

Under these assumptions ϑ is not M-embeddable in $\bigcup \mathrm{Rg}(F)$.

To prove this theorem we notice that each of the assumptions concerning ϑ, β and F is equivalent to the statement that a formula is satisfied in M. Thus (7) is equivalent to $\vdash_M H_1[\vartheta]$, where H_1 is formula (1). Assumption (8) is equivalent to $\vdash_M H_2[\vartheta, \vartheta]$, where H_2 is the formula which appears on the right side of equivalence (2). Assumption (9) can obviously be written as $\vdash_M H_3[\beta, \vartheta]$, where H_3 is the formula

$$(x_0 \in x_2) \wedge (|\omega| \leqslant |x_2|).$$

Assumption (10) is equivalent to $\vdash_M H_4[\beta, F]$, where H_4 is the formula

$$\mathbf{Fn}(x_1) \wedge (\mathbf{dl}(x_1) = x_0).$$

Finally, assumption (11) is equivalent to $\vdash_M H_5[\beta, F, \vartheta]$, where H_5 is the formula

$$(x)\{(x \in x_0) \rightarrow (Ey)[(\langle x, y\rangle \in x_1) \wedge (|y| \leqslant |x_2|) \wedge \neg(|x_2| \leqslant |y|)]\}$$

(the correlation of the free variables x_0, x_1, x_2 of H_5 with the elements β, F, ϑ is as follows: β is correlated with x_0, F with x_1 and ϑ with x_2).

Let P be the conjunction

$$H_1(x_2) \wedge H_2(x_2, x_2) \wedge H_3(x_0, x_2) \wedge H_4(x_0, x_1) \wedge H_5(x_0, x_1, x_2).$$

We now consider theorem 1.5, which was proved by means of axioms ZF with the help of the axiom of choice. The assumptions of this theorem written in the formal language of ZF become simply $\mathrm{AC} \wedge P$. The conclusion of the theorem is the formula

$$Q\colon \neg\left(|x_2| \leqslant \left|\bigcup (\mathbf{dp}\, x_1)\right|\right).$$

Hence we obtain $\vdash_M Q[F, \vartheta]$, which means that ϑ is not M-embeddable in $\bigcup \mathrm{Rg}(F)$. Theorem 4.2 is thus proved.

Of course one must be very careful when one applies the method of proof outlined above. In general, there are many formulae P, Q which satisfy equivalences (5) and (6) for given definable relations R, S, and from these many possibilities one has to select the ones for which condition (4) is indeed satisfied. We have not verified that our choice of P, Q meets these requirements and we do not intend to undertake this very cumbersome verification, which would require the formalization of the whole proof of 1.5. Thus proofs obtained by the method used above leave us somewhat frustrated; however, the method is essentially sound and we shall use it constantly in the future.

From theorem 2.5 and its provability in ZF (with AC added) we obtain in the same way the following result:

4.3. *Let M be a model of* ZF *in which the axiom of choice is valid; if $r \in M$ and r partially orders its field, then*

$$\vartheta(M, r) \in \mathrm{Card}(M), \qquad \vartheta(M, r) \neq \omega$$

and

$$\vartheta(M, r) = \mathrm{Cf}\big(M, \vartheta(M, r)\big).$$

5. Determination of the relative Souslin coefficient

In this section we shall determine the ordinal $\vartheta(M, r)$ in various cases corresponding to the examples discussed in Section 3. We recall that in 4.1 we constructed a formula θ:

$$\mathbf{Ord}(z) \wedge \mathbf{rel}(x) \wedge (Ey)\,[\mathbf{Dis}(x, y) \wedge |z| \leqslant |y|],$$

which defines the functor ϑ in the sense that for almost all M and all z, x in M the equivalence

(1) $$[z \in \vartheta(M, x)] \equiv\ \vdash_M \theta[z, x]$$

holds.

Let F, Ξ be two formulae such that $\mathrm{Fr}(F) = \{1, 2, \ldots, n\}$, $\mathrm{Fr}(\Xi) = \{0, 2, \ldots, n\}$. We denote by x the string $x_2, \ldots, x_n$ of $n-1$ variables and by a the sequence $a_2, \ldots, a_n$ of elements of a model M.

5.1. *If the formula*

(2) $$F(x_1, x) \to (x_0)[\theta(x_0, x_1) \to \Xi(x_0, x)],$$

is provable in ZF, *if M is a model of* ZF, *r, $a \in M$ and $\vdash_M F[r, a]$, then*

$$\vartheta(M, r) \subseteq \{\alpha \in M\colon\ \vdash_M \Xi[\alpha, a]\}.$$

PROOF. From (2) and the assumption of the theorem it follows that $\vdash_M \theta[\alpha, r]$ implies $\vdash_M \Xi[\alpha, a]$.

Example 1. Let $a \in M$ be a set and let $\Pi_1(a)$, $R_1(a)$ be defined as in XII.1. We remarked in XII.1.2 that $\Pi_1(a)$ and $R_1(a)$ are elements of M. We shall evaluate $\vartheta\big(M, R_1(a)\big)$.

We choose as Ξ the formula $|x_0| \leqslant |\omega|$ and as F the formula with the free variables x_0, x_1 such that for almost all A and all r, x in A

the condition $\vdash_A F[r, x]$ is equivalent to the conjunction of the following conditions:

(A_i) $\vdash_A$ AC;

(A_{ii}) r is a binary relation between pairs $\langle X, Y\rangle$, where $X \cap Y = 0$, $X \cup Y \subseteq x$ and $X \cup Y$ is finite;

(A_{iii}) $\langle X, Y\rangle r \langle X', Y'\rangle \equiv (X \subseteq X') \wedge (Y \subseteq Y')$.

It would be easy, though tedious, to write down such a formula explicitly.

From the properties of F we infer that if the axiom of choice is true in M, then

$$\vdash_M F[R_1(a), a].$$

From theorem 3.3 we infer that condition (2) is satisfied (here we use the fact that the theorems of Section 3 were proved with the help of ZF and the axiom of choice alone). From 5.1 we infer therefore that:

5.2. *If M is a model of* ZF, $a \in M$ *and the axiom of choice is valid in M, then*

$$\vartheta(M, R_1(a)) \leqslant \omega_1(M).$$

Example 2. Let a, $\alpha \in M$ and let $\Pi_2^\alpha(a)$, $R_2^\alpha(a)$ be defined as in XII.1. We know from XII.1.2, that $\Pi_2^\alpha(a)$ and $R_2^\alpha(a)$ belong to M. We choose the same formula Ξ as before and as F a formula with the free variables x_1, x_2, x_3, x_4 and with the following property: for almost all A and arbitrary r, p, x, m in A the condition $\vdash_A F[r, p, x, m]$ is equivalent to the conjunction of the following conditions:

(B_i) $\vdash_A$ AC;

(B_{ii}) p is the set of functions π satisfying $\mathrm{Dom}(\pi) \subseteq m$, $\mathrm{Dom}(\pi)$ is finite, $\mathrm{Rg}(\pi) \subseteq \Pi_1(x)$;

(B_{iii}) $r \subseteq p \times p$ and

$$\pi r \varrho \equiv \big\{(\mathrm{Dom}(\pi) \subseteq \mathrm{Dom}(\varrho)) \wedge (\xi)_{\mathrm{Dom}(\pi)}[\langle \pi(\xi), \varrho(\xi)\rangle \in R_1(x)]\big\}.$$

Again we dispense with the actual writing of F.

If M is a model in which the axiom of choice is valid, then obviously

$$\vdash_M F[R_2^\alpha(a), \Pi_2^\alpha(a), a, \alpha].$$

From 3.5 we infer that formula (2) is provable in ZF for this choice of F. Hence theorem 5.1 shows that

5.3. *If M is a model of* ZF *in which the axiom of choice is valid and a, $\alpha \in M$, then*

$$\vartheta\big(M, R_2^\alpha(a)\big) \leqslant \omega_1(M).$$

Example 3. Let M be a model of ZF in which the axiom of choice and the generalized continuum hypothesis are valid. Assume that $a, b \in M$ and that the relative cardinal $\beta = \mathrm{Card}(M, b)$ is infinite and regular in M, i.e., satisfies $\mathrm{Cf}(M, \beta) = \beta$. Denote by $\Pi_5(a, b) = \Pi$ the set of all finite functions π with $\mathrm{Dom}(\pi) \subseteq b$ and $\mathrm{Rg}(\pi) \subseteq a$. The relation R is defined as $\pi \subseteq \varrho$. Obviously Π and R belong to M.

We choose as Ξ the formula $|x_0| \leqslant |x_2|$ and as F the formula which describes R in the following sense: for almost all A and arbitrary r, p, a, b the condition $\vdash_A F[r, p, a, b]$ is equivalent to the conjunction of the following conditions:

($\mathrm{C_i}$) $\vdash_A \mathrm{AC} \wedge \mathrm{GCH}$;

($\mathrm{C_{ii}}$) $\mathrm{Cf}\big(A, \mathrm{Card}(A, b)\big) = \mathrm{Card}(A, b)$;

($\mathrm{C_{iii}}$) p is the set of finite functions with range contained in b and with domain contained in a;

($\mathrm{C_{iv}}$) $r \subseteq p \times p$ and $\pi r \varrho \equiv \pi \subseteq \varrho$.

Because of the assumptions concerning M and b we obtain $\vdash_M F[R, \Pi, a, b]$. From 3.6 and 1.3 we further infer that formula (2) of 5.1 is provable in ZF. Hence

5.4. *Under the assumptions enumerated above*

$$\vartheta(M, R) \leqslant \aleph\big(M, \mathrm{Card}(M, b)\big).$$

It would be easy to deal in a similar way with the case where $\mathrm{Cf}(M, \beta) < \beta$; we leave the discussion of this case to the reader.

6. Absoluteness of cardinals and of the cofinality index

In this section we place ourselves in the situation described in XI.5.2. Thus we have a model M of ZF and a model

$$N = N\big(M, \mathscr{X}, B, a(p), \Pi\big),$$

where $\mathscr{X}$, B, $a(p)$ and Π satisfy the assumptions of XI.5.2.

We call a relative cardinal $\alpha \in \mathrm{Card}(M)$ *absolute* if it belongs to $\mathrm{Card}(N)$; the cofinality index of α is *absolute* if $\mathrm{Cf}(M, \alpha) = \mathrm{Cf}(N, \alpha)$.

We first show on an example that, in general, not every relative cardinal is absolute.

6.1. *If* $N = N^{\mathrm{Z}}_{a,b}(p)$ *where* $a, b \in \mathrm{Card}(M)$ *and* $a > b \geqslant \omega$ (cf. XII.4.3), *then* $a \notin \mathrm{Card}(N)$.

PROOF. We saw in XII.5.5 that N contains a mapping of b onto a and thus a is not absolute (for this choice of N).

The reason why not all cardinals are absolute is simply this: N contains new elements which were not present in M and thus it may happen that N contains a mapping of a smaller ordinal onto a cardinal of M.

We shall now seek conditions which ensure the absoluteness of certain cardinals.

We shall denote by $\vartheta(M, \Pi)$ the ordinal $\vartheta(M, \prec)$, where $\prec$ is the partial ordering of Π defined by $\pi \prec \varrho \equiv U_\pi \supseteq U_\varrho$.

6.2. *Let M be a model in* ZF *in which the axiom of choice is valid and let*

$$N = N\big(M, \mathscr{X}, B, a(p_0), \Pi\big), \quad \textit{where} \quad B = B^0 \textit{ or } B = B^{\mathrm{Z}},$$

be one of the models constructed in theorem XI.5.2. *If* $\gamma \in \mathrm{Card}(M)$ *and* $\vartheta(M, \Pi) \leqslant \gamma$, *then* $\gamma \in \mathrm{Card}(N)$.

PROOF. The idea of the proof is as follows: we assume by way of contradiction that there exist a $\beta < \gamma$ and a function $f \in N$ which maps β onto γ. Thus f has the form $C_\varphi\big(a(p_0)\big)$ where we have omitted the upper index B.

For almost all p in a sufficiently small neighbourhood U_{π_0} around p_0 the set $C_\varphi\big(a(p)\big)$ is also a mapping f_p of β onto γ. The values of $f_p(\xi)$ for $\xi < \beta$ depend on ξ as well as on p. We leave ξ fixed and study the dependence of $f_p(\xi)$ on p. For almost all points p of U_{π_0} there is a neighbourhood U_{π_ξ} of p such that $f_q(\xi)$ is constant for almost all points q of this neighbourhood. The elements π_ξ will be put in a one-to-one correspondence (by means of a function which belongs to M) with elements of a $\prec$-disjoint set sel_ξ, which also belongs to M.

Since all ordinals $< \gamma$ are values of $f_p(\xi)$ for suitable p and ξ, we infer that γ is M-embeddable in the set $X = \bigcup \{\mathrm{sel}_\xi \times \{\xi\}: \xi < \beta\}$. However, this is impossible. For if $\gamma > \vartheta(M, \Pi)$, then $\max(\beta, \vartheta(M, \Pi)) < \gamma$ whereas X is in M of power at most $\max(\beta, \vartheta(M, \Pi))$ because sel_ξ has in M a cardinality $< \vartheta(M, \Pi)$. If $\gamma = \vartheta(M, \Pi)$, then $\beta < \vartheta(M, \Pi)$; using the relative regularity of $\vartheta(M, \Pi)$ we infer that X has in M a cardinality $< \vartheta(M, \Pi)$.

We now present the details of the proof. First we recall that each ordinal $\xi < \pi(M)$ can be represented in the form $C_{h(\xi)}(a(p))$, where the function $h(\xi) = \mathrm{pl}_{11}(\xi)$ is definable in M (see III.5.1 and V.2.5). Next we introduce two formulae H_0 and H. The formula H_0 is simply $\langle x_1, x_2 \rangle \in x_0$. The formula H says that x_0 is a one-to-one function with domain x_1 and range x_2; it is defined as follows

$$\mathbf{Fn}(x_0) \wedge (\mathbf{dl}(x_0) = x_1) \wedge (\mathbf{dp}(x_0) = x_2).$$

We then have $\vdash_N H[f, \beta, \gamma]$ and hence there is a π_0 in Π such that $p_0 \in U_{\pi_0}$ and

$$\text{(1)} \qquad \mathrm{Forc}_H(\pi_0, \varphi, h(\beta), h(\gamma)).$$

For each $\xi < \beta$ we have $\vdash_N H_0[f, \xi, f(\xi)]$ and hence there is a π_ξ in Π such that $p_0 \in U_{\pi_\xi}$, $\pi_0 \prec \pi_\xi$ and

$$\text{(2)} \qquad \mathrm{Forc}_{H_0}(\pi_\xi, \varphi, h(\xi), h(f(\xi))).$$

We now fix an ordinal $\xi < \beta$ and consider the set

$$F_\xi = \{\langle \pi, \eta \rangle \in \Pi \times \gamma: (\pi \succ \pi_0) \wedge \mathrm{Forc}_{H_0}(\pi, \varphi, h(\xi), h(\eta))\},$$

which obviously belongs to M. We shall show that F_ξ is a function. For let us assume that $\pi \succ \pi_0$ and

$$\text{(3)} \qquad \mathrm{Forc}_{H_0}(\pi, \varphi, h(\xi), h(\eta)), \quad \mathrm{Forc}_{H_0}(\pi, \varphi, h(\xi), h(\eta')).$$

From (1) we obtain that for almost all p in U_{π_0} the set $C_\varphi(a(p))$ is a function with domain $C_{h(\beta)}(a(p)) = \beta$ and range $C_{h(\gamma)}(a(p)) = \gamma$. From (3) we obtain that

$$\langle \xi, \eta \rangle \in C_\varphi(a(p)) \quad \text{and} \quad \langle \xi, \eta' \rangle \in C_\varphi(a(p))$$

for almost all p in U_π. Hence $\eta = \eta'$.

From (2) it follows that $\langle \pi_\xi, f(\xi) \rangle \in F_\xi$. Thus $f(\xi)$ belongs to the range of F_ξ.

Since $F_\xi \in M$ and the axiom of choice is valid in M we easily see that M contains a set which has exactly one element in common with each equivalence class of the relation

(4) $$\{\langle \pi', \pi'' \rangle : F_\xi(\pi') = F_\xi(\pi'')\}.$$

Moreover there is in M a function sel with domain β such that if $\xi < \beta$ then sel_ξ has exactly one element in common with each equivalence class of the relation (4).

To every $\alpha < \gamma$ corresponds a $\xi < \beta$ such that $\alpha \in \text{Rg}(F(\xi))$ because α is representable as $f(\xi)$. Hence we can correlate with each α a pair $\langle \pi, \xi \rangle$ such that $\pi \in \text{sel}_\xi$ and $\alpha = F_\xi(\pi)$. This mapping is one-to-one because if $\langle \pi, \xi \rangle = \langle \pi', \xi' \rangle$ then obviously $F_\xi(\pi) = F_{\xi'}(\pi')$. Moreover the mapping is definable in M. Thus γ is M-embeddable in the set

$$X = \bigcup \{\text{sel}_\xi \times \{\xi\} : \xi < \beta\}.$$

We shall now prove that this result is impossible. First we show that sel_ξ consists of $\prec$-disjoint elements. For assume that π' and π'' are two elements of sel_ξ and $\pi \succ \pi'$, $\pi \succ \pi''$. It follows that $F_\xi(\pi') \neq F_\xi(\pi'')$ and $\pi', \pi'' \succ \pi_0$. Using the definition of F_ξ, we infer that

$$\text{Forc}_{H_0}^{\ulcorner}\big(\pi, \varphi, h(\xi), h(F_\xi(\pi'))\big),$$

$$\text{Forc}_{H_0}^{\urcorner}\big(\pi, \varphi, h(\xi), h(F_\xi(\pi''))\big),$$

which contradicts the statement, proved above, that F_ξ is a function. It follows that

$$\text{Card}(M, \text{sel}_\xi) < \vartheta(M, \Pi).$$

We now distinguish two cases.

Case I. $\gamma > \vartheta(M, \Pi)$. Since $\text{Card}(M, \text{sel}_\xi \times \{\xi\}) < \vartheta(M, \Pi)$, we obtain

$$\text{Card}(M, X) \leqslant \beta \cdot \vartheta(M, \Pi) = \max(\beta, \vartheta(M, \Pi)) < \gamma.$$

Case II. $\gamma = \vartheta(M, \Pi)$. Since $\vartheta(M, \Pi) > \beta$ and also $\vartheta(M, \Pi) > \text{Card}(M, \text{sel}_\xi \times \{\xi\})$ and since $\vartheta(M, \Pi)$ is regular in M (that is is equal to $\text{Cf}(M, \vartheta(M, \Pi))$, see theorem 4.3) we can apply theorem 4.2 and find that $\vartheta(M, \Pi)$ is not M-embeddable into X.

Thus we obtain a contradiction in both cases and the theorem is proved.

We can easily show that the inclusion $\mathrm{Card}(M) \subseteq \mathrm{Card}(N)$ proved in theorem 6.2 cannot be strengthened to an equation. For let M_0 be the minimal model (cf. VI.4) and M its extension of the type described in theorem 6.1. Hence M contains an ordinal which is a cardinal of M_0 but not of M. Let N be a simple extension of M_0 satisfying the equation $\mathrm{Card}(M_0) = \mathrm{Card}(N)$; we shall show in an instant that such extensions exist and have the form $C^{\mathrm{Z}}_{\pi(M_0)}(a(p))$, where p is a generic point of a suitable space. Now if we start from M and construct from it the model $C^{\mathrm{Z}}_{\pi(M)}(a(p))$ using the same generic point p [1]), we obtain the model N. Hence $\mathrm{Card}(N) \neq \mathrm{Card}(M)$.

We now prove that in some cases the equation $\mathrm{Card}(M) = \mathrm{Card}(N)$ is true.

6.3. *If M and N are models of* ZF, $\pi(M) = \pi(N)$ *and* $M \subseteq N$, *then each cardinal of N is a cardinal of M.*

Proof. If $\gamma \in \mathrm{Card}(N)$, then $\gamma < \pi(M)$. For any $\beta < \gamma$ there is in N no function f with domain β and range γ. Hence no such function is in M and consequently $\gamma \in \mathrm{Card}(M)$.

6.4. *Under the assumptions of* 6.2 *if* $M \subseteq N$, *then conditions* $\gamma \in \mathrm{Card}(M)$ *and* $\gamma \in \mathrm{Card}(N)$ *are equivalent for each* $\gamma \geqslant \vartheta(M, \Pi)$.

This is an immediate corollary to 6.3 and 6.2.

We shall derive a similar result for the cofinality index.

6.5. *Let M be a model of* ZF *in which the axiom of choice is valid and let* $\mathscr{X}, \Pi, (A)\colon p \to a(p), \pi\colon \Pi \to U_\pi$ *be a space, a set and mappings which satisfy all assumptions of theorem* XI.5.2. *If* $p \in \mathrm{Gen}(\mathscr{X})$ *and* $N = N(p)$ *is the model* $C^{B}_{\pi(M)}(a(p))$ (*where B is one of the symbols* 0, Z), *then* $\mathrm{Cf}(M, \alpha) \geqslant \vartheta(M, \Pi)$ *implies that*

$$\mathrm{Cf}(N, \alpha) \geqslant \mathrm{Cf}(M, \alpha). \tag{5}$$

Proof. Let us denote $\beta = \mathrm{Cf}(N, \alpha)$. Then there is in $N(p)$ a function f whose domain is β and whose range has the supremum α. Hence for each $\xi < \alpha$ there is a smallest $\gamma(\xi) < \beta$ such that

$$f(\gamma(\xi)) > \xi. \tag{6}$$

[1]) This is permissible because the heights of M and N are the same, cf. remark on p. 136.

Since f is in $N(p)$, we may assume that $f = C_\varphi(a(p))$, where φ is an ordinal $< \pi(M)$. Also α and β can be represented as $C_\varrho(a(p))$ with suitable indices ϱ:

$$\alpha = C_{h(\alpha)}(a(p)), \quad \beta = C_{h(\beta)}(a(p)),$$

where the meaning of h is the same as in the proof of 6.2. We note that these equations are valid for arbitrary p in $\mathscr{X}$.

Using the notation introduced in 4.1 and the equivalence established in the proof of 4.1 (in the part devoted to the functor Cf) we obtain

$$\vdash_{N(p)} G[C_\varphi(a(p)), C_{h(\beta)}(a(p)), C_{h(\alpha)}(a(p))]. \tag{7}$$

We shall construct from f a function g which belongs to M, has the domain β and satisfies the condition $\bigcup \mathrm{Rg}(g) = \alpha$.

Since p is generic, we infer that there is a neighbourhood U_{π_0} of p such that (7) holds for almost all points p' in U_{π_0}. Thus with the exception of a set of the first category, for all p' in U_{π_0} the set $C_\varphi(a(p'))$ is a function mapping β into α whose range has the supremum α.

Let H_0 be the formula $\langle x_1, x_2\rangle \in x_0$.

For $\varrho < \beta$ and $\pi \succ \pi_0$ we put $t(\pi, \varrho) = \sigma$ if $\sigma < \alpha$ and

$$\mathrm{Forc}_{H_0}(\pi, \{\langle 0, \varphi\rangle, \langle 1, h(\varrho)\rangle, \langle 2, h(\sigma)\rangle\}); \tag{8}$$

if there is no such σ we put $t(\pi, \varrho) = 0$. Furthermore, we put $g(\varrho) = \sup\{t(\pi, \varrho)\colon \pi \succ \pi_0\}$.

We first show that $\sup\{g(\varrho)\colon \varrho < \beta\} = \alpha$. Thus let $\xi < \alpha$. We have to exhibit a $\varrho < \beta$ such that $g(\varrho) > \xi$. We shall show that $g(\gamma(\xi)) > \xi$, i.e., that there exists a $\zeta > \xi$ and a $\pi \succ \pi_0$ for which

$$\mathrm{Forc}_{H_0}\big(\pi, \{\langle 0, \varphi\rangle, \langle 1, h(\gamma(\xi))\rangle, \langle 2, h(\zeta)\rangle\}\big). \tag{9}$$

Put $\zeta = f(\gamma(\xi))$. Then $\zeta > \xi$ and

$$\vdash_{N(p)} H_0[C_\varphi(a(p)), C_{h(\gamma(\xi))}(a(p)), C_{h(\zeta)}(a(p))].$$

Since p is a generic point, we infer that there is a $\pi \succ \pi_0$ such that (9).

Next we show that $g(\varrho) < \alpha$ for each $\varrho < \beta$. Let ϱ be fixed. For each σ in the range of t select a $\pi_\sigma \in \Pi$ such that (8) is satisfied. The neighbourhoods U_{π_σ} and U_{π_τ} are disjoint whenever $\sigma \neq \tau$. This follows immediately if we reflect that disregarding a set X of the first category each p' in $U_{\pi_0} - X$ is such that there is exactly one η for which

$$\langle C_{h(\varrho)}(a(p)),\ C_{h(\eta)}(a(p))\rangle \in C_\varphi(a(p)).$$

We can obviously assume that the set F of pairs $\langle \sigma, \pi_\sigma \rangle$ is in M since the axiom of choice is valid in M. F is a one-to-one function. Since $\mathrm{Cf}(M, \alpha) \geqslant \vartheta(M, \Pi)$, there exist a $\xi < \mathrm{Cf}(M, \alpha)$ and a one-to-one function $s \in M$ which maps ξ onto the set consisting of all π_σ (i.e., onto $\mathrm{Rg}(F)$). It now follows that in M there is a one-to-one function which maps ξ onto the range of t. Hence the range of t is not cofinal with α and $g(\varrho) < \alpha$.

The function g is in M since the forcing relation is definable in M. Hence we find that $\sup\{g(\varrho)\colon \varrho < \beta\} = \alpha$ and therefore $\mathrm{Cf}(M, \alpha) \leqslant \beta$, which is the desired inequality.

In case where $M \subseteq N$ we can strengthen theorem 6.5 as follows:

6.6. *Under the assumptions of* 6.4 *if* $M \subseteq N$, *then*

$$\mathrm{Cf}(M, \alpha) = \mathrm{Cf}(N, \alpha).$$

PROOF. From the definition of $\mathrm{Cf}(M, \alpha)$ it follows that M contains an element f which is a mapping of $\mathrm{Cf}(M, \alpha)$ into α and which has a range cofinal with α. Since $f \in N$ the inequality $\mathrm{Cf}(M, \alpha) < \mathrm{Cf}(N, \alpha)$ is impossible, whence by 6.5 we obtain the equation stated in the theorem.

It is easy to construct examples of models M which are not contained in $N(p)$ and in which there are ordinals α such that $\mathrm{Cf}(N, \alpha)$ is strictly larger than $\mathrm{Cf}(M, \alpha)$.

7. The function exp of a model

Let M be a model of ZF in which the axiom of choice is valid. For every ordinal ξ of M there is then exactly one ordinal η of M such that

$$\mathrm{Card}\big(M,\ P(\omega_\xi(M)) \cap M\big) = \omega_\eta(M).$$

In other words, $\omega_\eta(M)$ is the relative cardinal (in M) of the "relative power set of $\omega_\xi(M)$", i.e., of the set of those subsets of $\omega_\xi(M)$ which are elements of M. We shall denote ω_η by $\exp(M, \xi)$ and call exp the *exponential function of M.*

If GCH is valid in M, then clearly $\exp(M, \xi) = \omega_{\xi+1}(M)$. It is an interesting and not yet completely solved problem which functions can be the exponential functions of models of ZF. In this section we shall establish some estimates for the exponential functions of models $N^{Z}(a(p))$ constructed by the method of theorem XI.5.2.

We assume as in XI.5.2 that $\mathscr{X}$ is a semi-regular space in which the theorem of Baire is valid. We denote by (A): $p \to a(p)$ a mapping of $\mathscr{X}$ into the class of transitive sequences of fixed length α_0. As usual, M will be a fixed denumerable model of ZF such that α_0 is an element of M, Π will be an element of M and $\pi \to U_\pi$ a mapping of Π onto a regular basis of $\mathscr{X}$. We shall assume that theorem XI.5.2 is applicable and thus that whenever p is a generic point of $\mathscr{X}$, the family

$$N^{Z}(p) = C^{B^{Z}}_{\pi(M)}(a(p))$$

is a model of ZF. Furthermore, we make three additional assumptions: first that the axiom of choice AC is valid in M, secondly that there are infinitely many disjoint neighbourhoods U_π and thirdly that M is contained in $N^{Z}(p)$. These assumptions are satisfied for instance when M is the minimal model and Π is one of the sets discussed in XII.1; for instance we can take as Π the set $\Pi^{\alpha}_{2}(r)$ assuming that $\alpha \geqslant \omega$.

From theorem 4.3 we know that $\vartheta(M, \Pi)$ is a cardinal of M and is different from ω. In view of the assumptions which we have made, it is infinite and hence can be represented as $\omega_\tau(M)$ where $\tau \neq 0$. If τ is not a limit ordinal, then we shall denote $\omega_{\tau-1}(M)$ by $\vartheta'(M, \Pi)$; otherwise we put $\vartheta'(M, \Pi) = \vartheta(M, \Pi)$.

Our first result concerning the exponential function is a simple corollary to theorem VII.8.1.

7.1. *If* $p \in \mathrm{Gen}(\mathscr{X})$ *and* $\alpha_0 < \omega_{\xi+1}(N^{Z}(p))$, *then*

$$\exp(N^{Z}(p), \xi) = \omega_{\xi+1}(M).$$

PROOF. The assumption says that

$$|\mathrm{Dom}(a(p))| \leqslant_{N^{Z}(p)} |\omega_\xi(N^{Z}(p))|$$

and hence the result follows immediately from theorem VII.8.1 in which we take $A = N^{Z}(p)$, $a = a(p)$, $B = B^{Z}$.

Theorem 7.1 is a restatement of our former result from Chapter VII, namely that GCH holds in all models of the form $N^Z(p)$ at least for sufficiently big cardinals.

We shall now give some estimates for cardinals smaller than α_0. First of all we must introduce some abbreviations.

For π and ϱ in Π we shall say that π and ϱ are *compatible* if $U_\pi \cap U_\varrho \neq 0$. This is of course equivalent to the statement that π and ϱ are not $\prec$-disjoint (see Sections 2 and 3).

A set $A \subseteq \Pi$ will be called *full* if for every π in Π there is a ϱ in A which is compatible with π.

If H is a formula and $\xi \in \pi(M)^{\mathrm{Fr}(H)}$, then we shall say that π *decides* H *at place* ξ (or briefly: *decides* H, ξ) if either $\mathrm{Forc}_H(\pi, \xi)$ or $\mathrm{Forc}_{\neg H}(\pi, \xi)$. It is obvious that if π and ϱ are compatible and both decide H, ξ, then

$$\mathrm{Forc}_H(\pi, \xi) \equiv \mathrm{Forc}_H(\varrho, \xi).$$

The following lemma will prove useful in the proof of theorem 7.3:

7.2. *For each formula H and each $\xi \in \pi(M)^{\mathrm{Fr}(H)}$ there is a full and $\prec$-disjoint set $A \subseteq \Pi$ such that $A \in M$ and each π in A decides H, ξ; the relative cardinal of A in M is $< \vartheta(M, \Pi)$.*

PROOF. Let X be the set of all those π in Π which decide H, ξ. Since $X \in M$ (because the forcing relation is parametrically definable in M), we conclude that $P(X) \cap M \in M$. Now the axiom of choice is valid in M and therefore there exists in M a maximal element of $P(X) \cap M$ consisting of mutually incompatible elements. This maximal element A is full and $\prec$-disjoint. Since it is contained in X, all its elements decide H, ξ. Finally the relative cardinal of A is smaller than $\vartheta(M, \Pi)$ because A consists of mutually incompatible elements. The lemma is thus proved.

We can now state and prove a theorem which is a special case of a result due to Solovay and Easton (see Easton [7]). This theorem gives an estimate for the exponential function of the model $N^Z(p)$ which does not depend on the length of the sequence $a(p)$ used in the construction.

7.3. *If $p \in \mathrm{Gen}(\mathscr{X})$ and $\xi < \pi(M)$, then*

$$\exp\left(N^Z(p), \xi\right) \leqslant \mathrm{Card}\,(M, \Pi^\lambda \cap M),$$

where $\lambda = \max\left(\omega_\xi\left(N^Z(p)\right), \vartheta'(M, \Pi)\right)$.

PROOF. In order to abbreviate the formulae we shall write $\gamma = \omega_\xi(N^Z(p))$. The left-hand side of the inequality to be proved is then the relative cardinal (with respect to $N^Z(p)$) of $P(\gamma) \cap N^Z(p)$.

We proceed as in the proof of VIII.2.1; that is, we correlate with each element of $P(\gamma) \cap N^Z(p)$ an object in the model M and calculate in M the cardinal number of the set consisting of those objects.

As in VIII.2.1, we denote the formulae $x_0 \in x_1$ and $(x_2)[(x_2 \in x_0) \to (x_2 \in x_1)]$ by H_0 and H_1.

Let K be the set of all triples $\langle \pi_0, A, s\rangle$ with the following properties: there exist a function $F \in M$ with $\mathrm{Dom}(F) = \gamma$ and an ordinal $\nu < \pi(M)$ such that:

(1) $$\pi_0 \in \Pi,$$

(2) $$A = \bigcup \mathrm{Rg}(F) \subseteq \Pi,$$

(3) For each $\xi < \gamma$ the set $F(\xi)$ is full, $\prec$-disjoint and each of its elements decides H_0, $(\mathrm{pl}_{11}(\xi), \nu)$,

(4) $$\mathrm{Forc}_{H_1}(\pi_0, \nu, \mathrm{pl}_{11}(\gamma)),$$

(5) $$s \subseteq A \times \gamma,$$

(6) $$\langle \pi, \xi\rangle \in s \equiv [(\pi \in F(\xi)) \wedge (\xi < \gamma) \wedge \mathrm{Forc}_{H_0}(\pi, \mathrm{pl}_{11}(\xi), \nu)].$$

In view of the parametrical definability of the relation Forc we easily see that $K \in M$.

For each $\langle \pi_0, A, s\rangle$ in K we denote by $\nu(\pi_0, A, s)$ the least ordinal for which there is a function $F \in M$ with domain γ satisfying (1)–(6). Finally, we put

$$\nu_0 = \sup\{\nu(\pi_0, A, s) \colon \langle \pi_0, A, s\rangle \in K\}.$$

It is then clear that $\nu_0 < \pi(M)$.

Let $x \in P(\gamma) \cap N^Z(p)$ and $\nu = \mathrm{Od}^{B^Z}(N^Z(p), x, a(p))$ or more concisely $\nu = \mathrm{Od}(x, a(p))$ (see VII.1.7). We claim that $\nu < \nu_0$.

Since

(7) $$C_\nu(a(p)) \subseteq \gamma,$$

there is a π_0 such that $p \in U_{\pi_0}$ and $\mathrm{Forc}_{H_1}(\pi_0, \nu, \mathrm{pl}_{11}(\gamma))$. For each $\xi < \gamma$ there exists a full set F_ξ such that each of its elements decides H_0, $(\mathrm{pl}_{11}(\xi), \nu)$ and any two of the elements of F_ξ are $\prec$-disjoint. Owing to the axiom of choice we can select for each ξ a set F_ξ in such a way that the function $F\colon \xi \to F_\xi$ be in M.

If we put

$$A = \bigcup \{F_\xi\colon \xi < \gamma\},$$

$$s = \{\langle \pi, \xi\rangle\colon (\pi \in F_\xi) \wedge (\xi \in \gamma) \wedge \mathrm{Forc}_{H_0}(\pi, \mathrm{pl}_{11}(\xi), \nu)\},$$

we obviously have formulae (1)–(6).

It follows that $\langle \pi_0, A, s\rangle \in K$. We put $\nu' = \nu(\pi_0, A, s)$ and want to show that $x = C_{\nu'}(a(p))$.

From the definition of ν' it follows that there is a function F' with domain γ such that (2), (3), (4), (6) remain valid if we replace in them F by F' and ν by ν'. We refer to the modified conditions as to (2′)–(6′). For symmetry we denote formulae (1) and (5) also by (1′) and (5′).

From (4′) it follows that for each generic q in U_{π_0} the set $C_{\nu'}(a(q))$ is contained in $C_{\mathrm{pl}_{11}(\gamma)}(a(q)) = \gamma$. Since $p \in U_{\pi_0}$, we obtain

$$(7') \qquad C_{\nu'}(a(p)) \subseteq \gamma.$$

We now have two completely symmetric sets of statements: one consists of statements (1)–(7) and the other of (1′)–(7′).

In order to prove the equation

$$C_\nu(a(p)) = C_{\nu'}(a(p))$$

we have to prove two implications:

$$(8) \qquad \xi \in C_\nu(a(p)) \to \xi \in C_{\nu'}(a(p)), \qquad \xi \in C_{\nu'}(a(p)) \to \xi \in C_\nu(a(p)).$$

In view of the symmetry of the assumptions it will be sufficient to prove only one of them, e.g. the first. Therefore let us assume that $\xi \in C_\nu(a(p))$. Then $\xi \in \gamma$ by (7). By way of contradiction we assume that $\xi \notin C_{\nu'}(a(p))$. Hence there is a π in Π such that $p \in U_\pi$, $\pi \succ \pi_0$, $\mathrm{Forc}_{H_0}(\pi, \mathrm{pl}_{11}(\xi), \nu)$ and

$$(9) \qquad \mathrm{Forc}_{\neg H_0}(\pi, \mathrm{pl}_{11}(\xi), \nu').$$

We choose a ϱ in F_ξ which is compatible with π. Hence we find that there is a $\varrho' \succ \varrho$ such that $\varrho' \succ \pi$ and $\mathrm{Forc}_{H_0}(\varrho', \mathrm{pl}_{11}(\xi), \nu)$. Since ϱ decides H_0, $(\mathrm{pl}_{11}(\xi), \nu)$ we can replace here ϱ' by ϱ and obtain $\langle \varrho, \xi\rangle \in s$. Now we use the definition of ν' and obtain by (6′) $\mathrm{Forc}_{H_0}(\varrho, \mathrm{pl}_{11}(\xi), \nu')$

and therefore also $\mathrm{Forc}_{H_0}(\varrho', \mathrm{pl}_{11}(\xi), \nu')$. But this result is clearly impossible in view of the relation $\varrho' \succ \pi$ and assumption (9).

Thus we have proved the first of the implications (8). Since the second can be proved in a symmetrical way, we can consider the equation $x = C_\nu(a(p)) = C_{\nu'}(a(p))$ as proved. It follows that $\mathrm{Od}(x, a(p)) \leqslant \nu'$ since $\mathrm{Od}(x, a(p))$ is the least ordinal α such that $x = C_\alpha(a(p))$ (cf. VII.1.7). Hence $\mathrm{Od}(x, a(p)) < \nu_0$. Since the function Od is parametrically definable in $N^Z(p)$ and is one-to-one in this set, we obtain the following result:

$$|P(\gamma) \cap N^Z(p)| \leqslant_{N^Z(p)} |\nu_0|.$$

We shall now evaluate the relative cardinal number of ν_0 in M. Obviously $\mathrm{Card}(M, \nu_0) \leqslant \mathrm{Card}(M, K)$ and so we shall evaluate $\mathrm{Card}(M, K)$.

Since K consists of triples $\langle \pi_0, A, s \rangle$, we shall evaluate the cardinalities of the ranges of the three components. The first component π_0 ranges over Π and the relative cardinality σ of this set is $\mathrm{Card}(M, \Pi)$. The second component A ranges over those subsets of Π which are representable as unions (2). Since, by (3), $F(\xi)$ is a $\prec$-disjoint set, we infer from the definition of ϑ' that

$$\mathrm{Card}(M, F(\xi)) \leqslant \vartheta'(M, \Pi),$$

whence by (2),

$$\mathrm{Card}(M, A) \leqslant \vartheta'(M, \Pi) \cdot \mathrm{Card}(M, \gamma) \leqslant \max(\vartheta'(M, \Pi), \gamma) = \lambda.$$

Thus A ranges over subsets of Π which belong to M and have in M a relative cardinality $\leqslant \lambda$. Now we resort to a well-known theorem provable in ZF with the help of the axiom of choice (see [17], p. 291):

If m is a cardinal and X an infinite set, then the set of those subsets of X whose power is $\leqslant m$ has the same cardinal number as X^m.

Since this theorem is provable from the axioms of ZF and the axiom of choice, we infer that it is valid in M. Hence A ranges over a set of the same (relative) cardinality as $\Pi^\lambda \cap M$.

For any fixed π_0 and A the set s ranges over subsets of $A \times \gamma$ and the relative cardinality of this set is $\leqslant \lambda \cdot \gamma = \max(\lambda, \gamma) = \lambda$.

Thus the relative cardinal of K in M is $\leqslant \mathrm{Card}(M, P(\lambda) \cap M)$. $\mathrm{Card}(M, \Pi) \cdot \mathrm{Card}(M, \Pi^\lambda) = \mathrm{Card}(M, \Pi^\lambda)$ and we obtain

(10) $$|\nu_0| \leqslant_M |\Pi^\lambda \cap M|.$$

We want to pass from this formula to an inequality between cardinals of $N^Z(p)$. Since $\Pi^\lambda \cap M$ is not necessarily an element of $N^Z(p)$, we pass first from $\Pi^\lambda \cap M$ to the ordinal $\mathrm{Card}(M, \Pi^\lambda \cap M)$, which obviously is an element of both $N^Z(p)$ and M. Thus we infer from (10) that

$$|\nu_0| \leqslant_M |\mathrm{Card}(M, \Pi^\lambda \cap M)|$$

and now replace $\leqslant_M$ by $\leqslant_{N^Z(p)}$, which is permissible in view of the inclusion $M \subseteq N^Z(p)$. Hence

$$|P(\gamma) \cap N^Z(p)| \leqslant_{N^Z(p)} |\mathrm{Card}(M, \Pi^\lambda \cap M)|.$$

This inequality can also be written as

$$\mathrm{Card}\big(N^Z(p), P(\gamma) \cap N^Z(p)\big) \leqslant \mathrm{Card}\big(N^Z(p), \mathrm{Card}(M, \Pi^\lambda \cap M)\big).$$

The left-hand side is by the definition of the function exp simply $\exp\big(N^Z(p), \xi\big)$.

In order to transform the right-hand side we put

$$\mathrm{Card}(M, \Pi^\lambda \cap M) = \mu.$$

Thus μ is an ordinal $< \pi(M)$ and an element of $\mathrm{Card}(M)$. Since Π has at least two elements, we see that

$$\mu > \mathrm{Card}(M, \lambda) \geqslant \vartheta'(M, \Pi) \quad \text{whence} \quad \mu \geqslant \vartheta(M, \Pi).$$

According to 6.2 μ is a cardinal of $N^Z(p)$ and hence

$$\mathrm{Card}\big(N^Z(p), \mu\big) = \mu.$$

Thus we obtain $\exp\big(N^Z(p), \xi\big) \leqslant \mu$, which is the desired result.

Example. Let GCH be valid in M and assume that

$$\vartheta(M, \Pi) = \omega_{\tau+1}(M), \quad \gamma = \omega_\xi(M), \quad \mathrm{Card}(M, \Pi) = \omega_\varrho(M).$$

In this case $\lambda = \omega_{\max(\xi, \tau)}(M)$. Since the formulae for the exponentiation of alephs (see [17], p. 303) are valid in M, we obtain the following values for the relative cardinal $\varkappa = \mathrm{Card}(M, \Pi^\lambda \cap M)$:

(i) $\varrho \notin \mathrm{Lim}(M)$, $\max(\xi, \tau) < \varrho$: $\varkappa = \omega_\varrho(M)$;

(ii) $\varrho \notin \mathrm{Lim}(M)$, $\max(\xi, \tau) \geqslant \varrho$: $\varkappa = \omega_{\max(\xi,\tau)+1}(M)$;

(iii) $\varrho \in \mathrm{Lim}(M)$, $\omega_{\max(\xi,\tau)}(M) < \mathrm{Cf}\big(M, \omega_\varrho(M)\big)$: $\varkappa = \omega_\varrho(M)$;

(iv) $\varrho \in \mathrm{Lim}(M)$, $\mathrm{Cf}\big(M, \omega_\varrho(M)\big) \leqslant \omega_{\max(\xi,\tau)}(M) < \omega_\varrho(M)$:

$$\varkappa = \omega_{\varrho+1}(M);$$

(v) $\varrho \in \mathrm{Lim}(M)$, $\max(\xi, \tau) \geqslant \varrho$: $\varkappa = \omega_{\max(\xi,\tau)+1}(M)$.

These values of $\varkappa$ give the upper estimates for the function $\exp\big(N^{\mathrm{Z}}(p), \xi\big)$ of the model $N^{\mathrm{Z}}(p)$ obtained from M by the method described in XI.5.2.

These estimates give better results than the one given in 7.1 especially in cases where $\mathrm{Dom}\big(a(p)\big) = \alpha_0$ is large. Moreover, estimates (i)–(v) can be applied in all cases whereas the estimate given in 7.1 is applicable only when ξ is sufficiently large.

8. The independence of the continuum hypothesis

In this section we shall discuss a model in which the continuum hypothesis is not valid and we shall determine the exponential function of that model. All the results of this section are due to Cohen [4], [6].

We specialize the assumptions made at the beginning of Section 7 as follows: M will be the minimal model, α_0 an infinite cardinal of M, $\mathscr{X}$ the space $[P(\omega)]^{\alpha_0}$ with the usual Tichonoff topology and Π the set $\Pi_2^{\alpha_0}(\{\omega\}^{\alpha_0})$ (see XII.1). The mapping of Π onto a regular basis of $\mathscr{X}$ was described in XII.1. For p in $\mathscr{X}$ we define $a(p)$ as the sequence whose initial terms are all integers; these terms are followed by coordinates of p:

$$a(p)\colon\ 0, 1, 2, \ldots, p_0, p_1, \ldots, p_\xi, \ldots \qquad (\xi < \alpha_0).$$

Since all assumptions of theorem XI.5.2 have been verified (see XII.1.1, 1.2 and XII.3.1), we obtain

8.1. *If* $p \in \mathrm{Gen}(\mathscr{X})$, *then* $N^{\mathrm{Z}}(p)$ *is a model of* ZF *and the axiom of choice is valid in* $N^{\mathrm{Z}}(p)$.

We assume in all the subsequent theorems that p is a generic point of $\mathscr{X}$.

The relative Souslin coefficient of Π was determined in XII.5.3, where we proved that $\vartheta(M, \Pi) = \omega_1(M)$. Hence by theorems 6.2, 6.3 and the definition of $\omega_\xi(M)$ we obtain

8.2. $\mathrm{Card}(M) = \mathrm{Card}\big(N^Z(p)\big)$ *and* $\omega_\xi(M) = \omega_\xi\big(N^Z(p)\big)$ *for* $\xi < \pi(M)$.

8.3. *If* $\alpha_0 > \omega_1(M)$, *then the continuum hypothesis is not valid in* $N^Z(p)$.

PROOF. We showed in XII.5.3 that $N^Z(p)$ contains a one-to-one mapping of α_0 into $P(\omega) \cap N^Z(p)$. Hence

$$(1) \quad \exp\big(N^Z(p), 0\big) = \mathrm{Card}\big(N^Z(p), P(\omega) \cap N^Z(p)\big) \geqslant \alpha_0 > \omega_1(M) = \omega_1\big(N^Z(p)\big).$$

We shall now calculate the function exp of the model $N^Z(p)$. We shall denote by ϱ an ordinal such that $\alpha_0 = \omega_\varrho(M)$. It is then obvious that $\mathrm{Card}(M, \Pi) = \omega_\varrho(M)$ because Π consists of finite functions whose domain is $\subset \alpha_0 = \omega_\varrho(M)$ and whose values are pairs of finite sets of integers.

8.4. *If* $\xi \geqslant \varrho$, *then*

$$\exp\big(N^Z(p), \xi\big) = \omega_{\xi+1}(M).$$

The proof is obtained directly from 7.1.

For $\xi < \varrho$ we have the estimate:

8.5. *If* $\xi < \varrho$, *then*

$$\omega_\varrho(M) \leqslant \exp\big(N^Z(p), \xi\big) \leqslant \omega_{\varrho+1}(M).$$

The estimation from above follows from the equation

$$\exp\big(N^Z(p), \varrho\big) = \omega_{\varrho+1}(M)$$

established in 8.4 and the remark that exp is an increasing function. The estimation from below results from (1), which can be written in the form

$$\exp\big(N^Z(p), 0\big) \geqslant \omega_\varrho(M).$$

Whether the value of the function exp is $\omega_\varrho(M)$ or $\omega_{\varrho+1}(M)$ depends on the relative cofinality character of $\omega_\varrho(M)$, i.e., on the number $\mathrm{Cf}(M, \alpha_0)$.

8.6. *If* $\mathrm{Cf}(M, \alpha_0) = \omega$, *then*

$$\exp\big(N^Z(p), \xi\big) = \omega_{\varrho+1}(M) \quad \textit{for all } \xi < \varrho.$$

PROOF. In view of 8.5 it is sufficient to show that

$$\exp\big(N^Z(p), 0\big) = \omega_{\varrho+1}(M).$$

Otherwise the relative cardinal of $P(\omega)\cap N^Z(p)$ in $N^Z(p)$ would be $\omega_\varrho(N^Z(p)) = \omega_\varrho(M) = \alpha_0$ and hence would be cofinal with ω (in M or, which in the present case is the same, in $N^Z(p)$, see theorem 6.5). This is impossible because König's theorem (see [17], p. 203) is valid in $N^Z(p)$ and that theorem implies that $P(\omega)$ is not cofinal with ω.

Now we have the corollary:

8.7. ZF *remains consistent if we add to it* AC *and the axioms*:

$$2^{\aleph_n} = \aleph_{\omega+1} \quad \textit{for} \quad n \leqslant \omega, \qquad 2^{\aleph_\tau} = \aleph_{\tau+1} \quad \textit{for} \quad \tau > \omega.$$

To prove this it is sufficient to take $\alpha_0 = \omega_\omega(M)$ in the previous theorems. Theorem 8.6 shows that in the resulting model the function exp is $= \omega_{\omega+1}(M)$ for all arguments $\leqslant \omega$.

Lusin [19] proposed in 1935 to discuss an alternative to the continuum hypothesis expressed by the equation $2^{\aleph_0} = 2^{\aleph_1}$. Corollary 8.7 shows that the hypothesis of Lusin is consistent with ZF and AC.

For $\mathrm{Cf}(M, \alpha_0) \neq \omega$ we have the following result:

8.8. *If* $\alpha_0 = \omega_\varrho(M)$ *is regular in* M (*i.e., if* $\mathrm{Cf}(M, \alpha_0) = \alpha_0$), *then*

$$\exp\big(N^Z(p), \xi\big) = \omega_\varrho(M) \quad \textit{for all } \xi < \varrho;$$

if α_0 *is singular, then*

$$\exp\big(N^Z(p), \xi\big) = \omega_\varrho(M)$$

for ξ *such that* $\omega_\xi(M) < \mathrm{Cf}(M, \alpha_0)$ *and*

$$\exp\big(N^Z(p), \xi\big) = \omega_{\varrho+1}(M)$$

for ξ *such that* $\mathrm{Cf}(M, \alpha_0) \leqslant \omega_\xi(M) \leqslant \alpha_0$.

PROOF. Let us put $\exp\big(N^Z(p), \xi\big) = \omega_\varepsilon(M)$; of course ε depends on ξ. It follows from the example given at the end of Section 7 that $\varepsilon \leqslant \varrho$ if $\omega_\varrho(M)$ is a regular cardinal of M. Thus $\varepsilon = \varrho$ in view of theorem 8.5. If $\omega_\varrho(M)$ is a singular cardinal of M and $\omega_\xi(M) < \mathrm{Cf}(M, \alpha_0)$, then we still have $\varepsilon = \varrho$ according to formula (iii) of the same example.

If $\mathrm{Cf}(M, \alpha_0) \leqslant \omega(M_\xi) \leqslant \alpha_0$, then the estimates given in Section 7 give only $\varepsilon \leqslant \varrho+1$, which we already know from theorem 8.5. We notice, however, that there is a theorem provable in ZF with the help of the axiom of choice which says that there is no infinite cardinal m for which the power of $P(m)$ would be cofinal with m (cf. [17], p. 290). This proves that there is no relative cardinal $\eta \geqslant \omega$ for which the relative cofinality index of Card$(N^Z(p), P(\eta) \cap N^Z(p))$ would be equal to η. If we substitute for η the relative cardinal $\mathrm{Cf}(M, \alpha_0) = \omega_\zeta(M)$ we find that $\exp(N^Z(p), \zeta)$ cannot be equal to $\omega_\varrho(M)$; for $\omega_\varrho(M)$ has the relative index of cofinality equal to $\omega_\zeta(M)$, and by the theorem just quoted $\exp(N^Z(p), \zeta)$ cannot have this index. It follows by 8.5 that $\exp(N^Z(p), \zeta) = \omega_{\varrho+1}(M)$, and hence the same equation follows for all ordinals between ζ and ϱ.

Theorem 8.8 is thus proved. Of course 8.6 is contained in 8.8.

The function $\exp(N^Z(p), \xi)$ has thus the following values: it is equal to $\omega_{\xi+1}(M)$ for all $\xi \geqslant \varrho$ and $= \omega_\varrho(M)$ for all $\xi < \varrho$ provided that α_0 is regular in M. If α_0 is singular in M, then $\exp(N^Z(p), \xi)$ is equal to $\omega_\varrho(M)$ for ξ such that $\omega_\xi(M) < \mathrm{Cf}(M, \alpha_0)$ and equal to $\omega_{\varrho+1}(M)$ for ξ such that $\mathrm{Cf}(M, \alpha_0) \leqslant \omega_\xi(M) < \alpha_0$. For larger values of ξ it is equal to $\omega_{\xi+1}(M)$.

These results show how the generalized continuum hypothesis can be violated in a suitable model. Much stronger results were established by Easton [7], who proved the following very general theorem:

Let M be a denumerable model for ZF *in which* AC *and* GCH *are valid, and let f be a non decreasing function parametrically definable in M whose domain is the set of cardinals of M which are regular in M, i.e., satisfy the equation* $\mathrm{Cf}(M, \alpha) = \alpha$. *Let* $\mathrm{Cf}(M, f(\alpha)) > \alpha$ *for each regular cardinal of M. Under these assumptions there is a model N such that* $N \supseteq M$, $\mathrm{Card}(N) = \mathrm{Card}(M)$, $\mathrm{Cf}(M, \alpha) = \mathrm{Cf}(N, \alpha)$ *for every α in* $\mathrm{Card}(M)$ *and such that*

$$\mathrm{Card}(N, P(\alpha) \cap N) = f(\alpha)$$

for every regular cardinal of M.

The proof of this theorem is much too involved to be included in the present book.

CHAPTER XIV

INDEPENDENCE OF THE AXIOM OF CHOICE

In the present chapter we shall discuss the independence of the axiom of choice from the axioms ZF and also several related problems. We shall work exclusively with models of the form $N(p) = C^{B^0}_{\pi(M)}(a(p))$; whenever we use a symbol which normally requires an index B indicating the operation used in the construction of the model, it will be tacitly understood that this index is B^0. In conformity with this convention we shall use symbols $\delta(\alpha)$, $K(\alpha)$, $L(\alpha)$, $M(\alpha)$ for what should be called $\delta(11, \alpha)$, $K(11, \alpha)$, etc. Sometimes we shall omit the parentheses and write shortly K_α, L_α, etc.

The main tool in our discussion will be homeomorphisms of the space $\mathscr{X}$, from which we draw generic points. We shall show that under special assumptions, to be formulated later, the forcing relation $\mathrm{Forc}_H(\pi, \xi)$ is invariant under suitable homeomorphisms of $\mathscr{X}$. This entails a certain kind of symmetry of the model $N(p)$, which is incompatible with the validity of the axiom of choice.

1. Action of homeomorphisms onto sets $C_\xi(a(p))$

We assume that $\mathscr{X}$ is a space, (A): $p \to a(p)$ a mapping of $\mathscr{X}$ into the class of transitive sequences of length α_0. Later on M will be a model of ZF and $N(p)$ will denote the set $C_{\pi(M)}(a(p))$.

Let f be a mapping of $\mathscr{X}$ onto itself. We wish to represent each $C_\xi(a(f(p)))$ as $C_{\varphi(\xi)}(a(p))$. Thus we wish to replace the action of f on the elements of $\mathscr{X}$ by a suitable change of the indices. A function φ of this sort does not always exist, but we formulate two conditions which together are sufficient for its existence:

(C1) *f is of finite order (i.e., there is an $n > 0$ such that $f^n(p) = p$ for each p);*

(C2) *If $\beta < \alpha_0$ and $\delta(\alpha) < \mathrm{pl}_{10}(\beta) < \delta(\alpha+1)$, then there is a ξ' such that $\delta(\alpha) < \xi' < \delta(\alpha+1)$ and the equation $a_\beta(f(p)) = C_{\xi'}(a(p))$ is true for each p in $\mathscr{X}$.*

1.1. *Each function f which satisfies* (C1) *and* (C2) *determines a mapping φ of ordinals into ordinals such that for arbitrary ordinals ξ, α and every p in $\mathscr{X}$:*

$$\delta(\alpha) < \xi < \delta(\alpha+1) \to \delta(\alpha) < \varphi(\xi) < \delta(\alpha+1), \tag{1}$$

$$C_{\delta(\alpha)}\big(a(f(p))\big) = C_{\delta(\alpha)}(a(p)), \tag{2}$$

$$C_\xi\big(a(f(p))\big) = C_{\varphi(\xi)}(a(p)). \tag{3}$$

PROOF. We let $\varphi(\xi) = \xi$ if $I(\xi) = 0$ or $I(\xi) = 11$ or $I(\xi) = 10$ and $\overline{\mathrm{pl}}_{10}(\xi) \geqslant \alpha_0$. If $1 \leqslant I(\xi) \leqslant 9$ and α is such that $\delta(\alpha) < \xi < \delta(\alpha+1)$, then we define $\varphi(\xi)$ as the first η such that $\delta(\alpha) < \eta < \delta(\alpha+1)$ and $I(\eta) = I(\xi)$, $K(\eta) = \varphi(K\xi)$, $L(\eta) = \varphi(L\xi)$, $M(\eta) = \varphi(M\xi)$. Finally, if $I(\xi) = 10$ and the ordinal $\beta = \overline{\mathrm{pl}}_{10}(\xi)$ is $< \alpha_0$, then we define $\varphi(\xi)$ as the least ξ' that satisfies (C2).

An obvious induction shows that φ is defined for each ξ and that (1) is true for arbitrary α and ξ.

Next we prove by induction on α that (2) is true for each ordinal α and each p in $\mathscr{X}$. For $\alpha = 0$ the formula is true for each p because $\delta(0) = 0$ and $C_0(a) = 0$ for any a. If (2) is valid for each p and all ordinals $< \alpha$ and if α is a positive limit number, then again the result is obtained immediately from the equation $C_{\delta(\alpha)}(a) = \bigcup_{\eta<\alpha} C_{\delta(\eta)}(a)$, which is valid for any a. It remains thus to deduce (2) for the ordinal $\alpha+1$ under the assumption that it is valid for each p and for the ordinal α.

The set $X = X_p = C_{\delta(\alpha+1)}\big(a(p)\big)$ consists of all $x_\xi = C_\xi\big(a(p)\big)$ with indices $\xi < \delta(\alpha+1)$ and similarly the set $Y = Y_p = C_{\delta(\alpha+1)}\big(a(f(p))\big)$ consists of all $y_\eta = C_\eta\big(a(f(p))\big)$ with $\eta < \delta(\alpha+1)$. If $\xi < \delta(\alpha)$, then $x_\xi \in Y$ in virtue of the inductive assumption, and similarly if $\eta < \delta(\alpha)$, then $y_\eta \in X$. If $\xi = \delta(\alpha)$, then $x_\xi = y_\xi$ in virtue of the inductive assumption; thus it is sufficient to discuss only the cases where ξ and η lie in the interval $(\delta(\alpha), \delta(\alpha+1))$. The values of $I(\xi)$ and $I(\eta)$ are then $\neq 0$.

If $1 \leqslant I(\xi) \leqslant 9$, then $K(\xi)$, $L(\xi)$, $M(\xi)$ are $< \delta(\alpha)$ and by inductive assumption we obtain $x_{K\xi}, x_{L\xi}, x_{M\xi} \in C_{\delta(\alpha)}\big(a(f(p))\big)$. Hence there are $\varrho, \sigma, \tau < \delta(\alpha)$ such that $x_{K\xi} = y_\varrho$, $x_{L\xi} = y_\sigma$, $x_{M\xi} = y_\tau$. Choosing η in the interval $(\delta(\alpha), \delta(\alpha+1))$ so that $I(\eta) = I(\xi)$, $K(\eta) = \varrho$, $L(\eta) = \sigma$, $M(\eta) = \tau$, we see that $x_\xi = y_\eta$ and hence $x_\xi \in Y$. We prove similarly that if $1 \leqslant I(\eta) \leqslant 9$, then $y_\eta \in X$.

If $I(\xi) = 11$, then $C_\xi(a) = \overline{\mathrm{pl}}_{11}(\xi)$ for any a, and thus $x_\xi = y_\xi$. Hence if $I(\xi) = 11$, then $x_\xi \in Y$ and $y_\xi \in X$. The proof is similar if $I(\xi) = 10$ and $\overline{\mathrm{pl}}_{10}(\xi) \geqslant \alpha_0$ since then $C_\xi(a) = 0$.

Finally we discuss the cases where $I(\eta) = 10$ and $I(\xi) = 10$. As we remarked above, we can assume that the ordinals $\beta = \overline{\mathrm{pl}}_{10}(\eta)$ and $\gamma = \overline{\mathrm{pl}}_{10}(\xi)$ are $< \alpha_0$.

If $I(\eta) = 10$, then $y_\eta = a_\beta(f(p))$ and hence, by (C2), $y_\eta = x_{\xi'}$, where ξ' is an ordinal which lies between $\delta(\alpha)$ and $\delta(\alpha+1)$. Hence $y_\eta \in X$. This proves that the inclusion $Y_p \subseteq X_p$ is true for each p. If $I(\xi) = 10$, then $x_\xi = a_\gamma(p)$ and hence, by (C1), $x_\xi = a_\gamma(f^n(p))$.

We put $p_1 = f(p)$, $p_2 = f(p_1)$, ..., $p_n = f(p_{n-1})$. Hence $p_n = p$. We prove by induction on i that for $i = 0, 1, \ldots, n-1$ there is an η_i, $\delta(\alpha) < \eta_i < \delta(\alpha+1)$, such that $a_\gamma(p) = C_{\eta_i}(p_{n-i})$. For $i = 0$ we take $\eta_i = \xi$. If the equation is valid for an i, then $a_\gamma(p) = C_{\eta_i}\big(a(f(p_{n-i-1}))\big)$ and using (C2) we obtain an ordinal η_i' satisfying $\delta(\alpha) < \eta_i' < \delta(\alpha+1)$ and $C_{\eta_i}\big(a(f(p_{n-i-1}))\big) = C_{\eta_i'}(a(p_{n-i-1}))$. Thus it is sufficient to take $\eta_{i+1} = \eta_i'$. For $i = n-1$ the equation becomes $a_\gamma(p) = C_{\eta_{n-1}}(f(p)) = y_{\eta_{n-1}}$ and thus $x_\xi \in Y_p$. This proves that $X_p \subseteq Y_p$ and the proof is complete.

Finally we prove (3). If $\xi = 0$, then the formula is true because $I(0) = 0$, whence $\varphi(0) = 0$, and we know that $C_0(a) = 0$ for each a. We now assume (3) for all ordinals $< \xi$ and discuss various cases.

If $I(\xi) = 0$, then ξ has the form $\delta(\alpha)$ and $\varphi(\xi) = \xi$. Thus in this case (3) follows from (2). If $1 \leqslant I(\xi) \leqslant 9$, then from the definition of φ we obtain $I\varphi(\xi) = I(\xi)$, $K\varphi(\xi) = \varphi(K\xi)$ and similar equations for the functions L and M. Hence

$$C_{\varphi(\xi)}(a(p)) = A_{I(\xi)}\big(C_{\varphi(K\xi)}(a(p)), C_{\varphi(L\xi)}(a(p))\big) \cap C_{\varphi(M\xi)}(a(p)),$$

whence we obtain (3) in virtue of the inductive assumption. If $I(\xi) = 11$, then $\varphi(\xi) = \xi$ and both sides of (3) are equal to $\overline{\mathrm{pl}}_{11}(\xi)$. The proof is similar in the case where $I(\xi) = 10$ and $\overline{\mathrm{pl}}_{10}(\xi) \geqslant \alpha_0$. Finally, if $I(\xi) = 10$ and $\overline{\mathrm{pl}}_{10}(\xi) < \alpha_0$, then $C_\xi\big(f(a(p))\big) = a_\beta\big(f(p)\big)$ where $\beta = \overline{\mathrm{pl}}_{10}(\xi)$. Since $\varphi(\xi)$ is one of the ordinals satisfying (C2), we obtain the desired result.

We note the following corollaries to 1.1.

1.2. *If f satisfies* (C1), (C2), *then* $N(p) = N\big(f(p)\big)$.

PROOF. This follows from (2) and the equation $\delta\big(\pi(M)\big) = \pi(M)$.

1.3. *If H is a formula, $\xi \in \pi(M)^{\mathrm{Fr}(H)}$ and φ satisfies* (1)–(3), *then*

$$p \in \mathscr{F}_{H,\varphi\circ\xi} \equiv f(p) \in \mathscr{F}_{H,\xi}. \tag{4}$$

PROOF. We use induction on H. If H is the formula $x_i \in x_j$ and the terms of ξ are ξ_i, ξ_j, then the left-hand side of (4) is equivalent to

$$C_{\varphi(\xi_i)}(a(p)) \in C_{\varphi(\xi_j)}(a(p)),$$

whence by (3) to

$$C_{\xi_i}\big(f(a(p))\big) \in C_{\xi_j}\big(a(f(p))\big),$$

i.e., to the right-hand side of (4). The proof is similar for the formula $x_i = x_j$. If (4) is valid for the formulae H and H', then it is valid for the formulae $H \wedge H'$, $\neg H$. Thus it remains to show that the validity of (4) for the formula H implies its validity for the formula $(x_n)H$, which we shall denote by H'. We shall assume that $n \in \mathrm{Fr}(H)$.

The left-hand side of (4) is equivalent to

$$(\eta)_{\pi(M)}[p \in \mathscr{F}_{H,(\varphi\circ\xi)\cup\{\langle n,\eta\rangle\}}]. \tag{5}$$

If we restrict the domain of η to ordinals which have the form $\varphi(\zeta)$ with $\zeta < \pi(M)$, then we obtain

$$(\zeta)_{\pi(M)}[p \in \mathscr{F}_{H,\varphi\circ(\xi\cup\{\langle n,\zeta\rangle\})}]. \tag{6}$$

We shall show that (6) implies (5). Let η be an ordinal $< \pi(M)$. There is an α such that $\eta < \delta(\alpha) < \pi(M)$, whence $C_\eta\big(a(p)\big) \in C_{\delta(\alpha)}\big(a(p)\big)$. In view of (2) we obtain $C_\eta\big(a(p)\big) \in C_{\delta(\alpha)}\Big(a\big(f(p)\big)\Big)$, and hence $C_\eta\big(a(p)\big)$ can be represented as $C_\zeta\Big(a\big(f(p)\big)\Big)$ with $\zeta < \delta(\alpha)$. Using (3) we obtain $C_\eta\big(a(p)\big) = C_{\varphi(\zeta)}\big(a(p)\big)$. From (6) it follows that

$$\vdash_{N(p)} H[C_{\varphi(\xi_1)}(a(p)), \ldots, C_{\varphi(\xi_k)}(a(p)), C_{\varphi(\zeta)}(a(p))]$$

(where $\xi_1, \xi_2, \dots, \xi_k$ are all terms of ξ). Thus we can replace $C_{\varphi(\zeta)}(a(p))$ by $C_\eta(a(p))$ and obtain

$$p \in \mathscr{F}_{H, (\varphi \circ \xi) \cup \{\langle n, \eta \rangle\}}.$$

Since η was arbitrary, we obtain (5). The equivalence of (5) and (6) is thus proved. It remains to apply to (6) the inductive assumption. We then find that (6) is equivalent to

$$(\zeta)_{\pi(M)}[f(p) \in \mathscr{F}_{H, \xi \cup \{\langle n, \zeta \rangle\}}],$$

i.e., to

$$f(p) \in \mathscr{F}_{H', \xi}.$$

Thus 1.3 is proved.

2. Homeomorphisms and forcing

In this section we assume that f is an auto-homeomorphism of $\mathscr{X}$ and determine what becomes of the forcing relation $\mathrm{Forc}_H(\pi, \xi)$ if U_π is transformed by f. More precisely, we want to find a sequence of ordinals ξ^* such that whenever $f^{-1}(U_\pi) = U_\sigma$, then

$$\mathrm{Forc}_H(\sigma, \xi^*) \equiv \mathrm{Forc}_H(\pi, \xi).$$

We place ourselves in the situation described in XI.5.2; thus M is a denumerable model of ZF, $\mathscr{X}$ a space, Π a set in M and $\pi \to U_\pi$ a mapping of Π onto an open basis of $\mathscr{X}$.

2.1. *Let f be an auto-homeomorphism of $\mathscr{X}$ which satisfies conditions* (C1), (C2) *given in Section* 1 *and let $\varphi = \varphi_f$ be a mapping of ordinals into ordinals satisfying* 1.1 (1)–(3). *Assume that π, ϱ, σ are elements of Π and*

$$f(U_\pi) \supseteq U_\sigma, \quad f^{-1}(U_\sigma) \supseteq U_\varrho.$$

If H is a formula and $\xi \in \pi(M)^{\mathrm{Fr}(H)}$, then

$$\mathrm{Forc}_H(\pi, \varphi \circ \xi) \quad \textit{implies} \quad \mathrm{Forc}_H(\sigma, \xi),$$
$$\mathrm{Forc}_H(\sigma, \xi) \quad \textit{implies} \quad \mathrm{Forc}_H(\varrho, \varphi \circ \xi).$$

PROOF. First we assume that $\mathrm{Forc}_H(\pi, \varphi \circ \xi)$. Hence

$$U_\pi - \mathscr{F}_{H, \varphi \circ \xi} \in I(\mathscr{X}).$$

Since f is a homeomorphism, it transforms sets of the first category into sets of the same kind. Hence

$$f(U_\pi)-f(\mathscr{F}_{H,\varphi\circ\xi}) \in I(\mathscr{X}).$$

By 1.3 $f(\mathscr{F}_{H,\varphi\circ\xi}) = \mathscr{F}_{H,\xi}$ and since $U_\sigma \subseteq f(U_\pi)$, we obtain

$$U_\sigma-\mathscr{F}_{H,\xi} \in I(\mathscr{X}), \quad \text{i.e.,} \quad \mathrm{Forc}_H(\sigma, \xi).$$

The second implication is proved similarly.

The proof of 2.1 can also be explained as follows:

The assumption $\mathrm{Forc}_H(\pi, \varphi\circ\xi)$ means that for almost all p in U_π the relation

$$\vdash_{N(p)} H[C_{\varphi(\xi_1)}(a(p)), \ldots, C_{\varphi(\xi_k)}(a(p))]$$

holds. In view of 1.2 and 1.1 (3) this means the same as

$$\vdash_{N(f(p))} H\Big[C_{\xi_1}\big(a(f(p))\big), \ldots, C_{\xi_k}\big(a(f(p))\big)\Big].$$

If p ranges over U_π, then points $f(p)$ fill up at least the whole of U_σ. Hence for almost all p in U_σ

$$\vdash_{N(p)} H[C_{\xi_1}(a(p)), \ldots, C_{\xi_k}(a(p))],$$

and we obtain $\mathrm{Forc}_H(\sigma, \xi)$.

We thus see that the implications proved in 2.1 are of "tautologuous" nature; in particular they do not allow us to infer that

$$\vdash_{N(p)} H[C_\xi(a(p))] \quad \text{implies} \quad \vdash_{N(p)} H\Big[C_\xi\big(a(f(p))\big)\Big].$$

Even for generic p such an implication would in general be false.

2.2. *Under the same assumptions as in* 2.1 *the conditions*

$$p \in \mathrm{Gen}(\mathscr{X}) \quad \textit{and} \quad f(p) \in \mathrm{Gen}(\mathscr{X})$$

are equivalent.

PROOF. If $p \in \mathrm{Gen}(\mathscr{X})$ and $f(p) \in \mathscr{F}_{H,\xi}$, then $p \in \mathscr{F}_{H,\varphi\circ\xi}$ and hence there is a neighbourhood U_π of p such that $\mathrm{Forc}_H(\pi, \varphi\circ\xi)$. Using 2.1 we obtain a neighbourhood U_σ of $f(p)$ such that

$$\mathrm{Forc}_H(\sigma, \xi), \quad \text{i.e.,} \quad U_\sigma - \mathscr{F}_{H,\xi} \in I(\mathscr{X}).$$

This proves that $f(p)$ is generic. The converse implication is proved similarly.

3. Invariance properties

Theorem 2.1 gains much strength in the case where for some terms ξ_i of ξ the equation

(1) $$C_{\varphi(\xi_i)}(a(p)) = C_{\xi_i}(a(p))$$

is identically true in p.

We deduce a theorem which in some cases allows us to prove equation (1).

We assume that G is a family of mappings of $\mathscr{X}$ onto $\mathscr{X}$ each of which has the properties (C1) and (C2) stated in Section 1. We denote by Γ a filter of subsets of G.

3.1. *Let Γ have the following property: for each $\xi < \alpha_0$ there is a G' in Γ such that $a_\xi(f(p)) = a_\xi(p)$ for all p in $\mathscr{X}$ and all f in G'.*

Then for each ordinal ξ there is a G' in Γ such that

$$C_\xi\big(a(f(p))\big) = C_\xi(a(p))$$

for each f in G' and each p in $\mathscr{X}$.

The proof is by induction on ξ. For $\xi = 0$ the theorem is obvious. We assume that it holds for all ordinals $< \xi$. If $I(\xi) = 0$, then there is an α such that $\delta(\alpha) = \xi$ and the result follows from 1.1 (2). If $1 \leqslant I(\xi) \leqslant 9$, then the theorem is valid for ordinals $K(\xi)$, $L(\xi)$, $M(\xi)$ and hence there is a G' in Γ such that for each p in $\mathscr{X}$ and each f in G' the equation $C_{K(\xi)}\big(a(f(p))\big) = C_{K(\xi)}(a(p))$ and similar equations for L and M are true. Since

$$C_\xi(a(p)) = A_{I(\xi)}\big(C_{K(\xi)}(a(p)), C_{L(\xi)}(a(p))\big) \cap C_{M(\xi)}(a(p))$$

the theorem is true for ξ. If $I(\xi) = 11$ or $I(\xi) = 10$ and $\overline{\mathrm{pl}}_{10}(\xi) \geqslant \alpha_0$, then $C_\xi(a(p))$ is independent of p. Finally, if $I(\xi) = 10$ and $\beta = \overline{\mathrm{pl}}_{10}(\xi) < \alpha_0$, then $C_\xi(a(p)) = a_\beta(p)$ and the theorem follows from the assumption.

4. Independence of the axiom of choice

In all our independence proofs we shall use models $N(p)$ defined in theorem XI.5.2. The space $\mathscr{X}$ will always be the product space $\mathbf{P}_{n<\omega} \mathscr{X}_n$ and the neighbourhoods U_π will be indexed by finite functions π with

$\mathrm{Dom}(\pi) \subseteq \omega$ such that $\pi(n)$ determines a neighbourhood in $\mathscr{X}_n$. The set Π will thus consist of such functions π. The choice of $a(p)$ will depend on the particular problem under discussion.

In Sections 4–6 we choose

$$\mathscr{X} = [P(\omega)]^\omega .$$

Each π in Π is thus a function with a finite domain contained in ω and such that $\pi(i)$ is an ordered pair $\langle X_i, Y_i \rangle$ of disjoint finite subsets of ω.

For any denumerable model M of ZF we obviously have $\Pi \in M$.

Points p of $\mathscr{X}$ are infinite sequences $(p_0, p_1, \ldots)$ of subsets of ω. We call p_i the ith coordinate of p. It will be convenient to use the abbreviated notation (n, k) for $2^n(2k+1)-1$. We put

$$u_n(p) = \{p_{(n,0)}, p_{(n,1)}, \ldots\},$$

$$u(p) = \{u_0(p), \ldots, u_n(p), \ldots\}$$

and let $a(p)$ be the sequence of type $\omega \cdot 3+1$

$$0, 1, 2, \ldots, p_0, p_1, \ldots, u_0(p), u_1(p), \ldots, u(p).$$

The sequence $a(p)$ is obviously transitive. It belongs to the first category discussed in XII.2. If $p_i \neq p_j$ for $i \neq j$ (this is the case, for instance, if p is a generic point), then $u(p)$ is a family of mutually disjoint sets.

4.1. *If* $p \in \mathrm{Gen}(\mathscr{X})$, *then* $N(p)$ *is a model of* ZF.

In the proof of this theorem we use theorem XI.5.2, whose assumptions were verified in XII.4.2.

In showing that the axiom of choice is not valid in $N(p)$ we shall use the following homeomorphisms f_ε of $\mathscr{X}$: for each permutation ε of ω we put $f_\varepsilon(p) = q$, where the coordinates q_i of q are $q_i = p_{\varepsilon^{-1}(i)}$. Thus $f_\varepsilon(p)$ is obtained from p by the permutation ε^{-1} of the coordinates. We denote by G the set of all f_ε where the permutation ε satisfies the equation $\varepsilon(i) = i$ for all but finitely many i and, moreover, transforms every integer of the form (n, k) into an integer (n, m) with the same n. By G_n we denote the subset of G consisting of functions f_ε for which $\varepsilon(i, j) = (i, j)$ for $i < n$ and arbitrary $j < \omega$.

The following simple facts concerning these notions are easily proved:

4.2. *The sets G_n form a basis of a filter of subsets of G.*

4.3. *G is a group of homeomorphisms of $\mathscr{X}$ and each f in G has a finite order.*

Next we describe the action of $f_\varepsilon \in G$ on the terms of $a(p)$:

4.4. *The sequence $a(f_\varepsilon(p))$ is equal to*

$$0, 1, 2, \ldots, p_{\varepsilon^{-1}(0)}, p_{\varepsilon^{-1}(1)}, \ldots, p_{\varepsilon^{-1}(n)}, \ldots, u_0(p), \ldots, u_n(p), \ldots, u(p).$$

4.5. *Each $f_\varepsilon \in G$ satisfies conditions* (C1), (C2).

PROOF. (C1) results from 4.3. In order to prove (C2) we assume that $\beta < \alpha_0$ $(= \omega \cdot 3+1)$ and $\delta(\alpha) < \mathrm{pl}_{10}(\beta) < \delta(\alpha+1)$. If $\beta < \omega$ or $\beta \geqslant \omega \cdot 2$, then $a_\beta(f(p)) = a_\beta(p) = C_{\mathrm{pl}_{10}(\beta)}(a(p))$ and so (C2) is satisfied with $\xi' = \mathrm{pl}_{1C}(\beta)$. If $\omega \leqslant \beta < \omega \cdot 2$, then $\delta(\omega) < \mathrm{pl}_{10}(\beta) < \delta(\omega+1)$ because $\mathrm{pl}_{10}(\beta)$ is the βth ordinal ξ satisfying $I(\xi) = 10$ and the interval $(\delta(\omega), \delta(\omega+1))$ contains a sequence of type ω^3 of such ordinals. Thus (C2) is vacuously satisfied if $\alpha \neq \omega$. If $\alpha = \omega$, then $a_\beta(f(p)) = p_{\varepsilon^{-1}(\beta-\omega)}$ $= C_{\xi'}(a(p))$, where $\xi' = \mathrm{pl}_{10}(\omega+\varepsilon^{-1}(\beta-\omega))$, and hence $\delta(\omega) < \xi'$ $< \delta(\omega+1)$.

From 4.5 and 1.1 we infer that:

4.6. *For each f_ε in G there is a function φ_ε satisfying conditions* (1)–(3), *of* 1.1.

Finally we observe that if ξ is a fixed ordinal $< \omega \cdot 3+1$, then there is an integer n such that if $f_\varepsilon \in G_n$, then $a_\xi(f_\varepsilon(p)) = a_\xi(p)$. For if $\xi < \omega$, then $a(p)$ is independent of p and if $\xi = \omega+j$, then it is sufficient to take any $n > j$. Finally if $\xi \geqslant \omega \cdot 2$, then $a_\xi(p) = a_\xi(f_\varepsilon(p))$.

Using 3.1 we infer therefore that:

4.7. *For any ξ there is an n such that if $f_\varepsilon \in G_n$, then*

$$C_\xi\big(a(f(p))\big) = C_\xi(a(p))$$

for each p in $\mathscr{X}$.

The main result of the present section is given in the next theorem:

4.8. *If $p \in \mathrm{Gen}(\mathscr{X})$, then no $C_\xi(a(p))$ is a selector of $u(p)$.*

PROOF. We assume by way of contradiction that $C_\xi(a(p))$ has exactly one element with each $u_m(p)$. Let n be an integer which satisfies 4.7

and let $p_{(n,j)}$ be the unique element of $C_\xi(a(p)) \cap u_n(p)$. We write $u_n(p)$ as $C_\alpha(a(p))$ where $\alpha = \text{pl}_{10}(\omega \cdot 2+n)$ and $p_{(n,j)}$ as $C_\beta(a(p))$ where $\beta = \text{pl}_{10}(\omega+(n,j))$. For each q in $\mathscr{X}$ and each f_ε in G we thus have

$$C_\alpha(a(q)) = C_\alpha\big(a(f_\varepsilon(q))\big) = u_n(q),$$

$$C_\beta\big(a\,(f_\varepsilon(q))\big) = q_{\varepsilon^{-1}(n,j)} = q_{(n,k)}\,,$$

where k is an integer determined by the equation $\varepsilon\big((n,k)\big) = (n,j)$.

According to our assumption the generic point p satisfies the formula

$$C_\beta(a(p)) \in C_\xi(a(p)), \tag{1}$$

which we can also write as

$$\vdash_{N(p)} H_0[C_\xi(a(p)),\ C_\beta(a(p))],$$

where H_0 is the formula $x_3 \in x_1$.

Furthermore,

$$\vdash_{N(p)} H[C_\xi(a(p)),\ C_\alpha(a(p)),\ C_\beta(a(p))], \tag{2}$$

where H is the formula

$$(x_0)[(x_0 \in x_1) \wedge (x_0 \in x_2) \to (x_0 = x_3)].$$

We shall obtain a contradiction by showing that there is a generic point q at which both (1) and (2) are true and for which there is an $h \neq j$ such that $q_{(n,h)} \in C_\xi(a(q))$. That this will be a contradiction follows from (2) since this formula (with p replaced by q) shows that if $q_{(n,j)}$ and $q_{(n,h)}$ both belong to $C_\xi(a(q))$, then $q_{(n,j)} = q_{(n,h)}$, whereas any two coordinates of a generic point are different from each other.

In order to find the required q and h we first notice that formulae (1) and (2) are valid not only for the point p but for all generic points of a sufficiently small neighbourhood U_π of p. As we know, π is a function with a finite domain such that if $i \in \text{Dom}(\pi)$, then $\pi(i) = \langle X_i, Y_i\rangle$, where X_i, Y_i are disjoint finite subsets of ω. Moreover, $q \in U_\pi$ if and only if $X_i \subseteq q_i$ and $Y_i \cap q_i = 0$ for each $i \in \text{Dom}(\pi)$. We can say that the requirement that q be an element of U_π imposes on the coordinates q_i finitely many conditions expressed by the above formulae.

We choose h so that $(n,h) \notin \text{Dom}(\pi)$ and put

$$\varrho = \pi \qquad \text{if} \quad (n,j) \notin \text{Dom}(\pi),$$
$$\varrho = \pi \cup \big\{\langle (n,h),\ \pi((n,j))\rangle\big\} \qquad \text{if} \quad (n,j) \in \text{Dom}(\pi).$$

Thus the requirement that $q \in U_\varrho$ imposes on the coordinate $q_{(n,h)}$ the same conditions as the requirement that q be an element of U_π imposed on $q_{(n,j)}$.

It is evident that $U_\varrho \subseteq U_\pi$.

The essential lemma is the following: *let ε be the transposition of (n,j) and (n,h); then for every q in $\mathscr{X}$*

$$q \in U_\varrho \equiv f_\varepsilon(q) \in U_\varrho. \tag{3}$$

To prove this lemma we put $f_\varepsilon(q) = r$ and call the condition

$$(X_i \subseteq q_i) \wedge (Y_i \cap q_i = 0)$$

simply $C_i(q)$. Condition $C_i(r)$ is defined similarly. Obviously $C_i(r) \equiv C_i(q)$ for $i \neq (n,j), (n,h)$ because then $q_i = r_i$. The left-hand side of (3) is equivalent to the conjunction of $C_i(q)$ for $i \in \mathrm{Dom}(\varrho)$ and the right-hand side to the conjunction of $C_i(r)$ for $i \in \mathrm{Dom}(\varrho)$.

If $(n,j) \notin \mathrm{Dom}(\pi)$, then $\varrho = \pi$ and neither (n,j) nor (n,h) belong to $\mathrm{Dom}(\varrho)$. Hence (3) is valid in this case.

If $(n,j) \in \mathrm{Dom}(\pi)$, then both (n,j) and (n,h) belong to $\mathrm{Dom}(\varrho)$ and thus (3) will be proved if we show that

$$C_{(n,j)}(q) \wedge C_{(n,h)}(q) \equiv C_{(n,h)}(r) \wedge C_{(n,j)}(r).$$

Since $q_{(n,j)} = r_{(n,h)}$ and $q_{(n,h)} = r_{(n,j)}$, this equivalence is obviously true. Thus (3) is proved.

We now choose a generic point q in U_ϱ. Since (1) is true in all generic points of U_ϱ, we obtain $\mathrm{Forc}_{H_0}(\varrho, \xi, \beta)$. By 2.1 we therefore obtain $\mathrm{Forc}_{H_0}(\varrho, \varphi(\xi), \varphi(\beta))$ where we abbreviated φ_{f_ε} to φ. We now use the fact that q is a generic point of U_ϱ and obtain

$$\vdash_{N(q)} H_0[C_{\varphi(\xi)}(a(q)), C_{\varphi(\beta)}(a(q))],$$

i.e.,

$$\vdash_{N(q)} H_0\big[C_\xi\big(a(f_\varepsilon(q))\big), C_\beta\big(a(f_\varepsilon(q))\big)\big],$$

whence

$$C_\beta\big(a(f_\varepsilon(q))\big) \in C_\xi\big(a(f_\varepsilon(q))\big),$$

i.e.,

$$q_{(n,h)} \in C_\xi\big(a(q)\big).$$

Thus we have obtained the desired contradiction and theorem 4.8 is proved.

As a corollary we infer that (cf. Cohen [6]):

4.9. *The existence of a well-ordering of $P(\omega)$ is not provable in* ZF.

We notice in addition that in the model defined in the proof of 4.8 no $C_\xi(a(p))$ is an infinite sequence of different p_i's. From this we easily deduce that one does not obtain a contradiction by admitting in ZF that there is a function f of the real variable which is not continuous at the point $x=0$ but for which $\lim_{n\to\infty} f(x_n)=f(0)$ for every sequence x_n convergent to 0. Cf. Jaegermann [15].

5. The ordering of $P(P(\omega))$

It requires but little change in the previous proofs in order to establish the independence of the statement that $P(P(\omega))$ can be ordered.

For p in $\mathscr{X} = [P(\omega)]^\omega$ we denote by $a(p)$ the sequence

$$0, 1, 2, \ldots, p_0, p_1, \ldots, u_0(p), u_1(p), \ldots, \{u_0(p), u_1(p)\},$$
$$\{u_2(p), u_3(p)\}, \ldots, \big\{\{u_0(p), u_1(p)\}, \{u_2(p), u_3(p)\}, \ldots\big\}$$

We can write this sequence more simply as

$$0, 1, 2, \ldots, p_0, p_1, \ldots, u_0(p), u_1(p), \ldots, v_0(p), v_1(p), \ldots, v(p)$$

where

$$v_j(p) = \{u_{2j}(p), u_{2j+1}(p)\} \quad \text{and} \quad v(p) = \{v_0(p), v_1(p), \ldots\}.$$

The length of $a(p)$ is $\omega\cdot 4+1$. It is a sequence of the first category discussed in XII.2. We let $N(p) = C_{\pi(M)}(a(p))$, where M is a denumerable model of ZF. Theorem XII.4.2 shows that

5.1. *If $p \in \mathrm{Gen}(\mathscr{X})$, then $N(p)$ is a model for* ZF.

We shall show that if $p \in \mathrm{Gen}(\mathscr{X})$, then no $C_\xi(a(p))$ is a selector of $v(p)$. We select as G the set of all functions f_ε, where ε is a permutation of ω with the following properties:

(1) There is an n such that for all $k \neq n$ and all $j \in \omega$

$$\varepsilon(2k, j) = (2k, j) \quad \text{and} \quad \varepsilon(2k+1, j) = (2k+1, j).$$

(2) $\varepsilon(2n, j)$ has the form $(2n+1, h)$ and conversely.

(3) The order of ε is 2.

For instance the following permutation ε belongs to G:

ε: $(3,0) \leftrightarrow (2,1)$; $(3,1) \leftrightarrow (2,0)$; $(3,j) \leftrightarrow (2,j)$ for $j > 1$, $n \leftrightarrow n$ for other values of n.

We denote by G_n the set of those f_ε in G which satisfy the equation $\varepsilon(k,j) = (k,j)$ for each $k < n$ and each j.

The following properties of f_ε are obvious:

5.2. *f_ε is a homeomorphism of $\mathscr{X}$ and its order is* 2.

5.3. *The following equations hold*:

$$a_\xi(f_\varepsilon(p)) = a_\xi(p) \quad \textit{for} \quad \xi < \omega \textit{ and } \xi \geqslant \omega \cdot 2;$$
$$a_{\omega+(j,h)}(f_\varepsilon(p)) = a_{\omega+\varepsilon^{-1}(j,h)}(p).$$

It follows from 5.2 and 5.3 that

5.4. *If $f_\varepsilon \in G$, then f_ε satisfies* (C1) *and* (C2) *of* 1.1.

By 1.1 we infer from 5.4 that:

5.5. *For each f_ε in G there is a function $\varphi = \varphi_{f_\varepsilon}$ which satisfies equations* (1)–(3) *of* 1.1.

Finally by 3.1 we infer that

5.6. *For each ξ there is an n such that $f_\varepsilon \in G_n$ implies*

$$C_\xi\big(a(f_\varepsilon(p))\big) = C_\xi(a(p)).$$

The main result of this section is the following:

5.7. *If $p_0 \in \mathrm{Gen}(\mathscr{X})$, then no $C_\xi(a(p_0))$ $(\xi < \pi(M))$ is a selector of $v(p_0)$.*

PROOF. Let ξ be an ordinal $< \pi(M)$. We choose n so that $C_\xi\big(a(f(p))\big) = C_\xi(a(p))$ for each $f \in G_n$ and each p in $\mathscr{X}$. Furthermore, we represent $u_{2n}(p)$ as $C_\alpha(a(p))$ and $u_{2n+1}(p)$ as $C_\beta(a(p))$ with $\alpha = \mathrm{pl}_{10}(\omega \cdot 2+2n)$ and $\beta = \mathrm{pl}_{10}(\omega \cdot 2+2n+1)$.

Let $f \in G_n$ and let us assume that there is a permutation ε such that:

(4) $f = f_\varepsilon$ and each $\varepsilon(2n,j)$ has the form $(2n+1,h)$ and each $\varepsilon(2n+1,h)$ has the form $(2n,j)$.

(cf. formula (2) on p. 234). Under these assumptions

$$C_\alpha\big(a(f(p))\big) = u_{2n+1}(p) \quad \text{and} \quad C_\beta\big(a(f(p))\big) = u_{2n}(p)$$

for each p in $\mathscr{X}$.

Let us assume that $C_\xi(a(p_0))$ contains exactly one element of $v_n(p_0)$, e.g., that

(5) $$u_{2n}(p_0) \in C_\xi(a(p_0)), \quad u_{2n+1}(p_0) \notin C_\xi(a(p_0)).$$

Since p_0 is a generic set, we find that there is a neighbourhood U_π of p_0 such that

(6) $$\mathrm{Forc}_{H_0}(\pi, \alpha, \xi) \quad \text{and} \quad \mathrm{Forc}_{\neg H_0}(\pi, \beta, \xi).$$

We now seek a neighbourhood $U_\varrho \subseteq U_\pi$ and a homeomorphism f_ε in G_n such that U_ϱ is invariant under f_ε and f_ε satisfies (4).

Since $\mathrm{Dom}(\pi)$ is a finite set, there is an integer s such that the integers $(2n, i)$, $(2n+1, i)$ are not in $\mathrm{Dom}(\pi)$ for any $i \geqslant s$. In order to simplify our discussion we shall assume that $\mathrm{Dom}(\pi)$ contains all pairs $(2n, j)$ and $(2n+1, j)$ with $j < s$. Thus if π does not have this property, we pass from U_π to a smaller neighbourhood $U_{\pi'}$, of p_0, where π' is obtained from π by extending it to a function whose domain contains the required integers. The extended function is again called π.

We put $\pi(2n, j) = \langle X_j, Y_j\rangle$, $\pi(2n+1, j) = \langle X'_j, Y'_j\rangle$ for $j < s$; hence X_j, X'_j, Y_j, Y'_j are finite sets of integers and the requirement $p \in U_\pi$ imposes on $p_{(2n, j)}$ the conditions

$$X_j \subseteq p_{(2n, j)}, \quad Y_j \cap p_{(2n, j)} = 0$$

and on $p_{(2n+1, j)}$ the conditions

$$X'_j \subseteq p_{(2n+1, j)}, \quad Y'_j \cap p_{(2n+1, j)} = 0.$$

Let us select s integers $\geqslant s$, e.g., the integers $s, s+1, \ldots, 2s-1$. We shall determine U_ϱ in such a way that the requirement $p \in U_\varrho$ imposes on $p_{(2n, s+j)}$ the same conditions as $p \in U_\pi$ imposed on $p_{(2n+1, j)}$; similarly $p \in U_\varrho$ imposes the same conditions on $p_{(2n+1, s+j)}$ as $p \in U_\pi$ imposed on $p_{(2n, j)}$. Thus we put

$$\varrho = \pi \cup \{\langle(2n, s+j), \langle X'_j, Y'_j\rangle\rangle : j < s\} \cup \\ \cup \{\langle(2n+1, s+j), \langle X_j, Y_j\rangle\rangle : j < s\}.$$

It is obvious that $U_\varrho \subseteq U_\pi$.

We now define a homeomorphism f_ε. Let ε be a permutation which is constant everywhere except on integers of the form $(2n, h)$ and $(2n+1, h)$. For $j \geqslant 2s$ let ε interchange $(2n, h)$ and $(2n+1, h)$; for

$j < s$ let ε interchange $(2n, j)$ with $(2n+1, j+s)$ and $(2n, j+s)$ with $(2n+1, j)$. Hence $f_\varepsilon \in G_n$ and f_ε satisfies (4).

With these definitions we easily show that for $x \in \mathscr{X}$

$$x \in U_\varrho \equiv f_\varepsilon(x) \in U_\varrho. \tag{7}$$

To see this we remark as in Section 4 that the left-hand side of the equivalence is true if for each $i \in \mathrm{Dom}(\pi)$ the ith coordinate of x satisfies certain conditions; the right-hand side of the equivalence requires that the same conditions be satisfied by the ith coordinate of $f_\varepsilon(x)$. If i does not have one of the forms $(2n, j)$ and $(2n+1, j)$, then x and $f_\varepsilon(x)$ have the same ith coordinates. Otherwise the $(2n, j)$th coordinate of $f_\varepsilon(x)$ is equal to the $(2n+1, h)$th coordinate of x, where $h = j$ if $h \geqslant 2s$ and $|h-j| = s$ otherwise. In the former case neither $(2n, j)$ nor $(2n+1, j)$ are in $\mathrm{Dom}(\pi)$, and thus no condition is imposed on the coordinates. If $h < 2s$, then because of our choice of ε the left-hand side of the equivalence requires that $x_{(2n,h)}$ should satisfy the same conditions as $x_{(2n+1,j)}$ and conversely. The equivalence is thus proved.

From (7) and (6) we obtain

$$\mathrm{Forc}_{H_0}(\varrho, \varphi(\alpha), \varphi(\xi)) \quad \text{and} \quad \mathrm{Forc}_{\neg H_0}(\varrho, \varphi(\beta), \varphi(\xi)),$$

where φ stands for φ_{f_ε}. This entails that for all generic points of U_ϱ

$$C_\alpha\big(a(f_\varepsilon(q))\big) \in C_\xi\big(a(f_\varepsilon(q))\big), \quad C_\beta\big(a(f_\varepsilon(q))\big) \notin C_\xi\big(a(f_\varepsilon(q))\big),$$

i.e.,

$$u_{2n+1}(q) \in C_\xi\big(a(q)\big), \quad u_{2n}(q) \notin C_\xi\big(a(q)\big),$$

which contradicts (6). Theorem 5.7 is thus proved.

As immediate corollaries from 5.7 we infer that (cf. Cohen [6]):

5.8. *If* $p_0 \in \mathrm{Gen}(\mathscr{X})$, *then the set* $v(p_0)$ *has no selector in* $N(p_0)$.

5.9. *The existence of an ordering of* $P(P(\omega))$ *is not provable in* ZF.

6. The existence of maximal ideals in $P(\omega)$

In this section we reproduce a proof, due to Feferman [10], that the existence of maximal non-principal ideals in the Boolean algebra $P(\omega)$ is not provable in ZF. We consider the same space $[P(\omega)]^\omega = \mathscr{X}$ with the Tichonoff topology. Let F_j be the sequence consisting of all finite subsets of ω and of all the complements of finite subsets of ω. We take as $a(p)$ the sequence of the second category (see XII.2) whose initial terms are consecutive integers and whose $(\omega+(n,j))$th term is $p_n \ast F_j = \mathscr{X}-(p_n \dot{-} F_j)$.

We consider homeomorphisms $f_{m,n}$ of $\mathscr{X}$ depending on two parameters m, n. The mth coordinate of the point $f_{m,n}(q)$ is $q_m \ast F_n$ and other coordinates are the same as in q. We easily show that:

6.1. *$f_{m,n}$ is an involutory homeomorphism of $\mathscr{X}$ and condition* (C2) *is satisfied.*

The proof that $f_{m,n}$ is of order 2 is obvious and so is the verification that $f_{m,n}$ is a homeomorphism of $\mathscr{X}$. Condition (C2) follows from the formulae

$$a_\xi(f_{m,n}(q)) = a_\xi(q) \quad \text{if} \quad \xi < \omega,$$

$$a_{\omega+(h,j)}(f_{m,n}(q)) = \begin{cases} a_{\omega+(h,j)}(q) & \text{if} \quad h \neq m, \\ q_m \ast (F_j \ast F_n) & \text{if} \quad h = m. \end{cases}$$

Thus $a_\xi(f_{m,n}(q)) = C_{\mathrm{pl}_{10}(\xi)}(a(q))$ if $\xi < \omega$ and $a_{\omega+(h,j)}(f_{m,n}(q))$ is $C_{\mathrm{pl}_{10}(\omega+s)}(a(q))$, where $s = (h,j)$ if $m \neq h$ and s is the index such that $F_s = F_j \ast F_n$ if $m = h$. Since $\omega < \mathrm{pl}_{10}(\omega+s) < \delta(\omega+1)$, we infer that condition (C2) is satisfied.

The rest of the proof follows the same general course as the previous proofs. We only sketch it very briefly. From XII.4.2 we infer that:

6.2. *If $p_0 \in \mathrm{Gen}(\mathscr{X})$ and $N(p_0) = C_{\pi(M)}(a(p_0))$, then $N(p_0)$ is a model of* ZF.

Using 6.1 we infer that:

6.3. *For any m, n there is a function $\varphi_{m,n}$ which satisfies* (1)–(3) *of* 1.1.

Let G_k be the set of functions $f_{m,n}$ with $m \geqslant k$; the set of all G_k, $k = 0, 1, 2, \ldots$ forms a basis of a filter of subsets of G_0. Using 3.1 we thus infer that:

6.4. *For each ξ there is a k such that for all p in $\mathscr{X}$ and all f in G_k*

$$C_\xi(a(p)) = C_\xi\big(a(f(p))\big).$$

We can now prove the main theorem of this section.

6.5. *If* $p \in \mathrm{Gen}(\mathscr{X})$, *then no element of* $N(p)$ *is a prime non-principal ideal in the Boolean algebra* $P(\omega) \cap N(p)$.

PROOF. We assume by way of contradiction that $C_\xi(a(p))$ is such an ideal. It follows that

$$\vdash_{N(p)} H[C_\xi(a(p))]$$

where H is the conjunction of the formulae

$$\neg(\omega \in x_1),$$
$$(x)(y)[(x \subseteq y) \wedge (y \in x_1) \to (x \in x_1)],$$
$$(x)(y)[(x \in x_1) \wedge (y \in x_1) \to (x \cup y \in x_1)],$$
$$(x)[x \in x_1 \to x \subseteq \omega],$$
$$(x)[(x \in \omega) \to (\{x\} \in x_1)],$$
$$(x)(y)\{[(x \cup y = \omega) \wedge (x \cap y = 0)] \to [(x \in x_1) \vee (y \in x_1)]\}.$$

Strictly speaking these formulae should be written without abbreviations such as ω, $\subseteq$, etc., but we retain them in order to simplify our exposition.

It follows that there is a π in Π such that $p \in U_\pi$ and $\mathrm{Forc}_H(\pi, \xi)$. Hence for any generic q in U_π the set $C_\xi(a(q))$ is a prime ideal of the Boolean algebra $P(\omega) \cap N(q)$; in particular, for each $x \in N(q)$ if $x \subseteq \omega$, then either x or $\omega - x$ belongs to $C_\xi(a(q))$.

Let k be an integer which satisfies 6.4:

$$C_\xi(a(q)) = C_\xi\big(a(f(q))\big) \quad \text{for} \quad f \in G_k \text{ and } q \text{ in } \mathscr{X}.$$

We fix arbitrarily an integer $n > k$ which does not belong to $\mathrm{Dom}(\pi)$ and notice that exactly one of the sets p_n, $\omega - p_n$ belongs to the ideal $C_\xi(a(p))$.

The rest of the proof must comprise two cases the first of which deals with the situation where p_n is an element of the ideal and the second with the situation where its complement is in the ideal. We shall discuss only the first case.

First we notice that $p_n = p_n * F_j$, where j is such that $F_j = \mathscr{X}$. Hence $p_n = a_{\omega+(n,j)}(p)$ and thus $p_n = C_\alpha(a(p))$ with $\alpha = \mathrm{pl}_{10}(\omega + (n,j))$. The equation

$$q_n = C_\alpha(a(q))$$

holds for each q in $\mathscr{X}$.

From $p_n \in C_\xi(a(p))$ we now find that $C_\alpha(a(p)) \in C_\xi(a(p))$, and hence there is a neighbourhood $U_\varrho \subseteq U_\pi$ of p such that

(1) $$q_n \in C_\xi(a(q))$$

for each generic q in U_ϱ. Denoting the formula $x_1 \in x_2$ by H_0, we can write

(2) $$\mathrm{Forc}_{H_0}(\varrho, \alpha, \xi).$$

Restricting U_ϱ, if necessary, we can ensure that $n \in \mathrm{Dom}(\varrho)$.

We now show that U_ϱ is invariant under a suitable $f_{n,m}$. Choose m so that $F_m = X_n \cup Y_n$, where $\varrho(n) = \langle X_n, Y_n \rangle$. The coordinates of $f_{n,m}(q)$ are the same as the coordinates of q with the exception of the nth coordinate, which is q_n for the point q and $q_n \star (X_n \cup Y_n)$ for the point $f_{n,m}(q)$. Since for $i \in X_n \cup Y_n$ we have the equivalence

$$i \in q_n \equiv i \in q_n \star (X_n \cup Y_n),$$

we infer that

$$X_n \subseteq q_n \equiv X_n \subseteq q_n \star (X_n \cup Y_n),$$
$$(Y_n \cap q_n = 0) \equiv \{Y_n \cap [q_n \star (X_n \cup Y_n)] = 0\}.$$

This shows that $q \in U_\varrho \equiv f_{n,m}(q) \in U_\varrho$. Using theorem 2.1 we infer from (2) that

$$\mathrm{Forc}_{H_0}(\varrho, \varphi_{n,m}(\alpha), \varphi_{n,m}(\xi)),$$

i.e., for an arbitrary generic q in U_ϱ

$$C_{\varphi_{n,m}(\alpha)}(a(q)) \in C_{\varphi_{n,m}(\xi)}(a(q)).$$

This means that $C_\alpha\big(a(f_{n,m}(q))\big) \in C_\xi\big(a(f_{n,m}(q))\big)$. From $n > k$ we infer that $C_\xi\big(a(f_{n,m}(q))\big) = C_\xi(a(q))$; from the definition of α it follows that $C_\alpha\big(a(f_{n,m}(q))\big)$ is equal to the nth coordinate of $f_{n,m}(q)$, i.e., to $q_n \star (X_n \cup Y_n)$. Thus we obtain

$$[q_n \cap (X_n \cup Y_n)] \cup [(\omega - q_n) \cap (\omega - (X_n \cup Y_n))] \in C_\xi(a(q)),$$

and since $C_\xi(a(q))$ is an ideal in $P(\omega) \cap N(q)$,

$$\omega - (q_n \cup X_n \cup Y_n) \in C_\xi(a(q)).$$

On the other hand, formula (1) proves that $q_n \cup X_n \cup Y_n \in C_\xi(a(q))$ because $C_\xi(a(q))$ is an ideal and finite subsets of ω belong to it. Hence we obtain $\omega \in C_\xi(a(q))$, which is a contradiction.

From 6.5 we obtain the following result of Feferman [10]:

6.6. *The existence of a prime non-principal ideal in $P(\omega)$ is not provable in* ZF.

7. Cofinality of ω_1

It is well known that if we allow the use of the axiom of choice, then we can show that ω_1 is not cofinal with ω. A. Lévy [18] proved that there are models of ZF in which ω_1 is cofinal with ω. Of course the axiom of choice is false in those models. In the present section we repeat the construction of Lévy.

Let M be the minimal model [1]) and let $\mathscr{X} = \underset{i<\omega}{\mathrm{P}} (\omega_i(M))^\omega$, the topology in the product space and also in the factors $\omega_i(M)^\omega$ being that of Tichonoff. Elements of $\mathscr{X}$ are sequences $p_0, p_1, \ldots$, where p_i is a mapping of ω into $\omega_i(M)$. Neighbourhoods in $\mathscr{X}$ are determined by functions π with finite domain, $\mathrm{Dom}(\pi) \subseteq \omega$, which satisfy the condition that $\pi(i)$ is a finite function with domain contained in ω and range contained in $\omega_i(M)$. A point p is in U_π if p_i is an extension of $\pi(i)$ for each i in $\mathrm{Dom}(\pi)$. We denote by Π the set of all functions π.

The definition of the sequence $a(p)$ is more involved than in the previous cases and the reasons for this complication are twofold. First of all we want the coordinates p_i of p to be terms of $a(p)$, and since $a(p)$ has to be a transitive sequence, we must include as terms of $a(p)$ all ordinals $\xi < \omega_\omega(M)$ together with pairs $\{n, \xi\}$, singletons $\{n\}$ and pairs $\langle n, \xi\rangle$. The second reason is that we shall use homeomorphisms f such that

$$(1) \qquad f(p) = (p_0 - \varphi_0) \cup \psi_0,\ (p_1 - \varphi_1) \cup \psi_1,\ \ldots$$

where φ_i and ψ_i are finite functions (finite set of pairs) with domains $\subseteq \omega$ and with ranges $\subseteq \omega_i(M)$. Since we want the conditions of 1.1

[1]) Much weaker assumptions concerning M would be sufficient; however, these generalizations are not very important.

to be satisfied, we must take care not only that p_i be terms of $a(p)$ but also that the sets $(p_i - \varphi_i) \cup \psi_i$ for all possible φ_i and ψ_i appear in the sequence $\{C_\xi\}$ at places ξ satisfying $\delta(\alpha) < \xi < \delta(\alpha+1)$ with a fixed α independent of p and of the particular φ_i, ψ_i used in (1).

We describe the choice of a sequence $a(p)$ of the second category (see XII.2), which meets these requirements. We put $\vartheta = \omega_\omega(M)$ and denote by

$$\xi \rightleftarrows (g_1(\xi), g_2(\xi))$$

a one-to-one mapping of ϑ onto $\vartheta \times \vartheta$; of this mapping we require that it be definable in M.

Furthermore, we select a mapping h of ϑ onto the set consisting of all finite sequences of ordinals $< \vartheta$. Let $h_1(\xi)$ be the domain of $h(\xi)$ and $\bar{\xi}_i$ the terms of the sequence $h(\xi)$:

$$h(\xi) = \{\langle i, \bar{\xi}_i \rangle : i \in h_1(\xi)\}.$$

Functions h, h_1 and $\bar{\xi}_i$ can be chosen so that they are definable in M. Now for $\xi < \vartheta$ and $n < \omega$ we take

$$a_\xi(p) = \xi, \quad a_{\vartheta+\xi}(p) = \{\xi\},$$

$$a_{\vartheta\cdot 2+\xi}(p) = \{g_1(\xi), g_2(\xi)\}, \quad a_{\vartheta\cdot 3+\xi}(p) = \langle g_1(\xi), g_2(\xi) \rangle,$$

$$a_{\vartheta\cdot 4+\xi}(p) = \{a_{\vartheta\cdot 3+\bar{\xi}_i}(p) : i \in h_1(\xi)\},$$

$$a_{\vartheta\cdot(5+n)+\xi}(p) = \big(p_n - a_{\vartheta\cdot 4+g_1(\xi)}(p)\big) \cup a_{\vartheta\cdot 4+g_2(\xi)}(p).$$

The order type of $a(p)$ is thus $\vartheta\cdot\omega$.

7.1. *$a(p)$ is a transitive sequence of the second category.*

Proof is obvious; in the notation of XII.2 the sequence Q consists of terms $a_\alpha(p)$ with indices $< \vartheta \cdot 5$.

Function (1) acts on the terms of $a(p)$ in the following way: the terms $a_\varrho(p)$ up to $\vartheta \cdot 5$ are unchanged and $a_{\vartheta\cdot(5+n)+\xi}(p)$ is transformed into

$$\{[(p_n - \varphi_n) \cup \psi_n] - a_{\vartheta\cdot 4+g_1(\xi)}(p)\} \cup a_{\vartheta\cdot 4+g_2(\xi)}(p),$$

i.e.,

$$[p_n - (\varphi_n \cup a_{\vartheta\cdot 4+g_1(\xi)}(p))] \cup \{[\psi_n - a_{\vartheta\cdot 4+g_1(\xi)}(p)] \cup a_{\vartheta\cdot 4+g_2(\xi)}(p)\}.$$

This set can evidently be represented as

$$[p_n - a_{\vartheta\cdot 4+\zeta}(p)] \cup a_{\vartheta\cdot 4+\eta}(p)$$

and hence in the form $a_{\vartheta\cdot(5+n)+\varrho}(p)$ for suitable $\eta, \zeta, \varrho < \vartheta$.

Thus we have proved that:

7.2. *If f is defined by* (1), *then $a_\xi(f(p))$ is for any $\xi < \vartheta$ equal to one of the terms $a_\varrho(p)$ with $\varrho < \vartheta$.*

We now want to determine the places in the sequence $C_\xi(a(p))$ which are occupied by the terms $a_\beta(p)$. As we know, $a_\beta(p) = C_\xi(a(p))$, where $\xi = \mathrm{pl}_{10}(\beta)$, and thus we must determine the values of $\mathrm{pl}_{10}(\beta)$.

We shall use the formulae

$$(\beta < \vartheta) \to (\delta(\beta) < \vartheta), \qquad \delta(\vartheta) = \vartheta,$$

which will be proved in the appendix to Chapter XV (p. 257).

Since $\beta \leqslant \mathrm{pl}_{10}(\beta) < \delta(\beta+1)$, we obtain from the above formulae that if $\beta < \vartheta$, then $\beta \leqslant \mathrm{pl}_{10}(\beta) < \vartheta$. Hence we have proved that:

7.3. *All terms $a_\beta(p)$ with $\beta < \vartheta$ appear in the sequence $C_\xi(a(p))$ at places with indices $< \vartheta$ and these indices form a set cofinal with ϑ.*

The interval $(\delta(\vartheta), \delta(\vartheta+1))$ contains ordinals ξ such that $I(\xi) = 10$ and $K(\xi)$, $L(\xi)$, $M(\xi)$ are arbitrary ordinals $< \vartheta$. Hence the order type of the set $\{\xi : (\vartheta < \xi < \delta(\vartheta+1)) \wedge (I(\xi) = 10)\}$ is ϑ^3. Therefore

7.4. *If β ranges over the set $\vartheta < \beta < \vartheta \cdot \omega$, then the values of* $\mathrm{pl}_{10}(\beta)$ *lie in the interval $(\vartheta, \delta(\vartheta+1))$.*

This theorem in conjunction with 7.2 shows that

7.5. *If f is defined by* (1), *then f satisfies condition* (C2) *of* 1.1.

We now turn to the construction of models. Since $a(p)$ is a sequence of the second category, we can apply theorem XII.4.2 and infer that:

7.6. *If $p \in \mathrm{Gen}(\mathscr{X})$, then $N(p) = C_{\pi(M)}(a(p))$ is a model of* ZF.

We shall show that $N(p)$ contains a mapping of ω onto $\omega_i(M)$.

7.7. *If $p \in \mathrm{Gen}(\mathscr{X})$, then* $\mathrm{Rg}(p_i) = \omega_i(M)$.

The proof is very similar to that of XII.5.5. Let us assume that there exist an i and $\xi < \omega_i(M)$ such that $p_i(n) \neq \xi$ for each n. Thus the formula

$$(2) \qquad (x, y)[(\langle x, y\rangle \in x_0) \to (y \neq x_1)]$$

is satisfied in $N(p)$ by p_i and ξ. There are ordinals α, β such that $C_\alpha(a(q)) = q_i$ and $C_\beta(a(q)) = \xi$ for each q in $\mathscr{X}$. Since p is generic, formula (2) is satisfied in $N(q)$ by q_i and ξ for almost all q which lie in a neighbourhood U_π of p. But this is evidently absurd because each neighbourhood of p contains a neighbourhood U_ϱ all points of which have the property $\xi \in \mathrm{Rg}(q_i)$.

Theorem 7.7 proves that

7.8. *If* $p \in \mathrm{Gen}(\mathscr{X})$, *then* $\omega_j(M) < \omega_1(N(p))$ *for every* $j < \omega$.

PROOF. $\omega_1(N(p))$ is by definition larger than any ordinal α for which there is in $N(p)$ a mapping with domain ω and range α.

7.9. *If* $p \in \mathrm{Gen}(\mathscr{X})$, *then* $\omega_\omega(M) \leqslant \omega_1(N(p))$.

PROOF. Since $\omega_\omega(M) = \sup\{\omega_j(M)\colon\ j < \omega\}$, the inequality $\omega_\omega(M) > \omega_1(N(p))$ would lead to a contradiction with 7.8.

The next lemmas will prepare the proof that 7.9 can be strengthened to an equation. We must first define suitable homeomorphisms of $\mathscr{X}$.

Let $p = (p_0, p_1, \ldots) \in \mathscr{X}$. We start our definition by describing a transformation of the ith coordinate of p.

Let ϱ_i, σ_i be two finite functions with the same domain $D_i \subseteq \omega$ and with values in $\omega_i(M)$. We let q_i be the function which coincides with p_i for arguments $n \notin D_i$ and which is defined as follows for the remaining arguments. If $n \in D_i$, then $q_i(n) = p_i(n)$ if $p_i(n) \neq \varrho_i(n)$ and $p_i(n) \neq \sigma_i(n)$; but if $p_i(n) = \varrho_i(n)$, then $q_i(n) = \sigma_i(n)$ and if $p_i(n) = \sigma_i(n)$, then $q_i(n) = \varrho_i(n)$. Thus $q_i(n)$ is obtained from $p_i(n)$ by the transposition $(\varrho_i(n), \sigma_i(n))$.

Each homeomorphism f will be determined by a pair of functions $\varrho, \sigma \in \Pi$, with a common domain D and such that for i in D the functions $\varrho(i)$ and $\sigma(i)$ have a common domain D_i. We let $f(p)$ or $f_{\varrho\sigma}(p)$ be the point q whose ith coordinate is obtained from p_i and the functions $\varrho(i)$, $\sigma(i)$ in the way indicated above. It is obvious that

7.10. $f_{\varrho\sigma}$ *is a homeomorphism of* $\mathscr{X}$ *and* $f^2(p) = p$ *for each* p.

7.11. *The homeomorphism* $f_{\varrho\sigma}$ *satisfies conditions* (C1) *and* (C2).

PROOF. Condition (C1) is satisfied because $f_{\varrho\sigma}$ is an involution. To prove (C2) it is sufficient to use 7.5 and notice that $f_{\varrho\sigma}$ has form (1): each coordinate q_i of $f_{\varrho\sigma}(p)$ is obtained from p_i by removing a number of pairs from p_i and adjoining the same number of other pairs.

We denote by G the set of all homeomorphisms $f_{\varrho\sigma}$ and by G_n the set of those f in G which for each point p leave the first n coordinates of p invariant. Notice that

$$\varrho|n = \sigma|n \to f_{\varrho\sigma} \in G_n.$$

Since the sets G_n form a basis of a filter of subsets of G, we conclude that:

7.12. *For each $\xi < \pi(M)$ there is an integer n such that $f \in G_n$ implies $C_\xi\big(a(f(p))\big) = C_\xi\big(a(p)\big)$ for each p in $\mathscr{X}$.*

We now prove the basic lemma:

7.13. *Let H be a formula, $\xi \in \pi(M)^{\mathrm{Fr}(H)}$ and let n be such that $C_{\xi_i}\big(a(f(p))\big) = C_{\xi_i}\big(a(p)\big)$ for each p in $\mathscr{X}$, each f in G_n and each i in* Fr(H). *Under these assumptions if $\pi \in \Pi$ and* $\mathrm{Forc}_H(\pi, \xi)$, *then* $\mathrm{Forc}_H(\pi|n, \xi)$.

PROOF. We assume by way of contradiction that there is a generic point q in $U_{\pi|n}$ such that

$$\vdash_{N(q)} \neg H[C_\xi(a(q))]. \tag{3}$$

It follows that $U_{\pi|n}$ contains a neighbourhood U_ϱ such that (3) is valid for each generic point q of U_ϱ. On the other hand, we know that $U_{\pi|n}$ contains a neighbourhood U_π such that the negation of (3) is valid at each generic point of U_π.

We shall determine neighbourhoods $U_{\varrho'} \subseteq U_\varrho$, $U_{\pi'} \subseteq U_\pi$ and a mapping f in G_n such that $f(U_{\varrho'}) = U_{\pi'}$.

First we extend π and ϱ arbitrarily to functions π^*, ϱ^* with a common domain D; if $i \in D$ and $\pi^*(i)$ and $\varrho^*(i)$ have different domains, we extend them arbitrarily to functions $\pi'(i)$ and $\varrho'(i)$ with a common domain D_i. If $\pi^*(i)$ and $\varrho^*(i)$ have the same domain D_i, then we take $\pi'(i) = \pi^*(i)$ and $\varrho'(i) = \varrho^*(i)$. Finally we put $f = f_{\pi'\varrho'}$.

Since each $\pi'(i)$ is an extension of $\pi(i)$ whenever $i \in \mathrm{Dom}(\pi)$, we obtain $U_{\pi'} \subseteq U_\pi$ and similarly $U_{\varrho'} \subseteq U_\varrho$. Denoting by $\pi'_i(n)$ the value of the function $\pi'(i)$ for the argument n and similarly for other functions, we have further the equivalences

$$p \in U_{\pi'} \equiv (i)_D(n)_{D_i}\big(p_i(n) = \pi'_i(n)\big),$$

$$q \in U_{\varrho'} \equiv (i)_D(n)_{D_i}\big(q_i(n) = \varrho'_i(n)\big).$$

These equivalences show that $p \in U_{\pi'} \equiv f(p) \in U_{\varrho'}$.

Finally, we notice that $\pi'|n = \varrho'|n$ because $U_\varrho \subseteq U_{\pi|n}$ and hence $\pi(i) = \varrho(i)$ for $i < n$, which proves that $\pi^*(i) = \varrho^*(i)$ and therefore $\pi'(i) = \varrho'(i)$. This shows that $f \in G_n$. The existence of elements π', ϱ' and of the homeomorphism f with the properties indicated above is thus established.

Now we use theorem 2.1 and infer from (3) that

$$\vdash_{N(q)} \neg H\Big[C_\xi\big(a(f(q))\big)\Big]$$

for almost all q in $U_{\pi'}$. Since $f \in G_n$, it follows that (3) is true in almost all q in $U_{\pi'}$, which is a contradiction. 7.13 is thus proved.

7.14. *If $p \in \mathrm{Gen}(\mathscr{X})$, then $\omega_1\big(N(p)\big) = \omega_\omega(M)$.*

Proof. We assume that $\omega_1\big(N(p)\big) > \omega_\omega(M)$, i.e., that there is in $N(p)$ a mapping of ω onto $\omega_\omega(M)$. Like every element of $N(p)$, this mapping can be represented as $C_\xi\big(a(p)\big)$. Thus the conjunction H of the following formulae H_1, H_2 is satisfied in $N(p)$ by $C_\xi\big(a(p)\big)$ and by the sets $\omega = C_{\mathrm{pl}_{11}(\omega)}\big(a(p)\big)$ and $\omega_\omega(M) = \vartheta = C_{\mathrm{pl}_{11}(\vartheta)}\big(a(p)\big)$:

$$H_1\colon\ (u)\{(u \in x_1) \rightarrow (E!v)[(v \in x_2) \wedge (\langle u, v\rangle \in x_3)]\},$$

$$H_2\colon\ (v)\{(v \in x_2) \rightarrow (Eu)[(u \in x_1) \wedge (\langle u, v\rangle \in x_3)]\};$$

(the correlation of the variables x_1, x_2, x_3 to the sets $C_\xi\big(a(p)\big)$, $\omega = C_{\mathrm{pl}_{11}(\omega)}\big(a(p)\big)$, $\vartheta = C_{\mathrm{pl}_{11}(\vartheta)}\big(a(p)\big)$ is this: x_1 is correlated with ω, x_2 with ϑ and x_3 with $C_\xi\big(a(p)\big)$). Since p is generic, we find that there is a π in Π such that for almost all q in U_π

(4) $$\vdash_{N(q)} H\big[C_{\mathrm{pl}_{11}(\omega)}\big(a(q)\big),\ C_{\mathrm{pl}_{11}(\vartheta)}\big(a(q)\big),\ C_\xi\big(a(q)\big)\big].$$

Let $\Pi_n = \{\pi \in \Pi\colon \mathrm{Dom}(\pi) \subseteq n\}$.

For each $\pi \in \Pi_n$ and $k \in \omega$ let $\gamma(\pi, k)$ be the least ordinal $\zeta < \omega_\omega(M)$ such that $\mathrm{Forc}_{H_0}\big(\pi, \mathrm{pl}_{11}(k), \mathrm{pl}_{11}(\zeta), \xi\big)$ or 0 if there is no such ordinal; here H_0 is the formula $\langle x_1, x_2\rangle \in x_3$. The function $\gamma(\pi, k)$ is parametrically definable in M and hence the set of its values has the relative cardinal number in M at most that of the set of its arguments. The set of the arguments of γ is $\Pi_n \times \omega$, which has in M the relative cardinal $\omega_0(M) \cdot \omega_1(M) \cdot \ldots \cdot \omega_{n-1}(M) \cdot \omega$ because the set of finite functions with a finite domain $\subset \omega$ and with range $\subset \omega_i(M)$ has the relative cardinal in M equal to $\omega_i(M)$. Thus $\mathrm{Card}(M, \Pi_n) < \omega_n(M)$. On the other hand, if we choose in (4) $q = p$, then for each $\eta < \omega_\omega(M)$ there is a k in ω satisfying

$$\langle k, \eta \rangle \in C_\xi(a(p)), \quad \text{i.e.,} \quad \vdash_{N(p)} H_0[\mathrm{pl}_{11}(k), \mathrm{pl}_{11}(\eta), \xi],$$

and hence using lemma 7.13 we can find an element π in Π_n for which $\mathrm{Forc}_{H_0}(\pi, \mathrm{pl}_{11}(k), \mathrm{pl}_{11}(\eta), \xi)$. Thus η belongs to the range of γ and the relative cardinal in M of the range of γ is $\geqslant \omega_\omega(M)$.

This contradiction shows that $\omega_\omega(M)$ is not denumerable in $N(p)$, and hence that $\omega_1(N(p)) = \omega_\omega(M)$.

We note two corollaries to theorem 7.14:

7.15. *There are models N of* ZF *in which $\omega_1(N)$ is cofinal with ω.*

PROOF. In view of V.3.10 the minimal model M is definable in $N(p)$, and hence so is the sequence $\omega_i(M)$. Hence this sequence belongs to $N(p)$ and its l.u.b. is $\omega_\omega(M)$, i.e., $\omega_1(N(p))$.

7.16. *The theorem*: "*the union of a sequence of denumerable sets is denumerable*" *is not provable in* ZF.

Corollary 7.16 can also be deduced from theorem 5.8.

CHAPTER XV

PROBLEMS OF DEFINABILITY

In models N obtained by simple extensions from a model M the axiom of choice is always valid. Under additional assumptions concerning M which we discussed in VII.8 even the generalized continuum hypothesis is true in the extended model. In spite of this no well-ordering of $P(\omega) \cap N$ is definable in N. This and similar phenomena will be discussed in the present chapter.

1. Definable relations between ordinals

As in the previous chapter, we shall consider a model $N(p) = C^{b^0}_{\pi(M)}(a(p))$ determined by a space $\mathscr{X}$, a mapping (A): $p \to a(p)$ of $\mathscr{X}$ into the class of transitive sequences of a given length $\alpha_0 < \pi(M)$, by a set Π in M and a mapping $\pi \to U_\pi$ of Π onto a regular open basis of $\mathscr{X}$. The model M is arbitrary in this section with the only stipulation that theorem XI.5.2 be applicable.

1.1. *Le A be a set and f_a $(a \in A)$ a family of auto-homeomorphisms of $\mathscr{X}$ such that each f_a satisfies conditions* (C1), (C2) *of* XIV.1.1 *and such that the set $\{f_a(p)\colon a \in A\}$ be dense in $\mathscr{X}$ for an arbitrary p in* Gen($\mathscr{X}$). *Let $p \in$ Gen($\mathscr{X}$) and let $R \subseteq \pi(M)^n$ be an n-ary relation definable in $N(p)$. Then R is parametrically definable in M.*

PROOF. The definability of R means that there is a formula H with n free variables $x_1, \ldots, x_n$ such that

$$(1) \qquad \xi \in R \equiv \vdash_{N(p)} H[\xi] \quad \text{for arbitrary } \xi \in \pi(M)^n.$$

Let $\mathrm{pl}_{11}(\xi)$ be a sequence whose terms are $\mathrm{pl}_{11}(\xi_i)$ for $i < n$. In order to prove the theorem it is sufficient (see IX.5.3) to show that

$$(2) \qquad \xi \in R \equiv (E\pi)_\Pi \mathrm{Forc}_H(\pi, \mathrm{pl}_{11}(\xi)).$$

The implication from left to right is immediate. We now assume that there is a π in Π such that $\mathrm{Forc}_H(\pi, \mathrm{pl}_{11}(\xi))$ but that $\xi \notin R$. In view of (1) we obtain $\vdash_{N(p)} \neg H[C_{\mathrm{pl}_{11}(\xi)}(a(p))]$, and since p is generic, there is a neighbourhood U_ϱ of p such that $\mathrm{Forc}_{\neg H}(\varrho, \mathrm{pl}_{11}(\xi))$. According to the assumptions of the theorem there is a homeomorphism $f = f_a$ which maps p into a point of U_π. By replacing U_ϱ by a smaller neighbourhood we can obtain $f(U_\varrho) \subseteq U_\pi$. Let U_σ be a neighbourhood of $f(p)$ such that

$$U_\sigma \subseteq f(U_\varrho) \subseteq U_\pi.$$

Since $\mathrm{Forc}_H(\sigma, \mathrm{pl}_{11}(\xi))$, we can use theorem XIV. 2.1 and obtain $\mathrm{Forc}_H(\varrho, \varphi_f \circ \mathrm{pl}_{11}(\xi))$, whence, p being generic,

(3) $$\vdash_{N(p)} H[C_{\varphi_f \circ \mathrm{pl}_{11}(\xi)}(a(p))].$$

The symbol φ_f denotes here of course the function determined by f according to XIV.1.1. Hence $C_{\varphi(\eta)}(a(p)) = C_\eta\big(a(f(p))\big)$ and, in particular for $\eta = \mathrm{pl}_{11}(\xi)$,

$$C_{\varphi(\mathrm{pl}_{11}(\xi))}(a(p)) = C_{\mathrm{pl}_{11}(\xi)}\big(a(f(p))\big) = \xi.$$

Formula (3) gives thus $\vdash_{N(p)} H[\xi]$, i.e., $\xi \in R$, which is a contradiction.

2. Non-definability of well-orderings of $P(\omega)$

We shall construct a model $N(p)$ in which no definable relation is a well-ordering of $P(\omega)$, although the axiom of choice and the generalized continuum hypothesis are valid in $N(p)$.

We take as $\mathscr{X}$ the space $P(\omega)$ with the usual Tichonoff topology. Let M be the minimal model of ZF and F_n an enumeration in M of finite subsets of ω. We put

$$a_k(p) = k \quad \text{for} \quad k < \omega$$

$$a_{\omega+(n,j)}(p) = (p - F_n) \cup F_j \quad \text{for} \quad n, j < \omega,$$

where, as in Chapter XIV, (n, j) stands for $2^n(2j+1) - 1$.

For each permutation ε of ω which leaves all but finitely many integers unchanged we define

$$f_\varepsilon(p) = \mathrm{Im}(\varepsilon, p) = \text{image of } p \text{ under } \varepsilon.$$

We denote by S the set of all permutations ε.

2.1. *Functions* f_ε *satisfy conditions* (C1) *and* (C2).

PROOF. If ε is of order n, then so is f_ε. The mapping f_ε is obviously an auto-homeomorphism. Since $a_n(f_\varepsilon(p)) = a_n(p)$, it remains to show that if $\beta = \omega+(n, j)$ and $\mathrm{pl}_{10}(\beta)$ lies in the interval $(\delta(\alpha), \delta(\alpha+1))$, then $a_\beta^*(f_\varepsilon(p))$ is representable as $C_{\xi'}(a(p))$ with ξ' in the same interval. It is easy to prove that $\omega < \mathrm{pl}_{10}(\beta) < \delta(\omega+1)$; thus we have to represent $a_\beta(f_\varepsilon(p))$ as $C_{\xi'}(a(p))$ with $\omega < \xi' < \delta(\omega+1)$. To see this we notice that $a_\beta(f_\varepsilon(p)) = (\mathrm{Im}(\varepsilon, p) - F_n) \cup F_j$, and since the symmetric difference $\mathrm{Im}(\varepsilon, p) \dot{-} p$ is finite, we can represent $a_\beta(f_\varepsilon(p))$ in the form $(p - F_k) \cup \cup F_m$. Thus $a_\beta(f_\varepsilon(p))$ is equal to $a_{\omega+(k,m)}(p)$, which proves our assertion.

2.2. *If* $p \in \mathscr{X}$ *and* p *and* $\omega - p$ *are infinite, then the set* $\{f_\varepsilon(p)\colon \varepsilon \in S\}$ *is dense in* $\mathscr{X}$.

PROOF. If X, Y are disjoint finite subsets of ω we can find a permutation ε in S which interchanges the elements of X with some elements of p and elements of Y with some elements of $\omega - p$.

2.3. (Lévy [18].) *If* $p \in \mathrm{Gen}(\mathscr{X})$, *then the axiom of choice and the generalized continuum hypothesis hold in* $N(p)$ *but no well-ordering of* $P(\omega) \cap N(p)$ *is definable in* $N(p)$.

PROOF. We first show the second part of the theorem. Since M is the minimal model, its elements have the form $C_\xi(0)$ where $\xi < \pi(M) = \pi(N)$. It follows in view of V.3.10 that M is a definable subset of $N(p)$. Since $p \in P(\omega) \cap N(p) - M$ the difference $P(\omega) \cap N(p) - M$ is definable in $N(p)$ and not void. Now assume that $P(\omega) \cap N(p)$ can be well-ordered by a relation R definable in $N(p)$. The first element of the difference $P(\omega) \cap N(p) - M$ is then a definable subset of ω and hence, according to 1.1, belongs to M, which is a contradiction.

According to VII.1.9 the axiom of choice is valid in $N(p)$ if $a(p) \in N(p)$. We now verify this condition. $a(p)$ has as its initial segment the sequence of all integers; this segment obviously belongs to $N(p)$. The rest of $a(p)$ is the sequence with terms $(p - F_n) \cup F_j$. The mapping $(n, j) \to \langle F_n, F_j\rangle$ belongs to M; moreover, $p \in N(p)$ since $p = a_{\omega+(n_0, n_0)}(p)$ where n_0 is such that $F_{n_0} = 0$. Hence the mapping $(n, j) \to (p - F_n) \cup F_j$ belongs to M, which proves that the sequence with terms $(p - F_n) \cup F_j$ belongs to M. This proves that the axiom of choice is valid in $N(p)$

If ξ is an ordinal in $N(p)$, $\xi \geqslant \omega$, then $N(p)$ contains a mapping of ξ onto $\mathrm{Dom}\big(a(p)\big)$ because $\mathrm{Dom}\big(a(p)\big) = \omega\cdot 2$. Theorem VII.8.1 proves thus that the generalized continuum hypothesis is valid in $N(p)$. Theorem 2.3 is thus proved. As a corollary we have

2.4. *The axiom of extensionality is not valid in the family D of definable subsets of* $N(p)$.

PROOF. The difference $P(\omega)\cap N(p) - M$ is definable in $N(p)$ but has no definable elements.

3. Definable well-ordered subsets of $P(\omega)$

We shall construct (after Lévy [18]) a model in which the axiom of choice and the generalized continuum hypothesis are valid but in which every subset of $P(\omega)$ well-ordered by a definable relation is at most denumerable. The main idea is to construct an extension $N(p)$ of the minimal model in which $\omega_1\big(N(p)\big) > \omega_1(M)$ and to which theorem 1.1 is applicable.

Let M be the minimal model. We take as $\mathscr{X}$ the subspace of $[\omega_1(M)]^\omega$ consisting of one-to-one mappings of ω into $\omega_1(M)$. The topology in the space $[\omega_1(M)]^\omega$ is that of Tichonoff and the topology in $\mathscr{X}$ is induced by the topology in $[\omega_1(M)]^\omega$.

The space $\mathscr{X}$ is closed in $[\omega_1(M)]^\omega$ since if f is not a one-to-one mapping, e.g. if $f(m) = f(n)$ $(m \neq n)$, then the neighbourhood determined by the partial function $f|\{m, n\}$ is disjoint from $\mathscr{X}$. It follows that the Baire theorem is valid in $\mathscr{X}$.

$\mathscr{X}$ has a regular basis consisting of sets U_π where π is a one-to-one mapping of a finite subset of ω into $\omega_1(M)$. We denote by Π the set of all such finite one-to-one functions π.

We now define the mapping (A): $p \to a(p)$.

First of all we consider a transitive sequence Q of type $\omega_1(M)$ which belongs to M, contains all ordinals $< \omega_1(M)$ and is such that whenever $\xi, \eta < \omega_1(M)$, then $\{\xi, \eta\}$ and $\langle\xi, \eta\rangle$ are terms in Q. It is easy to construct such a sequence by stages: at the stage $\lambda+1 < \omega_1(M)$ we add to the sequence constructed at the stage λ the first ordinal $\varrho < \omega_1(M)$ not yet used, its singleton $\{\varrho\}$ and all the pairs $\{\varrho, \xi\}$, $\langle\xi, \varrho\rangle$, $\langle\varrho, \xi\rangle$ (in this order) with ξ in the part already constructed. At the limit stages we take the union of the parts previously constructed. This inductive definition is expressible in ZF, and hence the Q satisfying this definition is an element of M.

Let F be a function definable in M with $\mathrm{Dom}(F) = \omega_1(M)$ such that $F(\xi)$ enumerates all finite sets whose elements are terms of Q. Furthermore, let $\xi \rightleftarrows (\xi', \xi'')$ be a one-to-one mapping definable in M of $\omega_1(M)$ onto $\omega_1(M) \times \omega_1(M)$. We define $a(p)$ for $p \in \mathscr{X}$ by putting

$$a_\xi(p) = Q_\xi \quad \text{for} \quad \xi < \omega_1(M),$$
$$a_{\omega_1(M)+\xi}(p) = [p - F(\xi')] \cup F(\xi'').$$

Thus the order type of $a(p)$ is $\omega_1(M) \cdot 2$ and $a(p)$ is a sequence of the second category.

With p generic we construct the model

$$N(p) = N\big(M, \mathscr{X}, B^0, a(p), \Pi\big)$$

(cf. XII.4) and infer by remarks following XII.4.3 that:

3.1. *If* $p \in \mathrm{Gen}(\mathscr{X})$, *then* $N(p)$ *is a model of* ZF.

Repeating the proof given in 2.3 we infer that:

3.2. *The axiom of choice and the generalized continuum hypothesis are valid in* $N(p)$.

Next we show that the assumptions of 1.1 are satisfied in the present case.

For every permutation ε of ω we define an auto-homeomorphism f_ε of $\mathscr{X}$ by means of the equation $f(p) = p \circ \varepsilon^{-1}$. Let G be the set of all f_ε where ε is any permutation which moves only finitely many integers.

3.3. *All homeomorphisms f in G satisfy conditions* (C1) *and* (C2) *of* XIV.1.1.

PROOF. (C1) is satisfied because ε and f_ε have the same order. To prove that (C2) is satisfied we have to represent $a_\beta\big(f_\varepsilon(p)\big)$ in the form $C_{\xi'}\big(a(p)\big)$, where the ordinals $\xi = \mathrm{pl}_{10}(\beta)$ and ξ' lie in the same interval $\big(\delta(\alpha), \delta(\alpha+1)\big)$.

If $\beta < \omega_1(M)$, then $a_\beta(p)$ is independent of p. Thus we can choose $\xi' = \xi$. Now assume that $\omega_1(M) \leqslant \beta < \omega_1(M) \cdot 2$. By the usual argument $\delta\big(\omega_1(M)\big) = \omega_1(M)$ (see Appendix, p. 257) and $\delta\big(\omega_1(M)+1\big) > \omega_1(M) \cdot 2$, and thus for all β satisfying the inequalities $\omega_1(M) \leqslant \beta < \omega_1(M) \cdot 2$ the ordinals $\mathrm{pl}_{10}(\beta)$ and β lie in the same interval $\big(\omega_1(M), \delta(\omega_1(M)+1)\big)$. To prove (C2) for these ordinals it is therefore sufficient to show that $a_\beta(f_\varepsilon(p))$ occurs in the sequence $a(p)$ with an index $\geqslant \omega_1(M)$. To see this we remark that $f_\varepsilon(p)$ is obtained from p by changing finitely many values of p, i.e., $f_\varepsilon(p) = (p-A) \cup B$ where A and B are finite subsets of $\mathrm{Rg}(Q)$. It follows that if $\omega_1(M) \leqslant \beta < \omega_1(M)\cdot 2$, then

$$a_\beta(f_\varepsilon(p)) = [f_\varepsilon(p) - F(\beta')] \cup F(\beta'')$$
$$= [p-(A \cup F(\beta'))] \cup [(B-F(\beta')) \cup F(\beta'')],$$

and hence $a_\beta(f_\varepsilon(p))$ has the form $a_\eta(p)$. Lemma 3.3 is thus proved.

3.4. *If* $p \in \mathrm{Gen}(\mathscr{X})$, *then the set* $\{f(p)\colon f \in G\}$ *is dense in* $\mathscr{X}$.

PROOF. Let π be a one-to-one finite function with $\mathrm{Dom}(\pi) \subset \omega$ and $\mathrm{Rg}(\pi) \subset \omega_1(M)$. Since p is generic, it maps ω onto $\omega_1(M)$ (cf. theorem XII.5.5). Hence there is a finite set $X \subset \omega$ which is transformed by p onto $\mathrm{Rg}(\pi)$. Since p and π are one-to-one, the sets X and $\mathrm{Dom}(\pi)$ have the same number of elements, which proves that there exists a permutation ε of ω such that $p(\varepsilon^{-1}(j)) = \pi(j)$ for each $j \in \mathrm{Dom}(\pi)$. We can assume that ε moves only finitely many elements. In this way we obtain $f_\varepsilon(p) \in U_\pi$ with f_ε in G.

Lemma 3.4, which we have just proved, shows that theorem 1.1 is applicable and hence that a relation between ordinals which is definable in $N(p)$ is parametrically definable in M. We can now state our main result (Lévy [18]):

3.5. *If* $X \subseteq P(\omega) \cap N(p)$ *and there is in* $N(p)$ *a relation definable in* $N(p)$ *which well-orders* X, *then* $\mathrm{Card}\big(N(p), X\big) \leqslant \omega$.

PROOF. Let τ be the order type of X. It follows from the assumptions of the theorem that there is an order-preserving mapping φ of τ onto X which is definable in $N(p)$. The relation

$$\{\langle \xi, n\rangle \in \tau \times \omega\colon\ n \in \varphi(\xi)\}$$

is definable in $N(p)$. It follows that this relation is parametrically definable in M, and since it is contained in the set $\tau\times\omega$ which belongs to M, it belongs itself to M. This shows that $X \in M$. We now use the fact that the continuum hypothesis holds in M. Hence $\mathrm{Card}\,(M, P(\omega) \cap M) \leqslant \omega_1(M)$ and therefore $\mathrm{Card}(M, X) \leqslant \omega_1(M)$. Thus M contains a one-to-one mapping of X into $\omega_1(M)$. The same mapping is an element of $N(p)$ since M is the minimal model. It follows that

$$\text{Card}(N(p), X) \leqslant \text{Card}(N(p), \omega_1(M)).$$

Now we notice that $p \in N(p)$ and that p is a one-to-one mapping of ω onto $\omega_1(M)$. Thus the relative cardinal of $\omega_1(M)$ in $N(p)$ is ω and we obtain $\text{Card}(N(p), X) \leqslant \omega$.

As a corollary we infer that:

3.6. *The set $M \cap P(\omega)$ has in $N(p)$ the relative cardinal ω and in M the relative cardinal $\omega_1(M)$.*

PROOF. We saw in VII.3 that there is a well-ordering of M definable in M and hence in $N(p)$ since $M = C^{\min}_{\pi(M)}(0)$ is definable in $N(p)$.

Theorem 3.6 shows that the proposition "subsets of ω constructible with respect to the void sequence form a denumerable set" is undecidable in ZF even if we adjoin the axiom of choice and the generalized continuum hypothesis as new axioms. We have thus obtained a relatively simple example of an undecidable proposition, which shows very convincingly the incompleteness of the axiomatic set theory [1]).

[1]) The incompleteness of ZF results also from the so called "first" incompleteness theorem of Gödel. From this theorem it does not follow, however, that there exist two transitive families A, B of sets such that $A \not\equiv B$ (see. I.5) and both A and B are models of ZF. This much stronger incompleteness results immediately from the remark made above. It can also be derived from the consistency and independence of AC from the axioms of ZF and also from the consistency and independence of GCH established in the previous chapters. Moreover, the models A and B may be assumed to be denumerable and have the same height.

APPENDIX

We assume that $M = C_\mu^{B^0}(0)$ is a model of ZF; thus, in particular, M can be the minimal model.

THEOREM. *If f is an increasing continuous uniformly definable function with domain On and range $\subseteq$ On, then for any α in $\pi(M)$ the ordinal $\omega_\alpha(M)$ is a critical number of f.*

PROOF. We first consider the case where $\alpha = \beta+1$. Let F be a formula with two free variables x_0, x_1 which defines f (cf. V.1 and IV.1). Hence for almost all sets A and arbitrary ξ, η in $\pi(A)$

$$f(\xi) \in A, \tag{1}$$

$$[\eta = f(\xi)] \equiv \vdash_A F[\eta, \xi]. \tag{2}$$

The correlation of the variables of F and the ordinals η, ξ is this: η is correlated with x_0 and ξ with x_1. Thus the right-hand side of (2) should be written as $\vdash_A F[\{\langle 0, \eta\rangle, \langle 1, \xi\rangle\}]$.

The expression "for almost all" means that there are finitely many axioms $K_1, \ldots, K_r$ of ZF such that whenever A is a transitive set in which these axioms are valid, then formulae (1), (2) hold for arbitrary $\xi, \eta < \pi(A)$.

Let us assume that $\xi < \omega_\alpha(M)$ and put $s = \omega \cup \xi \cup \{\xi\}$. It is obvious that s is M-embeddable in $\omega_\alpha(M)$:

$$|s| \leqslant_M |\omega_\beta(M)|.$$

Let H be the conjunction of the following formulae: the axioms $K_1, \ldots, K_r$, the formula $\mathbf{Ord}(x_1)$ and the formula

$$G\colon\ (x_1)\{\mathbf{Ord}(x_1) \to (E!x_0)[\mathbf{Ord}(x_0) \wedge F]\}.$$

The last formula "says" that for each ordinal x_1 there is exactly one x_0 such that $F(x_0, x_1)$.

We can assume that the axiom of extensionality is among the axioms

K_i. Since all the axioms of ZF are valid in M, we find from (1) and (2) that for all $\zeta < \pi(M)$

(3) $$\vdash_M G,$$

(4) $$\vdash_M K_1 \wedge \ldots \wedge K_r,$$

(5) $$\vdash_M \mathbf{Ord}[\zeta].$$

We now use theorem VII.7.3, in which we put $A_0 = M$ and replace ξ by $\omega_\beta(M)$; in view of the definition of M we also have $A_0' = M$, where the meaning of A_0' is explained in VII.7.3. Hence we obtain a set m in M such that

(6) $$s \subseteq m, \quad |m| \leqslant_M |\omega_\beta(M)|,$$

(7) m is an H-elementary subset of M.

The contracting function φ of m belongs to M (VII.6.5). Putting $m^* = \mathrm{Im}(\varphi, m)$ we obtain therefore a set $m^* \in M$ such that

(8) $$|m^*| \leqslant_M |\omega_\beta(M)|,$$

(9) $$\varphi(x) = x \quad \text{for} \quad x \in s,$$

(10) φ maps m isomorphically onto m^*,

(11) m^* is transitive.

(10) and (11) follow from the properties of the contracting function (see I.6). (8) results from (6) and the remark that $\varphi \in M$ and φ is one-to-one. Finally, (9) results from the theorem stating that the contracting function of m is equal to identity on each transitive subset of m (cf. I.6.3).

Put $\zeta = \xi$ in (4) and (5). By (7) and (6) we obtain $\vdash_m \mathbf{Ord}[\xi]$ and from (3) and (7) we infer that $\vdash_m G$, and hence there is an element $y \in m$ such that $\vdash_m F[y, \xi]$ and $\vdash_m \mathbf{Ord}[y]$. Applying the isomorphism φ and putting $\eta = \varphi(y)$, we obtain therefore

$$\vdash_{m^*} F[\eta, \xi], \quad \vdash_{m^*} \mathbf{Ord}[\eta]$$

because φ transforms ξ into itself.

It follows that η is an ordinal.

From (2) we now obtain $\eta = f(\xi)$. Since $\eta \in m^*$, we have $\eta \subseteq m^*$ and hence $|\eta| \leqslant_M |\omega_\beta(M)|$. Thus

$$|f(\xi)| \leqslant_M |\omega_\beta(M)|$$

and therefore

$$f(\xi) < \omega_{\beta+1}(M) = \omega_\alpha(M).$$

Thus we have shown that

$$[\xi < \omega_\alpha(M)] \rightarrow [f(\xi) < \omega_\alpha(M)],$$

and hence $\omega_\alpha(M)$ is a critical number of f.

If α is a limit number, then $\omega_\alpha(M) = \lim_{\beta<\alpha} \omega_\beta(M)$, and the theorem results from the previous case because a limit of critical numbers is itself a critical number.

APPLICATION. If we take in the theorem $f(\xi) = \delta(\xi)$ and $\alpha = \omega$, we obtain

$$[\beta < \omega_\omega(M)] \rightarrow [\delta(\beta) < \omega_\omega(M)],$$
$$\omega_\omega(M) = \delta(\omega_\omega(M)).$$

These two formulas were used in XIV.7, p. 243. In a similar way we can derive the formula $\delta(\omega_1(M)) = \omega_1(M)$, which we used on p. 252.

BIBLIOGRAPHY

(This bibliography lists only the works quoted in the text and does not claim completeness in any sense of the word.)

[1] J. W. Addison, *Some consequences of the axiom of constructibility*, Fundamenta Mathematicae 46 (1959), pp. 337–357.

[2] P. Bernays, *A system of axiomatic set theory I*, Journal of Symbolic Logic 2 (1937), pp. 65–67.

[3] —, A. A. Fraenkel, *Axiomatic set theory*, Studies in Logic and the Foundations of Mathematics, North Holland Publishing Co., Amsterdam, 1958.

[4] P. J. Cohen, *The independence of the continuum hypothesis I, II*, Proceedings of the National Academy of the U.S.A. 50 (1963), pp. 1143–1148; 51 (1964), pp. 105–110.

[5] — *A minimal model for set theory*, Bulletin of the American Mathematical Society 69 (1963), pp. 537–540.

[6] — *Set theory and the continuum hypothesis*, W. A. Benjamin, New York, 1966.

[7] W. B. Easton, *Powers of regular cardinals*, Princeton Doctoral Dissertation (mimeographed), 1964.

[8] P. Erdös, R. Rado, *A partition calculus in set theory*, Bulletin of the American Mathematical Society 62 (1956), pp. 427–489.

[9] —, A. Tarski, *On families of mutually exclusive sets*, Annals of Mathematics 44 (1943), pp. 315–329.

[10] S. Feferman, *Some applications of the notion of forcing and generic sets*, Fundamenta Mathematicae 56 (1965), pp. 325–345.

[11] K. Gödel, *Consistency proofs for the generalized continuum hypothesis*, Proceedings of the National Academy of Science of the U.S.A. 25 (1939), pp. 220–224.

[12] — *What is Cantor's continuum problem*? American Mathematical Monthly 54 (1947), pp. 515–525.

[13] — *The consistency of the axiom of choice and of the generalized continuum hypothesis with the axioms of set theory*, 4th printing, Princeton, 1958.

[14] A. Hajnal, *On a consistency problem connected with the generalized continuum hypothesis*, Zeitschrift für mathematische Logik und Grundlagen der Mathematik 2 (1956), pp. 131–136.

[15] M. Jaegerman, *The axiom of choice and two definitions of continuity*, Bulletin de l'Académie Polonaise des Sciences, série des sciences mathématiques, astronomiques et physiques 13 (1965), pp. 699–704.

[16] J. L. Kelley, *General topology*, Van Nostrand Co., Princeton, 1955.

[17] K. Kuratowski, A. Mostowski, *Set theory*, Studies in Logic and the Foundations of Mathematics, North Holland Publishing Co., Państwowe Wydawnictwo Naukowe, Amsterdam and Warsaw, 1967.

[18] A. Lévy, (Mimeographed Notes), 1963, pp. 1–32.

[19] N. Lusin, *Sur les ensembles analytiques nuls*, Fundamenta Mathematicae 25 (1935), pp. 109–131.

[20] E. Marczewski (Szpilrajn), *Remarque sur les produits cartesiens d'espaces topologiques*, Doklady Akademii Nauk SSSR 31 (1941), pp. 525–528.

[21] W. Marek, *On families of sets*, Bulletin de l'Académie Polonaise des Sciences, série des sciences mathématiques, astronomiques et physiques 12 (1964), pp. 443–448.

[22] — J. Onyszkiewicz, *Some results in the foundations of the set theory*, Bulletin de l'Académie Polonaise des Sciences, série des sciences mathématiques, astronomiques et physiques 15 (1967), pp. 51–52. See also correction to this paper, ibidem.

[23] R. M. Montague, R. L. Vaught, *Natural models of set theory*, Fundamenta Mathematicae 47 (1959), pp. 219–242.

[24] A. Morse, *A theory of sets*, Academic Press, New York, 1965.

[25] A. Mostowski, *Recent results in set theory*, Problems in the Philosophy of Mathematics. Studies in Logic and the Foundations of Mathematics, North Holland Publishing Co., Amsterdam, 1967, pp. 82–96.

[26] J. v. Neumann, *Die Axiomatisierung der Mengenlehre*, Mathematische Zeitschrift 27 (1928), pp. 669–752.

[27] A. Robinson, *Introduction to model theory and the metamathematics of algebra*, Studies in Logic and Foundations of Mathematics, North Holland Publishng Co., Amsterdam, 1963.

[28] R. M. Robinson, *The theory of classes. A modification of von Neumann's system*, Journal of Symbolic Logic 2 (1937), pp. 29–36.

[29] B. Scarpellini, *On a family of models of Zermelo-Fraenkel set theory*, Zeitschrift für mathematische Logik und Grundlagen der Mathematik 12 (1966), pp. 191–204.

[30] J. C. Shepherdson, *Inner models of set theory*, part III, Journal of Symbolic Logic 18 (1955), pp. 145–167.

[31] R. Solovay, $2^{\aleph_0}$ *can be anything it ought to be. The Theory of Models*, Studies in Logic and the Foundations of Mathematics, North Holland Publishing Co., Amsterdam, 1965, p. 435.

[32] G. Takeuti, *Topological spaces and forcing*, to appear.

[33] — *On the axiom of constructibility*, to appear.

[34] A. Tarski, *The concept of truth in formalized languages. Logic, semantics, metamathematics*, Clarendon Press, Oxford, 1956.

LIST OF IMPORTANT SYMBOLS

$\neg H$	negation 1
$H \wedge H'$	conjunction 1
$(x_i)H$	universal quantifier 1
$H \vee H'$	(inclusive) disjunction 1
$H \rightarrow H'$	implication 1
$H \equiv H'$	equivalence 1
(Ex_i)	existential quantifier 1
$\text{Fr}(H)$	set of integers i such that x_i occurs freely in H 1
$H(x_j, \ldots, x_k)$	formula which has free occurrences of the variables $x_j, \ldots, x_k$ 1
$(E!y)H$	"there is exactly one y such that H" 2
$x \cup y$	union of x and y 3
$x \cap y$	intersection of x and y 3
$-x$	complement of x 3
$x - y$	difference of x and y 4
0	void class 4
V	universal class 4
$\bigcap x$	intersection of sets which belong to x 4
$\bigcup x$	union of sets which belong to x 4
$x \subseteq y$	inclusion 4
$P(x)$	class of all subsets of x 4
$\{x\}$	singleton of x 4
$\{x, y\}$	pair of x and y 4
$\langle x, y \rangle$	ordered pair of x and y 4
$\langle x_1, \ldots, x_n \rangle$	ordered n-tuple 4
x^n	nth power of x 4
$x \times y$	Cartesian product of x and y 4
$\text{Rel}(x)$	"x is a relation" 4
$x \bigcirc y$	composition of x and y 4

S	class of all transfinite sequences 39
$\mathrm{lh}(a)$	length of a sequence a 39
B	function satisfying conditions (B.0)–(B.4) 39
$K^B(a)$	class consisting of all sets $C_\xi^B(a)$ 40
Trans (x)	formula: "x is transitive" 45
Ord (x)	formula: "x is an ordinal" 45
$B^{\min}$	smallest function satisfying (B.1)–(B.4) 48
B^0	smallest function satisfying (B.1)–(B.5) 48
B^Z	smallest function satisfying (B.1)–(B.6) 48
Dis (x)	formula: "x is a family of disjoint non void sets" 99
Sel (x, w)	formula: "w is a selector of x" 99
$\lvert a \rvert \leqslant_A \lvert b \rvert$	"a is A-embeddable in b" 102
Sc (x_i, x_j)	formula: "x_j is a successor of x_i" 106
I or $I(\mathscr{X})$	family of sets of the first category of the space $\mathscr{X}$ 128
$\dot{-}$	symmetric difference 129
$\mathrm{P}_{t \in T} \mathscr{X}_t$	Cartesian product of sets $\mathscr{X}_t$ 129
$\mathscr{F}$ or $\mathscr{F}_{H,t}$	valuation 130
$G_{H,t}$	open set congruent mod $I(\mathscr{X})$ to $\mathscr{F}_{H,t}$ 131
$N_{H,n,t}$	nowhere dense sets such that $\mathscr{F}_{H,t} \dot{-} G_{H,t} \subseteq \bigcup_n N_{H,n,t}$ 131
$\mathrm{Forc}_H(\pi, t) \equiv U_\pi - \mathscr{F}_{H,t} \in I$	forcing relation 132
$\pi \to U_\pi$	mapping of set Π onto an open basis of $\mathscr{X}$ 132
(A)	mapping $p \to a(p)$ of $\mathscr{X}$ into the class of transitive sequences 135
$\pi \prec \varrho$	relation which condition π bears to ϱ if $U_\varrho \subseteq U_\pi$ 135
$\mathscr{E}_{\alpha\beta}$ or $\mathscr{E}^B_{\alpha\beta}$	set of points p such that $C^B_\alpha(a(p)) \in C^B_\beta(a(p))$ 136, 141
$\mathscr{I}_{\alpha\beta}$ or $\mathscr{I}^B_{\alpha\beta}$	set of points p such that $C^B_\alpha(a(p)) = C^B_\beta(a(p))$ 136, 141
Gen $(\mathscr{X})$	set of generic points 136
Φ	family of functions whose values are subsets of $\mathscr{X}$ and whose domains are contained in $\pi(M)^2$ 141
$\varphi * \psi$	complement of the symmetric difference 143
$\ll$	irreflexive relation with the field $\pi(M)^2$ 145
$e \mid (\alpha, \beta)$	function e restricted to arguments $\ll (\alpha, \beta)$ 145

Φ^*	set of functions whose values are 0 or 1 and which have three arguments the first of which ranges over Π and the remaining two over $\pi(M)$ 147
$\mathscr{E}^*$	characteristic function of the relation $U_\pi - \mathscr{E}_{\alpha\beta} \in I$ 147
$\mathscr{I}^*$	characteristic function of the relation $U_\pi - \mathscr{I}_{\alpha\beta} \in I$ 147
R_φ	relation associated with a polynomial φ 147
$\leqslant_0$	partial ordering of $\pi(M)^2$ 155
D_1	set of pairs $\langle\alpha, \alpha\rangle$ with $\alpha < \pi(M)$ 155
D_2, D_3	sets of special and ordinary pairs 155
$\mathscr{E}^B \mid (\alpha, \beta)$, $\mathscr{I}^B \mid (\alpha, \beta)$	functions $\mathscr{E}^B_{\xi\eta}$, $\mathscr{I}^B_{\xi\eta}$ restricted to arguments satisfying $\langle\xi, \eta\rangle \leqslant_\alpha \langle\alpha, \beta\rangle$ 155
$e_{\xi\eta}$	set of points p such that $a_\xi(p) \in a_\eta(p)$ 164
$i_{\xi\eta}$	set of points p such that $a_\xi(p) = a_\eta(p)$ 164
$\Pi_1(r_0)$	set of pairs $\langle X, Y\rangle$ where X, Y are disjoint finite subsets of a set r_0 170
$\Pi_2^\alpha(r)$	set of finite functions π such that $\pi_i \in \Pi_1(r_i)$ for each i in $\mathrm{Dom}(\pi)$ 170
$R_1(r_0)$, $R_2^\alpha(r)$	inclusion relations between neighbourhoods determined by elements of $\Pi_1(r_0)$ or $\Pi_2^\alpha(r)$ 170
$\Pi_{3,J}(r_0)$	set of ordered pairs of disjoint elements of J 171
$\Pi_{4,J,K}(r)$	set of functions π with domains in K such that $\pi_i \in \Pi_{3,J}(r_i)$ for each i in $\mathrm{Dom}(\pi)$ 171
$\Pi_5(a, b)$	set of all finite functions with domain $\subseteq b$ and values in a 171
$N(M, \mathscr{X}, B, a(p), \Pi)$	generic extension of M determined by space $\mathscr{X}$, function B, sequence $a(p)$ and set of conditions Π 182
$N_1^B(r_0, p)$	simple extension determined by a generic subset p of r_0 182
$N_\alpha^B(r, p)$, $N_{\alpha, J, K}(r, p)$	multiple extensions determined by a generic sequence p whose terms are subsets of terms of r 183
$N^B_{a,b}(p)$	simple functional extension determined by a generic mapping p of b into a 183
$N^Z(p)$	abbreviated notation for $N^{B^Z}(r, p)$ 187
α'	smallest ordinal cofinal with α 190

Functors of the first and the second kind*

* Formulae of ZF which define functors are printed in bold face.

$\mathrm{constr}_{B,T}(A, \xi, p)$	functor with value $C_\xi^B(T(A, p))$ 81
$\mathrm{Konstr}_T^B(p)$	functor with value $C_{\pi(A)}^B(T(A, p))$ 81
$\mathrm{Od}^B(A, x, a)$	functor whose value is the index ξ such that $x = C_\xi^B(a)$ 101
$\aleph(A, a)$	functor whose value is the least ordinal not A-embeddable in a 103
$\mathrm{Card}(M)$	functor whose value is the set of relative cardinals of M 199
$\mathrm{Cf}(M, \alpha)$	functor whose value is the relative cofinality index of α 199
$\vartheta(M, \alpha)$	functor whose value is the relative Souslin coefficient of r 199
$\omega_\xi(M)$	functor whose value is the ξth relative cardinal of M 202

AUTHOR INDEX

SUBJECT INDEX